The First Bite: A Comprehensive Guide to Establishing and Growing Your Career in Veterinary Medicine

"*The First Bite: A Comprehensive Guide to Establishing and Growing Your Career in Veterinary Medicine* should be required reading for any graduating veterinarian! The content is relevant, practical, and invaluable. My thanks to Dr. John Tait and Dr. Brian Ausman for providing our profession with this excellent resource."

Lisa M. Miller DVM, PhD, MEd, Diplomate ACVP
Associate Dean of Academic Affairs
Atlantic Veterinary College
University of Prince Edward Island
Charlottetown, PEI

"This is the most comprehensive text on the business of what it is to be a veterinarian. The opportunities and challenges and how to approach them are clearly identified. This is a must read for anyone contemplating entering the profession as well as for those already a part of it."

Dana Allen, DVM, MSc, Diplomate ACVIM (Internal Medicine)
Professor and Chair, Deptartment of Clinical Studies
Ontario Veterinary College
University of Guelph
Guelph, Ontario

THE FIRST BITE

A Comprehensive Guide
to Establishing and
Growing Your Career
in Veterinary Medicine

John Tait and Brian Ausman

WITH A FOREWORD BY
Susan Jones

EDITED BY
Walt Ingwersen

The First Bite: A Comprehensive Guide to Establishing and Growing Your Career in Veterinary Medicine

ISBN-10: 0-9782525-0-0
ISBN-13: 978-0-9782525-0-2

Printed in Canada

Second Edition
10 9 8 7 6 5 4 3 2 1

Cover Painting by: Christine Stec, DVM

Cover Design by: Pandora Press

Interior Design by: Dianne Nelson, Shadow Canyon Graphics

John Tait, BSc, DVM, MBA, CFP, ADR, has owned or managed private and corporate veterinary practices in Canada and the United States. He is an Assistant Professor at the University of Guelph, as well as an adjunct Professor at two other Universities, Managing Partner of the Ontario Veterinary Group, a consultant for small business medical professionals, and a former Editor for the Practice Management section of the *Canadian Veterinary Journal*. He currently sits on the Board of Directors of the National Commission on Veterinary Economic Issues and the American Animal Hospital Association (AAHA), both as Secretary Treasurer. In 2009-2010 he was the 2nd Canadian President of AAHA.

Brian Ausman BSc (Agr), DVM, MBA, LL.B, is a lawyer, veterinarian, and practice owner who advises professionals on a wide range of legal issues throughout their careers. Brian has written, published, and lectured on topics of decision-making, in one's professional, business, and private lives.

Walt Ingwersen, DVM, DVSc, Diplomate ACVIM, has enjoyed careers in private general and specialty small animal practice, academia, scientific writing, and industry. He is past editor of the *Journal of the American Animal Hospital Association* and currently works as a Technical Services veterinarian for Boehringer Ingelheim Canada Ltd.

We would like to thank our sponsors –
Hill's Pet Nutrition Canada,
Pfizer Animal Health,
and RBC Royal Bank® –
for their ongoing commitment
to the veterinary profession.
Their support is greatly appreciated.

 Pfizer Animal Health

 **RBC Royal Bank®**

Group Insurance Solutions

*This book is dedicated to the
animals that enrich our lives
and provide us with
such rewarding vocations.*

Contents

Foreword by Susan Jones xvii

SECTION 1
FACING THE CHALLENGES:
The Transition from Student to Professional 1
  Section Introduction by John Tait

Chapter 1-1
Getting Started 5
  John Tait

Chapter 1-2
Mentorship 9
  John Tait

Chapter 1-3
Your Support Team 15
  Brian Ausman

Chapter 1-4
Learning a Living 27
  Carl Osborne

Chapter 1-5
What Organizations Do I Join? 41
  John Tait

Chapter 1-6
Should I Buy, Join or
Set Up My Own Practice? 45
  Darrell Tracey, CA

Chapter 1-7
Leadership 53
  John Tait

Chapter 1-8
The Gender Perspective in Veterinary Medicine:
Will Feminizing the Profession Make It More Efficient? 57
  Darren Osborne

Chapter 1-9
What Industry Can Do For You 67
  Rob Bell

SECTION 2
A PARADE OF PRACTITIONER PERSPECTIVES 81
  Section Introduction by John Tait

Chapter 2-1
Professional Issues Unique to Female Veterinarians 83
  Laurie Dunbar

Chapter 2-2
Veterinary Medicine in the Province of Quebec 95
  Laurie Dunbar

Chapter 2-3
Veterinary Medicine in Canada's Atlantic Provinces 103
  Steve Noonan

Chapter 2-4
A Female Practitioner Owner, Wife, and Mother
from Prince Edward Island 111
  Jane MacMillan-Bondt

Chapter 2-5
Getting Started from the Perspective of a Toronto
Multiple Practice Owner 115
  Ian Sandler

Chapter 2-6
A Locum Veterinarian in Calgary 123
  Laura Hunt

Chapter 2-7
Food Animal Practice 129
  William Armstrong

Chapter 2-8
Life as an Intern and Resident 135
  John Tait and Danielle Richardson

Chapter 2-9
Veterinary Emergency Medicine 139
  Jen LeBel

Chapter 2-10
Veterinary Medicine Beyond the Books 145
  Rob Ashburner

Chapter 2-11
Practicing and Living in the United States 151
  John Tait

SECTION 3
ON THE HUNT: Job-Seeking Strategies 155
  Section Introduction by Sharon Graham

Chapter 3-1
Types of Private Practices 159
  John Tait

Chapter 3-2
Résumés and Cover Letters 163
  Heather Erskine

Chapter 3-3
Interview Skills: Putting Your Best Foot Forward 191
  John Tait

Chapter 3-4
Negotiating Strategies and How to "Sell Yourself" 197
    John Tait

Chapter 3-5
The Right Fit: Recruiting for Performance and Mutual Gain 203
    Mark Woolnough

SECTION 4
ACQUIRING WEALTH:
Financial Planning for Tomorrow and the Future 217
    Section Introduction by Stephen Prime

Chapter 4-1
Planning for Financial Life Stages 221
    John Tait

Chapter 4-2
Debt and Debt Management 233
    John Tait

Chapter 4-3
Tax Management and Employment Compensation Strategies 237
    Andrew Shalit and John Tait

Chapter 4-4
Compensation and Employment Contracts 249
    John Tait

Chapter 4-5
Protecting Your Income 257
    Brian Clegg

Chapter 4-6
Understanding Insurance and Its Role in Risk Management 269
    Claire Walker

Chapter 4-7
Investing Strategies During Your Career 281
    Jay Stark

Chapter 4-8
The Move to Practice Ownership 293
John Tait

Chapter 4-9
Developing Your Banking Relationship 307
Stephen Prime

Chapter 4-10
Selecting a Trusted Business Advisor 315
Andrea Chan

SECTION 5
LEGAL AND ETHICAL ISSUES IN VETERINARY MEDICINE 323
Section Introduction by Brian Ausman

Chapter 5-1
An Introduction to Ethics in Veterinary Medicine 327
Bernard E. Rollin

Chapter 5-2
The Proactive Veterinary Practitioner:
Veterinary Risk-Management Planning 335
Douglas C. Jack

Chapter 5-3
The Equine Pre-Purchase Examination:
Standard of Care and Legal Tips 347
Catherine E. Willson

Chapter 5-4
Non-Competition Agreements:
Walk a Mile in Another's Moccasins 355
Brian Ausman

Chapter 5-5
Being an Expert Witness 361
Ian Stauffer and Maura Kehoe

Chapter 5-6
People, Pets, and Wills: Taking Care of Our Pets 371
  Brian Ausman

SECTION 6
MAKING SENSE OF THE UNEXPECTED 375
  Section Introduction by Brian Ausman

Chapter 6-1
"Here Comes 'da Judge": Defending or Starting a
Court Action—A Primer on the Canadian Court System 379
  Douglas C. Jack

Chapter 6-2
Why Me? Surviving a Client Lawsuit or a
Professional Misconduct Complaint 387
  Brian Ausman

Chapter 6-3
Responding to a Complaint 393
  Alec Martin

Chapter 6-4
Family Law: Unravelling the Web We Weave 407
  Poroshad Mahdi

Chapter 6-5
Affairs of the Heart: Marriage Contracts for Professionals 417
  Brian Ausman

Chapter 6-6
Pet Health Insurance 423
  Peter R. Beaumont

SECTION 7
LIFE OUTSIDE THE HERD: Other Career Options 439
  Section Introduction by Clayton MacKay

Chapter 7-1
Career Paths in Veterinary Medicine: Pharmaceutical Industry 443
Walt Ingwersen

Chapter 7-2
Career Paths in Veterinary Medicine: Pet Food Industry 453
Nicole Judge

Chapter 7-3
Career Paths in Veterinary Medicine: Teaching and Academia 463
Brigitte Brisson

Chapter 7-4
Career Paths in Veterinary Medicine:
Part-Time and Locum Work 469
Hélène Bouchard

Chapter 7-5
Career Paths in Veterinary Medicine: Government 475
Gwen Zellen and Tom Baker

Chapter 7-6
Career Paths in Veterinary Medicine: Shelter Medicine 483
Miranda Spindel and Lila Miller

Chapter 7-7
Career Paths in Veterinary Medicine:
Laboratory Animal Medicine 491
Michel Bailey

Chapter 7-8
Career Paths in Veterinary Medicine:
International Work 499
David Waltner-Toews

SECTION 8
YOU AND YOURS: Preserving Your Good Health
and Achieving Balance in Your Life 505
Section Introduction by Michael Kaufmann

Chapter 8-1
Compassion Fatigue 509
    Debbie Stoewen

Chapter 8-2
Burnout 533
    Michael Kaufmann and Robin Robertson

Chapter 8-3
Depressive Conditions 551
    Joy Albuquerque

Chapter 8-4
Substance Abuse and Addiction:
Recognition, Intervention, and Recovery 561
    Michael Kaufmann

Chapter 8-5
After the Call: Accessing Substance Abuse
Assistance Programs 571
    Michael Kaufmann

Chapter 8-6
Emotional Intelligence for Veterinary Professionals 577
    Patsy Marshall

Chapter 8-7
Break Away From Work: The Restorative Value
of Effective Vacationing 583
    Michael Kaufmann

Chapter 8-8
Giving Something Back 589
    John Tait

Foreword

Nothing endures but change.
Heraclitus, Greek philosopher (540 BC - 480 BC)

While we are in veterinary school, most of us have a firmly-established vision of our lives after graduation. We long for the day when we can begin to implement that vision in the real world.

Regardless of whether we see ourselves in practice or in some other area of veterinary medicine, veterinarians areunited by a common goal to provide care for animals.Many of us stay true to our original vision; increasingly, more and more veterinarians find different ways to participate in delivering healthcare to animals and value to society. Either way, our veterinary education provides us with a wide variety of skillsets and opportunities.

You will experience changes throughout your career—from student to professional, from associate to practice owner, from full-time to part-time, from professional to academic, from practitioner to industr —the transitions and options are many.

Whether you are a veterinary student, a recent graduate, or a not-so-recent graduate considering a career transition, you will find valuable information and guidance in this book.I hope that you will keep it on your bookshel —I'm confident you will find many reasons to reach for it along the way.

Best wishes to you throughout your career, wherever our wonderful profession takes you.

Susan Jones, DVM
Director of Veterinary Affairs, Hill's Pet Nutrition Canada Inc.
Mississauga, Ontario

Dr. Susan Jones is currently the Director of Veterinary Affairs at Hill's Pet Nutrition Canada Inc. She has had a varied career in veterinary medicine, beginning as a small animal practitioner with subsequent experience in the animal health industry in marketing, communications and market research before joining Hill's.

Section 1

FACING THE CHALLENGES:

The Transition from Student to Professional

Introduction

I recall entering veterinary school with the thought and vision that after graduation, veterinary medicine would be all about preventing disease, repairing the injured, and fixing the sick. Twenty years later, I've come to realize that the clinical component of veterinary medicine, while the core of the profession, is only part of the business of veterinary medicine and the many career paths, planning decisions, issues, and influencing factors that go along with being a veterinarian.

As careers evolve (no matter what the career path), needs, goals, priorities, and worries change and are often in a state of flux. Entry-level and early career veterinarians face many clinical and non-clinical issues and challenges for the first time, many of which will affect and influence their initial and lasting contentment with the profession and what it has to offer. Veterinary medicine is a niche profession in many respects, with many excellent organizational and individual resources to draw upon to help us at various points during our careers. This guide is but one of them, designed as a reference for many issues that may occur not only at the outset or early years of your career but also repeatedly throughout your careers.

Dr. Brian Ausman and I have attempted to address the pertinent areas in as wide, informative, meaningful, and succinct a manner as possible. From financial issues to stress management, to legal issues to career paths, we have gathered input from experts and experienced veterinarians in a variety of areas, and this guide would not have been possible without their assistance.

We hope you find this guide helpful as you begin and grow your career in veterinary medicine.

Section 1 covers a number of lifestyle and resource identification issues that can be addressed even well before graduation, to create a resource base that prepares you well as you enter the profession.

John Tait, BSc, DVM, MBA, CFP, ADR Managing Partner,
Ontario Veterinary Group,
Toronto, Ontario
Assistant Professor, Ontario Veterinary College,
Guelph, Ontario

John Tait, BSc, DVM, MBA, CFP, ADR, has owned or managed private and corporate veterinary practices in Canada and the United States. He is an Assistant Professor at the University of Guelph, as well as an adjunct Professor at two other Universities, Managing Partner of the Ontario Veterinary Group, a consultant for small business medical professionals, and a former Editor for the Practice Management section of the *Canadian Veterinary Journal*. He currently sits on the Board of Directors of the National Commission on Veterinary Economic Issues and the American Animal Hospital Association (AAHA), both as Secretary Treasurer. In 2009-2010 he will become the second Canadian President of AAHA.

CHAPTER 1-1

Getting Started

John Tait, BSc, DVM, MBA, CFP, ADR
Managing Partner, Ontario Veterinary Group,
Toronto, Ontario
Assistant Professor, Ontario Veterinary College,
Guelph, Ontario

> *Nothing happens unless first a dream.*
>
> — Carl Sandburg

The conclusion of veterinary school marks both an end and a beginning. For you, the time spent exclusively in school and focusing on graduating has come to an end, but a challenging, multifaceted, and demanding (yet rewarding) career has begun. Also, graduation from veterinary school represents the beginning of an entirely new set of decisions to be made and planning to be done—a transition that is introduced here and expanded upon later in this book.

The transition from full-time student to full- or part-time professional means more than having to pay income taxes regularly. The completion of school and entry into the workplace (like any other major transition) presents new and unfamiliar issues, many of which require decisions that have a great deal of uncertainty attached to them. There will be decisions about your short-term and long-term planning horizon, and these will further affect your security, wealth accumulation, workplace experience, family planning, and career aspirations.

Transition itself begins with the planning stage, commencing with a "laundry list" of items to consider, evaluate, weigh alternatives against, and complete at various times prior to or upon entering the work force. There are really three major overlapping categories of planning issues: personal financial planning, employment terms and workplace entry, and lifestyle issues. All of these are interrelated and should be considered jointly in either an initial or subsequent career move. Important elements in arriving at informed decisions in these three critical categories are effectively timing your decisions and identifying who your resource base will be for advice and information. Upon entering the job marketplace or when transitioning between jobs, think about your own personal, financial, and career goals. What benefits are important to you? How much risk are you willing to take to achieve your goals? How do you define life balance? Does the move in question make sense, given where you would like your career to be in two, five, or 10 years?

Before you set foot in your first job, you should determine the valuable resources you will call on for advice—whether simply for information or in times of difficulty. Typically, a primary resource base will consist of an accountant or tax-planning individual or firm, a financial planner, an income-protection individual or insurance representative, a bank representative, and legal counsel. For all of these categories of individuals and functions, knowledge and expertise with respect to the issues surrounding early career professionals (and veterinarians in particular) will help to facilitate informed and more effective decision-making. The final element of a resource base that will be of value to you as a new professional is a mentor/experienced individual who has been through many of the same decisions and priority-setting that you are experiencing and will continue to experience as your career expands.

Geographic proximity, qualifications, service standards, fees charged, and age will further influence choices for your primary resource base. These individuals all represent relationships, so your resource personnel should be comfortably accessible to you, provide a level or depth of service and frequency of contact that meets your needs, charge a fair and competitive rate that is commensurate with your expectations for perceived value, and (because these are likely to be long-term relationships) be at a point in their career where they will build and maintain a relationship with you for a period of years.

Inside the category of financial planning, there are three areas of concern that should be addressed: protecting your income, budgeting to live off your income, and growing your income—all of which are addressed later in this book. Effective financial planning is a matter of balance between these three areas, beginning at entry level and continuing throughout your career, thereby ensuring you meet your current and future needs and goals.

Employment terms (i.e., finding the perfect job) can occupy relatively little or a considerably large amount of time, depending on the breadth of your search and time spent previewing the position and living area, evaluating how this position may "bridge" to future positions, and negotiating terms and conditions of your employment.

When it comes to choosing a career position, lifestyle issues are generally regarded as the most important for newer graduates in today's marketplace. Whether it be working hours, community activities and amenities, education, or proximity to family, your own interests, values, and priorities will drive your lifestyle preferences.

Like with most tasks, an effective and organized approach to settling into or changing your career path/lifestyle will minimize the potential for hidden and unwanted surprises along the way. Start with a plan, use your mentor, rank your priorities, shop around, and critically evaluate your lifestyle needs. The stresses of the practical or applied side of the profession can be challenging enough to deal with; by defining your values and priorities and using your resource base and reference material, you can maximize your employment experience and career satisfaction.

Additional Recommended Reading

Building the Successful Veterinary Practice, Volume 1,2,3. Catanzaro T. Iowa State University Press; 1998.
Associate's Survival Guide. Fassig SM ed. AAHA Press, Denver, CO; 2005.
New Business Ventures and the Entrepreneur. Stevenson H, Roberts M, Grousbeck H. Irwin Press; 1994.

Biography

For Dr. Tait's biography, please see the Section 1 Introduction on page 3.

CHAPTER 1-2

Mentorship

John Tait, BSc, DVM, MBA, CFP, ADR
Managing Partner, Ontario Veterinary Group,
Toronto, Ontario
Assistant Professor, Ontario Veterinary College,
Guelph, Ontario

> *The most important single influence in the life
> of a person is another person . . . who is worthy of emulation.*
>
> — Paul D. Schafer

The Merriam Webster's Collegiate Dictionary classifies the word *mentor* as both a noun ("a trusted counselor or guide") and a verb ("to serve as a mentor for"). The idea of "mentorship" for many in veterinary medicine encompasses a process that combines both applications of the word. Mentoring is an ongoing relationship between two individuals seeking to improve their environment and success in the workplace. In a practice setting, mentoring is a means to improve the culture, efficiency, and productivity in a practice environment.

At various points in a person's life, it is common to identify, seek to learn from, and often emulate a mentor(s). New graduates often enter practice with an element of fear, uncertainty, and without a frame of reference. Mentors become models for proper problem-solving and decision-making techniques, teaching of technical and interpersonal skills, and for the provisions of personal guidance. Mentorship has taken on increased awareness in veterinary medicine today, particularly among new veterinary graduates and new practice owners who find themselves in unfamiliar roles and face the challenges of high expectations, information overload, and little time to learn how to master all of the new responsibilities. Both mentors and mentees can benefit from the mentoring relationship. A culture of effective mentoring can enhance recruitment and retention. Employees who better integrate into a practice will be less stressed and experience a greater level of job satisfaction, and mentoring will help this integration. Solutions are often made quicker and with less conflict, and better patient care is facilitated. Mentees can benefit from a mentor by receiving assistance and input into developing their medical, business, and interpersonal skills. Part of being a successful professional is being able to think independently and effective mentoring will encourage such evolution.

Ironically, veterinary schools face these same challenges when educating veterinary students. While veterinary students graduate with sound knowledge and adequate (or better) entry-level technical skills, the schools cannot be expected to send these students into their new roles as practitioners with a complete and versed set of skills and coping abilities. Additionally, individual graduates will enter the workplace with differing levels of confidence and experience, thus creating great variability in their need for mentoring.

The need for further education and training, therefore, continues for some time following graduation and is significantly influenced by the experienced veterinarian's willingness to teach and coach, and by the new graduate's confidence and willingness to listen and take direction.

The stumbling block in many mentoring relationships is defining exactly what mentorship means to the individuals involved. The interpretation of mentorship is largely subjective; therefore, the process and contents therein need to be well defined at the inception in order for the mentoring relationship to be effective for both parties. Without open communication between mentor and pupil, unrealistic expectations may be set on both sides of the relationship. Frustration will mount, performance will be affected, and, inevitably, the relationship will dissolve unnecessarily. A successful mentoring relationship is based on mutual effort, respect, trust, and willingness to communicate openly about professional and personal issues.

There are five types of mentoring relationships:

1. Formal mentoring which includes written expectations and contracts between mentor and mentee regardless of where they are located
2. Informal mentoring which is more casual and does not include written expectations but does include a reciprocal understanding of expectations

3. Virtual mentoring is a form of mentoring where the mentor and mentee are not in the same location and must rely on finding a means of communication when they are not physically in the same place
4. Face to face mentoring, which is where mentor and mentee always meet in person
5. Peer to peer which is when mentor and mentee are colleagues at the same level sharing experiences for personal growth

New or recent graduates and/or associates who identify one or more areas requiring further development should be encouraged to openly express their need for assistance. This should not be perceived as a weakness to be hidden and resolved independently, but as an area(s) that, once developed and refined, will further help the individual and the practice achieve their goals. It is conceivable that a new graduate, particularly one lacking in self-confidence, may be seeking some continuance of the student environment where reinforcement and observation was received on a frequent basis. Others, who are extremely independent from the beginning, simply need to know the voice of assistance is but a phone call or yell for help away.

Practice owners or more seasoned veterinary mentors and coaches should define how they propose to bring and transition a new veterinarian into the practice, what they expect in terms of feedback with respect to difficulties the new associate may have, what the ascending levels of responsibility and challenges will be, and when and how to be accessible for questions, conversation, and hands-on guidance if necessary. Employers should also set some kind of reasonable timeline or end date with respect to performance goals for these new employees. While mentorship is an ongoing process, it should taper off in its intensity and not be an endless process.

Focus groups that I annually conduct among new graduates always identify the scenario of being thrust into a practice on day one with little or no guidance because the owner or experienced veterinarian is unavailable (either physically or due to a lack of time). This is a major source of frustration. The concept of being part of a team working toward a collective goal is quickly lost in this type of setting and that is a key factor leading toward unnecessarily high turnover rates for new graduates within our profession. While formal continuing education plays a valuable role for veterinarians of any experience level, the more immediate issue with newer graduates is simply to have someone available to reinforce their decisions, thereby helping them to build both their self-confidence and a sound clinical frame of reference for the future.

The goal of any mentoring activity should be to create an environment that allows new associates to progress as rapidly as possible down the learning curve and mature their practice skills. The mentoring environment can be laid out during discussions that lead to defining the terms of employment and then ultimately in writing by creating an employment contract. Good mentors generally exhibit a number of skills, including the ability to listen well, to keep in touch on a regular basis, understand ethics and their application, and be a role model in terms of clinical guidance, teamwork, communication, writing, organizing, and conflict resolution. Current and potential mentors identify good "mentees" as having characteristics that include high levels of dedication and initiative, a good work ethic, and an orientation to self-directed learning.

New associates generally are pleased to have the terms of the mentoring relationship defined for them. Those requiring more intensive mentoring feel that easing into full responsibilities and decision-making provides a temporary security net for them and sets a more comfortable level of what is expected during the initial phase of their employment. Defining the mentoring relationship in an employment contract can be done by outlining progressive independent scheduling and responsibilities, defining time and/or activities spent working directly with other veterinarians, establishing regular times for meetings during the workweek (e.g., in-hospital case rounds), and scheduling performance reviews at specific periods over the duration of the contract, during which time the mentoring activities can be reviewed and tapered off in their intensity as the new associate progresses.

The issue is much the same for new practice owners, who now have the added responsibilities of running a business in addition to the day-to-day clinical practice. If a new owner or owners are inside the practice already, hopefully much of that mentoring has happened by observation and a sharing of the business activities. For purchasers coming from outside the practice, transitioning with an outgoing vendor is important both for maintaining the culture of the business and for helping to guide the new owner(s) with respect to the management and leadership of the new practice.

The strategy of finding a good mentor or mentee is critical to the success of the relationship. The selection should be based on primarily on attributes including respective levels of education, areas of interest, what type of relationship you prefer, and the time commitment involved. A face to face meeting is always the best way to kick off the relationship where expectations can be discussed.

As the relationship matures, the need of both parties will change. Reviewing the relationship periodically and celebrating victories will continue to keep the relationship fresh and the mentor and mentee engaged. At some point the relationship in the context of mentor and mentee will end. It is possible that the goals set out will have been reached, one or both parties will have moved on to different positions, or the mentee will evolve themselves into a mentor.

If you are interested in one of these roles, an action plan is a good idea so the relationship has a "road map" to follow. An investment in this type of relationship will be good for you, your practice, career, and the profession.

Biography

For Dr. John Tait's biography, please see the Section 1 Introduction on page 3.

CHAPTER 1-3

Your Support Team

Brian Ausman, BSc (Agr), DVM, MBA, LL.B
Real Estate and Business Broker, Lawyer, and
Practice Co-Owner,
Guelph, Ontario

> *The only things worth counting on*
> *are people you can count on.*
>
> — Dwight D. Eisenhower

Introduction

As you undergo the transition from student to professional, you will notice a marked difference in how you are treated. You suddenly have economic clout; miraculously, your opinion matters. Individuals and organizations want your time and your business. Your academic and professional achievements have opened the door to options you never had before. However, along with the incredible privilege of having these choices comes the responsibility of making the decisions that go along with them. Your support team can help and should consist of professional advisors, mentors, and company representatives.

Professional Advisors

You went to school to practice veterinary medicine. But it seems you are expected to make a myriad of business and legal decisions that you may be ill prepared to make, not have the time to research properly, or, quite frankly, bore you silly. You know that these decisions are important, but where do you get the resources, time, and energy to make informed and thoughtful choices? This is why you should assemble your team of professional advisors. This would typically include an accountant, a lawyer, a banker, a financial advisor, and an insurance broker—all of whom have contributed chapters to this book.

Choosing Your Professional Advisors: The Framework

Choosing your advisors is like surfing the Internet. You can mindlessly click from one site to the next, wasting countless hours of your time. Or you can have a plan. Step one is a qualification process that provides a short list from which to choose. This is followed by step two, where you apply key relationship questions to the professionals on your short list in order to determine the one that best fits your individual needs and personality. Once you have chosen your advisors, you should have a strategy to initiate and maintain these relations. Thus, the final components of this framework provide you with guidelines for achieving long-term, win-win relationships with your professional advisors.

The initial qualification phase is intended to ensure that your potential advisors have the core competencies to perform the services you will require during your professional career. Evaluate their knowledge of the business and art of veterinary practice. Find out if they have other veterinarians as clients. Do they write or speak on veterinary topics? Do they have other health professionals as clients? Have they any particular experience, knowledge, or background in veterinary medicine? Do they understand the key success factors that make for both clinical and financial success? Apart from having a background and experience in the veterinary industry, there are some core competencies that are specific for each of your future professional advisors. These include educational achievements and professional qualifications. Ask prospective advisors for a professional biography. Find out when they achieved particular designations, and if you are unclear or unfamiliar about a particular designation, ask them to explain what it means, who issued it, what it took to achieve, and what it means to you, their future client. In short, a professional education, professional designations, and commitment to continuing education are important. Do not hesitate to ask about them. As well as evaluating past performance and achievements, look to the future. Ask them what form of continuing education they participate in to stay at the forefront of what is going on in both their profession and your industry.

Talk to other professionals in the field and ask for their recommendations. For example, a lawyer that works extensively with veterinarians will know of accountants with a similar practice focus. If done discretely, you can often acquire information that goes beyond mere recommendation. It would be revealing to ask your co-professionals if they have enough knowledge about your prospective professional advisors to critique their strengths and weaknesses, describe their reputations within the veterinary service community, and if, in their experience, they have demonstrated a willingness to be team players.

Big firm or small firm? That is often the question. Especially for lawyers and accountants, there is a marked dichotomy in the size of the firm. Do you choose one with hundreds of professionals or a small one with as few as one practitioner? Large firms offer a large number of professionals under one umbrella, are great for multi-national corporations, and cater to the fortune 500 companies. Small practices that specialize in a given industry or discipline are known as boutique practices. Boutique firms are able to be flexible and creative in the way that large firms cannot. For the veterinary practitioner, a small boutique firm is often your best value if it has shown a commitment to your industry and a willingness to bring in other professionals within and outside the profession as needed.

Whatever size of office that your prospective advisors work from, it is essential that they have the willingness and temperament to work as an integral part of your team of professional advisors. Ask about their philosophy of working with members of other professions in general and, specifically, with the team of professional advisors that you are building. Ensure that they do not always insist on "conducting the orchestra." Are they creative and aggressive in forming strategic alliances and good relationships with other professionals? However, ensure that they are not so aligned within a group of professionals that they will not work effectively or cooperatively with your choices.

Choosing Your Accountant

What services could an accountant provide for you during the course of your professional career? On the most basic level, accountants help us deal with our tax and bank reporting. We are all required to complete and file tax information, both personally and professionally, on at least an annual basis. Thus, your accountant must have the technical competence to complete your annual tax return and GST filings. Furthermore, many financial institutions require annual, and (in some cases) even quarterly, reporting on your financial situation.

The true measure of an accountant takes place not when things go right, but when you are challenged. When you are questioned by an auditor from CCRA (Canada Customs and Revenue Agency, formerly "Revenue Canada") or by your bank manager, you want your accountant at your side. It is his or her professional credibility and familiarity with your finances and reporting methodology that will ensure things go well.

One can easily justify the effort and resources in finding and retaining the right accountant, even if you only engage him or her to prepare tax filings and bank reporting statements and be there for you during audits. However, by limiting your accountant's role to these basic functions, you are indeed missing the added value s/he can provide. Your accountant can help you evaluate where you are, right now, financially. Armed with a detailed assessment of your current situation and having a good grasp of your personal and professional goals, an accountant can help answer the "what if" questions when you are presented with choices as you proceed down your chosen career path.

Consider the education and common professional designations for an accountant, including Chartered Accountant (CA), Certified Management Accountant (CMA), and Certified General Accountant (CGA). When interviewing prospective accountants, ask them about their designations and what they mean to you as the client. Among other things, these designations are important credibility signals.

Evaluate your potential accountant's tax expertise. There are critical times in your practice and personal life when you need specialized tax advice (e.g., setting up your corporate structure, buy-ins, sales, etc.). Find an accounting firm that can provide this service either in house or is comfortable with you going through another firm for tax advice. It is not an uncommon situation and quite appropriate, when challenging tax issues arise, for either you or your accountant to request a second opinion or go to a "tax expert" outside of the accounting firm you are using.

Consider timeliness. This is not the time to be timid; the direct approach is best. It is best to address your expectations before you engage an accountant. Does your prospective accountant genuinely have the time to do your work when you need it done? Many accountants are virtually unavailable for the two or three months leading up to the end-of-April deadline for filing personal returns. Unfortunately, like any group, some accountants take on more work than they can handle. Ask if your work is going to be delegated to a "junior." There is nothing wrong with someone else doing the mechanical part of your accounting—just as your technicians can perform technical services, so too can an accountant's bookkeeper or junior associate. However, it is prudent to insist that a senior professional review the reports generated and sit down with you to explain the consequences, make recommendations, and answer your questions—all in a timely fashion. The fact that "time is money" is true in accounting like few other fields. Keep in mind that your banker will not tolerate frequently missed reporting dates, and the deadlines that the government imposes on filings for both corporations and individuals are broken only at the price of increasing costly penalties for filing late.

Inquire, also, about your prospective accountant's access to comparative databases. One of the most valuable services your accountant can provide is management advice; specifically, you will want to know how your professional financial performance compares to your cohorts. Having these benchmark numbers, you might find you need to re-evaluate your management focus or decide you need some specific continuing education in a particular management area—or perhaps what you really need is someone else to take over these responsibilities. Your accountant should be able to help you make these decisions and guide you to the resources needed to achieve your financial goals.

Keep in mind that the cohorts you want to compare your professional financial performance with are important. While the Income Tax Act is a federal law, there are numerous provincial nuances (e.g., Provincial tax rates, subsidies, grants, etc.) that make it imperative to compare numbers within the province. The type of practice you are involved in is also very important as well. Specifically, the size of your practice in terms of numbers of doctors and gross revenue are key differentials.

Choosing Your Lawyer

What services could and should a lawyer provide for you throughout your professional career? Even as a student, you may have legal needs (e.g., if you or your family purchases a home, wills, powers of attorney, etc.). Around the time of graduation, most of you will be looking at job offers, and your lawyer's advice during the negotiation process and his or her review of your employment contract before you sign it is time and effort well invested.

If you go into private practice within a year or two, many of you will find yourselves choosing between buying an existing practice in its entirety or becoming a partner in an existing practice. Both of these moves typically require both partnership and shareholder agreements. Alternatively, starting your own practice requires a whole new set of challenges, from arranging your financing to negotiating leases and/or purchasing real estate, incorporation, registration of practice names, and so on. The time to get your lawyer involved is at the preliminary stage so as to guide rather than correct choices made.

As you progress through your professional career, some of your legal needs become more sophisticated (e.g., a simple will that was adequate when you were a student may evolve into a fairly complex estate plan involving trusts, complicated insurance policies, etc.). Further, you cannot separate your personal and professional lives. Just as changes in your professional situation should trigger a review of your legal arrangements and accompanying documentation, so should any major changes in your personal life or family situation. For example, the development of a new personal relationship may find you wondering if you need a marriage or cohabitation agreement. Likewise, births and deaths among your family and friends may necessitate the review of your will and estate arrangements or other critical planning. Most of you will purchase a series of homes to meet your changing personal and family needs. Some of you will become involved in investments and business outside of and/or within the profession that require your lawyer's assistance in such matters as negotiations, documentation, registration, and financing arrangements.

To be an informed consumer of legal services, it is important to understand that lawyers have traditionally practised in two broad areas of law, based on the traditional English system—Barristers or Solicitors. A litigator is the Canadian equivalent of an English Barrister, and these lawyers principally do courtroom or trial work in one of two broad areas: criminal work (when the state takes action against the individual) and civil litigation (when a person or group takes private action against another person or group). Solicitors are lawyers who do the non-courtroom work, and they typically focus on business law, taking care of your "day-to-day financial health."

Some lawyers devote their practice to serving the needs of health professionals. Similar to the discussion under accountants, it is important for your lawyer to know and not be reluctant to refer you to a legal specialist, should the need arise. Just as there are medical specialists, there are legal specialists, and these include tax, intellectual property, employment, litigation, and administrative law specialists. Administrative law deals with the specialized rules administered by your provincial licensing body. Therefore, one of the requirements of your chosen solicitor should be that he or she has a well-established network and working relationship with a variety of specialists that will likely need to be consulted with on your behalf over the course of your professional career.

Relationship Phase

Now that you have chosen a short list of those professionals that meet your needs and qualifications, the next step is to apply key relationship questions to assist in making your final decision. These include questions related to being a team player, having shared values, and, perhaps most importantly, providing the required level of comfort.

It is absolutely critical that you choose professionals who are team players. Your team of professionals is like an orchestra, with a rotating conductor—sometimes the accountant must lead the band, and other times it is essential that the lawyer or insurance broker take the lead. To achieve the best results for you, all of your professional advisors must be prepared to lead and to follow, depending on your needs in that particular circumstance. For example, there may be a particular thorny tax issue your accountant has identified. Often your lawyer must work with the accountant to ensure the appropriate solution. Likewise, your bank manager may have to appreciate and cooperate in reorganising the financing terms and timing of funds availability to create the critical audit trail. This is no time for prima donnas. The time spent posturing is time you are paying for; if communication is not complete and timely, you may suffer financially.

If you practice small animal medicine, inquire of the professional you are considering employing if they have a pet, and if so, how they take care of it and what role that pet plays in their life. In short, do they have an appreciation and respect for animals? And more importantly, do they walk the same walk that you do? It is certainly not essential that your professional advisors share your same hobbies and passions, but it is important that they appreciate and, if at all possible, share your core values (e.g., if certain social issues are important to you, does your financial advisor provide an array of investments that respect your ethical believes?).

Consider the comfort level you feel with your potential advisor. Are you relaxed and at ease in his or her company, and, most importantly, do you feel you can trust your potential advisor? Do your homework. Do what business people call "due diligence." However, once you have selected your short list, listen to your gut. If you just don't feel you like or trust or want to work with an individual, then don't. On the other hand, if there is an almost instantaneous rapport and interest between you, you probably have found the professional that is right for you in that category. Since you will be discussing many of your most important decisions, both professionally and personally, with this individual, and your goal is to have a long-term professional relationship with this individual, it is wise to pick someone you feel you can trust and would enjoy working with.

Initiating and Maintaining Relationships with Your Professional Advisors

Your big-picture goal should be to develop an ongoing relationship with your professional advisor and not have a one-off transactional arrangement; once you select your professional advisor (especially your lawyer and accountant), become a client even before you need their services! Keep in mind that in many situations, a professional advisor can only work for one party or the other; by developing an ongoing relationship, you will ensure that you get your first "draft pick" (so to speak) should a representation conflict arise.

Like every relation, matching and managing expectations is the key to ensuring the relationship works smoothly and increases the likelihood of achieving your goals and expected outcomes. When describing goals or expectations, use the "SMART formula" (Specific, Measurable, Action, Realistic, Timetable). Be as specific as possible (e.g., "I want you to have my draft tax return completed by April 1 of each year."); use measurable criteria (e.g., "I will return your phone calls within two business days."); be action oriented (e.g., "Prepare my GST returns."); be realistic (e.g., recognize that if you cannot return phone calls every day, you should not commit to doing so); and finally, use a timetable (e.g., set target dates, whenever possible).

Attend some of your potential advisor's speaking engagements or read what s/he writes. Find out how s/he likes to communicate, and share your communication style (e.g., some professionals are available by phone at certain times of the day, while others prefer email or faxes). Become self aware, and let your professional advisor know what works for you—specifically, how to contact you, how often you expect to be contacted, what times are good or bad, and if you prefer email, phone, fax, or letter.

Mentors

You are accountable for the degree of success of your own professional career, but there is no need to go it alone. One of the best ways to reach a professional goal is to find who has what you want and ask them to guide you to a similar achievement. Mentors guide, coach, and open doors to help you achieve your professional goals. Mentors are never paid.

Finding a Mentor

Your mentor might be a senior practitioner in the first practice you work, a veterinary college professor you worked for one summer, or the practitioner you volunteered with as a high school student. Finding a mentor can be hard work, and it may require a lot of perseverance to find a right fit. Professional organizations (e.g., Canadian Veterinary Medical Association, Ontario Veterinary Medical Association, etc.) are great places to go for assistance in finding your mentor.

Maintaining the Relationship With Your Mentor

In short, respect your mentor's time, advice, and experience. See your mentor regularly and at times that are convenient for him or her. Always express your appreciation and respect. Listen to what your mentor suggests, and respond accordingly. At the least, give his or her ideas serious consideration. Report back regarding what is working and what is not working for you.

It is often said that we learn from our mistakes; however, we can also learn from the mistakes of others. Ask your mentor about the things that s/he would do differently if his or her professional career could begin all over again. What were the obstacles that were overcome? How were the challenges handled? What was the smartest thing he or she did career-wise? Ask probing questions. Take good notes, and listen hard. Learn from the other person's mistakes and successes. Identify and repeat behaviour and attitudes that have led to your mentor's success. Report back to your mentor both your successes and failures.

Just as every actor must find his or her own "voice," each practitioner must discover the practice style that is authentic for him or her. Your mentor can provide invaluable critical feedback and positive reinforcement to help you grow personally and professionally. The goal is for you to develop confidence in your own judgments and abilities to self-evaluate your own competencies. However, do not make the mistake of thinking that you'll outgrow the feedback of knowledgeable and experienced co-professionals. One only has to look to the field of coaching in sports, where it is well recognized that top athletes reach and stay at their peak performance through the positive reinforcement and critical reality checks provided by their coaches.

There may come a time in a mentoring relationship when you must bring your relationship to a close. Let your mentor know at the start of the relationship that you realize this possibility, and set the ground rules for an exit strategy for either party. Indicators that it is time to move on include: you have outgrown the mentor, one or both of you is wasting the other's time; the enjoyment goes out of the relationship; you find your mentor is too negative or critical in nonconstructive ways; or you lose respect for one another. Losing a trusted mentor may be painful, but move on and find another.

Company Representatives

Pharmaceutical, pet food, and other suppliers of specialized products and/or services to the veterinary profession typically supply a range of support. Company representatives are also known by a variety of other names, including detail person, service representative, or sales manager. They may or may not be veterinarians, but regardless, they can become one of your most valuable resources in practice.

Company Representatives: What to Expect of Them

Detailed people primarily provide technical information and assistance. Their background can be everything from technical to veterinary practitioners; likewise, their academic and research background can include masters and PhD qualifications, whereas others are "street smart" about their company, products, and industry. Typically, company representatives will provide you with detailed information regarding the safe use and efficacy of their company's products and will back up these claims with peer-reviewed, published references on supportive clinical trials. It is important to distinguish between the published, peer-reviewed clinical trials and self-serving literature published by a company to extol the virtues of its products. Critically review the claimed product features and resulting benefits. If the time allocated is not enough, book another appointment. If you want more written materials, ask for them.

Discussions are usually geared toward safety, efficacy, and indications and contraindications of various products. It is an opportunity for the practitioner to make an informed opinion and base future decisions on product use and recommendations to clients. In short, the company representative provides the science from an applied perspective. Depending on your perspective and the needs of your practice, interactive discussion involving the practitioner, technicians, and other staff can be very useful.

When you have a problem with a company's product, the representative is the person to start with, and they should work quickly to resolve the problem. Finding solutions may involve other people in the company, and they are the ones that know best who to contact and what levers to pull to get things done expediently. A good company representative will return phone calls promptly, usually the same day or next, and provide any requested information in a timely fashion.

Company Representatives: What They Expect of You

Most problems involving company representatives revolve around proper etiquette. Company representatives expect to and should be seen on time, except in cases of genuine emergencies. Like you, they are professionals and have schedules to adhere to, and time is often our most precious commodity. If you must reschedule an appointment, let the company representative know as soon as possible; it is best to schedule time for telephone discussions or callbacks, as "telephone tag" is a time-waster for everyone. Always try to leave a message containing the purpose of your call and when you can be reached for a callback. Email is a tremendous resource in this area. Most company representatives make appointments. Insist that they all do.

While company representatives expect to be asked about clinical trials, they typically cannot or do not provide information on a competitor's products.

Don't try to put them in the difficult position of "bashing" their competitor's products. However, questions about research are important. Inquire about quantity of resources and types of research the company is doing. Also find out if there are research projects in which you might participate.

It is a good practice to take the time to get to know your company representative; don't underestimate the knowledge that can be gained from this person, as s/he often attends more conferences and is on the leading edge of continuing education. Don't be afraid to ask about articles from proceedings, etc., that you would find useful.

Be realistic and understand that the resources that various companies allocate to various activities differ. Furthermore, the budget that any given company representative may have to assist you in your activities depends on a variety of factors, including your purchases and potential purchasers from the parent company, your true worth as a key influencer of other professional purchasers, and your value in field studies and research studies. In any case, don't limit your discussions with company representatives to product promotions. Furthermore, consider the relationship with your company representative as a form of strategic alliance, in which the principle of fair-trading demands a win-win scenario for all parties involved.

Summary

Most of you entered veterinary school with a passion to become a clinician, and your professional education provides you with superb training to practice. However, as a professional graduate, you are entering a chaotic landscape in which you will be constantly forced to make decisions in areas outside your clinical training. The choices that you make regarding these non-clinical decisions will, among other things, profoundly influence the quality of life for you and your family as well as the success of your practice career. However, there is no need to go it alone. A key success factor for today's veterinary graduate is the power of the team. Use the techniques presented here to develop your own strategies to develop your support team of professional advisors, mentors, and company representatives.

Biography

Upon graduation from the Ontario Agricultural College, Dr. Brian Ausman went on to complete his DVM at the Ontario Veterinary College (OVC) in 1984. Following graduation Dr. Ausman ran a bovine herd health practice and worked for Agriculture Canada until his recruitment by the Canadian President of the Chow division of Ralston Purina Feeds to manage an extensive line of livestock feeds. His responsibilities included crafting and implementing detailed annual strategic business plans for which he won the highest international sales and marketing award. This led to his completing an MBA at Wilfred Laurier University.

Intrigued by the workings of our legal system, Dr. Ausman went on to do a law degree at the University of Western Ontario. Convinced that litigation was totally inappropriate for resolving most commercial disagreements, Dr. Ausman also became certified as a Mediator of Dispute Resolution and his current practice focuses on non-litigious and win-win outcomes. He advises and assists veterinarians across Canada on multidisciplinary legal and business challenges. Together with his qualifications as a real estate and business broker, he is uniquely qualified to assist professionals in buying and selling veterinary practices.

Believing strongly in the importance of "giving back" and the responsibility of veterinarians as animal advocates, Dr. Ausman became one of the founding Directors and provides pro bono legal counsel to Veterinarians Without Borders-Canada. As a volunteer guest lecturer, Dr. Ausman speaks annually to third year students at the OVC and to students at AVC on topics germane to the transition from student to professional.

Over the years, Dr. Ausman, along with his business partner and wife, Dr. Christine Stec, established three new veterinary hospitals and revitalized one existing practice.

Dr. Ausman enjoys life on a farm just north of Guelph with his wife Christine and their pet family of dogs and horses.

CHAPTER **1-4**

Learning a Living

Carl A. Osborne, DVM, PhD, Diplomate ACVIM
Veterinary Clinical Sciences Department,
College of Veterinary Medicine,
University of Minnesota,
St. Paul, Minnesota USA

> *Wisdom is the prime thing. Acquire wisdom and with
> all that you acquire, acquire understanding.*
>
> — Proverbs 4:7

Introduction

It is with great enthusiasm that I respond to the invitation to pen my thoughts about my ongoing journey of discovery. If you have innate curiosity about life, if you enjoy learning and teaching, if you are teachable, if you enjoy helping others grow, and you recognize that you may be asked to be a leader and a follower (both roles require desire and ability), then you would enjoy a career as a veterinarian.

In the following essay, I will provide answers to the following questions:

1. What are the definitions of the terms "knowledge," "wisdom," and "understanding," and how do they relate to each other?

2.   What is the important relationship between how, when, and why treatment of specific diseases should be understood?
3.   How would you define learning?
4.   Should students be expected to apply the concept of academism to their patients?
5.   What is the greatest barrier to acquisition of knowledge, wisdom, and understanding about various aspects of veterinary medicine?
6.   In what way is expression of compassion a basic expectation of veterinarians?
7.   What is the ultimate goal of veterinary curricula?
8.   If one accepts the premise that it is never too late to learn, in what context can we learn things too late?
9.   When studying for an examination, what criteria can learners use to determine when they understand and can apply the material?
10.   What is the literal meaning of the term "doctor," and how does this meaning relate to knowledge, wisdom, and understanding?
11.   In the context of "learning a living," what is required in addition to the desire to learn?
12.   What is our purpose in life?
13.   What can we do to bring true happiness to others and ourselves?
14.   What is the greatest reward for doing?

Learning and Study Defined

How would you define learning? Webster's dictionary defines "learning" as acquiring knowledge or skill by study or experience.[1] Webster's dictionary defines "study" as the act or process of applying our mind in order to acquire knowledge by reading or investigating.[1] Unfortunately, Webster's definition of study emphasizes learning knowledge without emphasizing the importance of learning wisdom. What is the difference?

Knowledge stems from the Greek term "gnosis" (as in the words diagnosis and ignorance) and when translated as "knowledge," it indicates familiarity with relevant information (or facts) acquired by personal experience, observation, or study. Unfortunately, many of us have been taught to over-emphasize the accumulation of new knowledge to a point where we neglect the development of two other essential components of learning – wisdom and understanding. How would you compare the attribute of knowledge to the attributes of wisdom and understanding? How is knowledge of this difference of practical value?

Wisdom consists of acquiring a combination of knowledge and understanding that enables us to successfully apply knowledge. Those who acquire wisdom recognize the importance of acquiring sufficient breadth of knowledge and depth of understanding to provide sound clinical judgment. Although essential, facts per se are usually of little value to our patients. Medical facts only become useful to the extent they can be used to define and solve clinical problems. If we acquire knowledge but do not learn how to properly apply it, we will not acquire wisdom. Wisdom is a blend of many attributes in addition to knowledge. They include understanding, discernment, thinking ability, intelligence, experience, diligence, shrewdness (the opposite of gullibilty or naivete), and good judgment. Let us consider the attribute of understanding in greater detail.

Acquiring understanding calls for contemplating how new information fits in with the knowledge we already have. Understanding is related to our ability to see how various aspects of a subject (such as specific functions of a kidney) relate to each other, and also our ability to grasp how individual parts work together to form the whole (i.e., how individual renal functions work together to maintain homeostasis). Those who seek to understand accurate knowledge are not satisfied with the superficial view of a subject. As with a puzzle, a person who understands a subject can put separate pieces together so s/he can see the whole. In other words, the person who understands a subject can see the entire forest in addition to individual trees.

This aspect of understanding is important, because we are unlikely to be able to retain and properly apply new knowledge unless we understand it. When we attend lectures or seminars, we are likely to become frustrated unless we understand where each new piece of information fits into the scheme of things. For example, the priority of information to be learned about therapy of a specific disease should initially encompass why treatment is needed, followed by learning about when and how to give specific, supportive, symptomatic, and/or palliative forms of treatment. The why and when of the learning process provides us with a firm foundation for determining how to treat and prevent various diseases. If a veterinarian knows how to treat or prevent a disease, but does not understand why or when such action is warranted, misapplication of acquired knowledge is inevitable. The results can be catastrophic. However, if we continue to keep our minds open in context of learning more about a subject, then time, continued study, and experience will help us to gain greater understanding. In contrast, selfish pride, stubbornness, self-will, over-confidence, and independence can stunt the growth of our power of understanding.

Now that we have defined knowledge, wisdom, and understanding, how would you redefine learning? I propose that Webster's dictionary definition of learning and study be expanded such that they become acts or processes of applying the mind in order to acquire knowledge, wisdom, and understanding. As we personally experience the deep satisfaction of saving a patient's life or restoring their health as a result of application of our knowledge, wisdom, and understanding, learning often becomes an energy-deriving and exhilarating process. What at first seems to be a disciplined exercise becomes, with time, a source of great satisfaction.

Being an "Academic Practitioner"

How do these principles relate to private, academic, or practitioner choices? Perhaps we should begin to answer this question by thinking about the meaning of the word academic. Although the exact definition of academic may vary depending on the context in which this term is used, in context of medical vernacular an "academic" diagnosis often is associated with the stereotype of being theoretical or something that has no direct or practical application. Likewise, an "academic" clinician is often perceived as one who is associated with the "ivory tower" and one who lacks practical experience in dealing with the "real world." However, in context of providing quality patient care, is this perception valid?

Please consider this point: differences in missions of university veterinary teaching hospitals and missions of veterinary hospitals staffed by colleagues in private practice have often been misinterpreted to reflect the mistaken notion that "academic" problem-solving by university faculty is fundamentally different from "practical" problem-solving by primary care practitioners. Again I ask the question: is this distinction valid? When viewed in context of appropriate application of knowledge, wisdom, and understanding in caring for patients, it is apparent that this difference is conceptually inaccurate. True, differences are unavoidable in the quantity of readily available knowledge, wisdom, and understanding in veterinary teaching hospitals that are typically staffed by many board-certified specialists compared to private practices that are staffed by one or more primary care veterinarians. However, no barrier exists, except a self-imposed one, to acquisition and use of available knowledge, wisdom, and understanding that aids in management of patients in either environment. Please let me illustrate my point by asking you to consider this question: If you or a member of your family were faced with a life-threatening illness, would you have more confidence in the recommendations of a physician trained to think in an "academic" way that incorporated the fundamentals of evidence-based medicine, or in the advice of a physician who adopted the philosophy of empirical thinking in a "practical" way?

What is the point? In context of appropriate patient care, the point is that the true nature of academism relates primarily to the orientation of our thoughts, rather than to our relationship to a private practice, specialty practice, or veterinary teaching hospital. The key issue is realization of the need to think in an academic or scientific way. It involves the way we look at things. In providing care for our patients, shouldn't we seek and rely upon verifiable diagnostic and therapeutic observations that could, if necessary, be reproduced by other members of our hospital? To illustrate, would you continue to rely upon a thermometer that measured a normal temperature of 38.5°C on one day and a normal temperature of 41°C the next day?

In context of quality patient care, scientific thinking is a major responsibility for all of us. We should all be striving to practice academic ways of thinking. The concept of "academic practitioner" should be encouraged. Why? Because the application of such thinking to our patients allows us to demonstrate our compassion in the way most expected of us – namely, that we strive at all times to be professionally competent. One of the most important goals of our profession is to foster, encourage, promote, and demand academism from ourselves and from our colleagues. Of course, in the process, we should not minimize the need for practicality. However, our allegiance to practicality should not be misdirected. Practicality may be a virtue, provided one does not hide behind it as an expedient excuse for ignorance.

Learning How to Learn

When will we stop becoming students? Is it after we formally receive our DVM degrees? Is it when an accredited specialty board certifies us? Of course not! Our formal course of study in colleges of veterinary medicine is designed primarily to help us to learn how to learn. Ralph Waldo Emerson summarized it this way: "The things taught in schools and colleges are not an education, but the means of an education."[2] The ultimate goal of our formal veterinary curricula should be to shift the responsibility of pursuing education from teachers to each individual student. In this context, we become educated when we realize that college merely prepares us to learn intelligently. As Alan Gregg, a physician educator put it, "A good education should leave much to be desired."[3] In other words, it's never too late to learn.

The axiom "it is never too late to learn" is conceptually true. In practice, however, some things can be learned too late to be of optimum value. For example, our patients may suffer serious and even fatal adverse consequences if we fail to learn and follow directions when using various diagnostic and therapeutic techniques. This is sometimes called "learning in the school of hard knocks" (e.g., by experiencing difficulties first hand). Although experience is an effective teacher, she is often a tough one for the ignorant. Why? Because she gives the test first and the lesson afterward. Therefore, to minimize learning by the method of experiencing the unwanted consequences of our mistakes, we must seek opportunities to learn in a timely fashion. Keeping in mind that "almost right" is still wrong, we must also be discriminating of what we learn and how and where we learn it. When we are wise, we are most likely to learn lessons from the mistakes of others (i.e., we are teachable); when we are ignorant, we often learn too late from our own.

To Teach Is To Learn Twice

When studying for an examination, what criteria can learners use to determine when they understand and can apply the material? Consider the following situation. Have you ever told a classmate or colleague that you know the information, but you cannot express the concepts in words? If so, it is likely that you are stating that you do not understand the information to the extent that you can apply it in properly caring for your patients. Let us return to the question, "How do you know when you know?" The criteria that I find most reliable in assessing when I understand the information well enough to put it into practice is the point at which I can readily and accurately explain it to others in a straightforward fashion. It is one thing to learn a subject for our own use; it is often a greater thing to learn a subject with the goal of teaching it to others.

Please consider learning from the following point of view. The word "doctor" is derived from the Latin term "docere," meaning "to teach." Doesn't it follow that doctors teach? Now, if it is true that we can lead horses to water but can't make them drink, does it follow that in our role as teachers we can lead students to knowledge, but we can't make them think? The analogy is clear, but it is not positive. A more effective approach to teaching would be to embrace the concept, "I can lead students to knowledge, but how can I help them to think?" The challenge is clear, and teachers (doctors) who respond to it will benefit themselves as well as others. Why so? Because to teach is to learn twice!

"Learning a Living"

The Veterinarian's Oath states in part, "I accept as a lifelong obligation the continual improvement of my professional knowledge and competence."[4] Isn't this a solemn promise that we will strive to "learn a living"? Our awareness of the need for knowledge and wisdom opens the door to our acquiring them. Our desire to learn means that we are teachable. In contrast, my experience has been that it is difficult for us to begin to learn what we think we already know. To paraphrase, the person who knows everything has a lot to learn.

But more is required than our desire to learn. That desire must be translated into action. Learning a living encompasses mastering and continually applying effective methods of learning in addition to mastering end points of learning. We must continually train our brain to learn a living. Just as physical fitness ebbs as a result of physical inactivity, effective learning vanishes with mental inactivity. The well-known adage, "use it or lose it," applies to our learning a living. To this end, King Solomon penned this enduring principle several thousand years ago: "A wise person will listen and take in more instruction, and a man of understanding is the one who acquires skillful direction" (Proverbs 1:5). Isn't it obvious that we must continually train our brain to "learn a living"?

What Is Our Purpose In Life?

Have you ever contemplated the answer to this question? What can we do to bring true happiness to ourselves and to others? After having the privilege of spending more than four decades as an "academic" member of the veterinary profession, I would like to share my answer with you.

Albert Einstein, one of the world's most famous scientists and philosophers, wrote the following admonition concerning the purpose of life. He said, "Strive not to be a man (or woman) of success, strive to be a person of value."[2] What does being a person of value encompass? How does it differ from being a person of success? How can we put this principle into practice?

I interpret Einstein's admonition to mean that the value of what we unselfishly do to benefit others is of greater overall benefit than the value of what we do ourselves to achieve personal success. In this context, we become selfish not by pursing our own needs, but rather by neglecting the needs of others. It follows that our true value in life should be measured in context of what it accomplishes on behalf of others, and not just in light of what it does for us in the way of income or prestige.

The definition of a profession encompasses the concept of an occupation guided by an ethical code that has a service motive rather than a profit motive. In this context, wouldn't it be reasonable to expect that the conduct of members of a profession motivated to serve others would be primarily based on giving rather than getting? Whereas companies like General Motors and Microsoft are primarily motivated by making a monetary profit, it is my interpretation that the health professions should be primarily motivated by a desire to direct their talents and resources toward the care of living beings – animal and human.[5] Thus, we must use caution to avoid the tendency to selfishly exploit circumstances so as to unduly profit from the illnesses of others. Rather, we strive to be compassionate by having empathy for the distress and misfortunes of others combined with a compelling heartfelt desire to help them.

If ethical conduct directs the veterinary profession primarily toward a service rather than a profit orientation, should the amount of our net incomes be the primary measure of our success? If we adhere to Einstein's admonition to strive to be persons of value, perhaps the norm of success should be viewed in context of the overall impact of our professional services on the health and welfare of animals under our care rather than "the bottom line." Perhaps in addition to evaluating our year-end fiscal balance, we should include the number of clients and patients that have benefited by our efforts to serve their needs.[5]

Returning to the question, "What is our purpose in life?" as veterinarians, our mission is to serve rather than be served. Therefore, we must uphold the traditional value of caring and sharing by avoiding the contemporary code of making and taking with indifference toward the needs of others. As members of a "profession," we should use our God-given energy, talents, and resources to provide for the needs and welfare of other beings.

What can we do to bring true happiness to others and ourselves? Being guided by the enduring principle that there is greater happiness in giving than receiving, it becomes apparent that true happiness comes with helping others in need. In this context, happiness is a by-product of doing things for others, and it is not an end in itself.

In reflecting on the activities and accomplishments of colleagues, friends, and family that I have known during my lifetime, it is my conclusion that what we do for ourselves dies with us. In contrast, what we do for others lives on. Therefore, until the day arrives when our lamp of service is extinguished, let us continue to give of our talents and energies in behalf of the welfare of others.

What Is the Greatest Reward for Doing?

Recently, Dr. John Wright, past-president of the American Association of Human Animal Bond Veterinarians, asked me what I considered to be the most significant changes in the human-animal bond in context of my career as a veterinarian. I began to reflect on the phenomenal changes that have occurred in the practice of veterinary medicine since I graduated from Purdue University's School of Veterinary Medicine in 1964. Many advances in patient care that have occurred during the past 44 years are related to the emergence of an evidence-based approach to diagnosis and therapy. This in turn has resulted in a huge paradigm shift in the philosophy of the practice of veterinary medicine from an art based largely on empiricism, to a science built on the foundations of verifiable observations (knowledge) and advances in technology. However, in my instance, a more significant change that has occurred in context of the human-animal bond is related to my perspective of the high value that I place on the lives of animals. Please consider the following:

At one time, I accepted the scientific premise that evolutionary random mutations and natural selection were responsible for the complex structural and functional design of living things.[6] However, as I learned more about the anatomical, physiological, biochemical, and genetic complexities of biological systems, I began to diligently search for answers about the origin and purpose of life. As I have described elsewhere,[7] my search for answers to these questions uncovered convincing evidence that life could not originate by chance. Rather, scientific logic based on probability, and the principle of cause and effect, point to the conclusion that an intelligent designer is responsible for the amazing structural and functional design found in living beings – animal and human. This conclusion heightened my appreciation and respect for all forms of life. Although in my role as a veterinarian I have been trained to provide care primarily for companion animals, I am not a "species racist." Like many others before me, I recognize that of all professions, the veterinary profession should champion respect for, and appreciation of, all forms of life.

In the context of the practice of veterinary medicine and the human-animal bond, why is the issue of the origin and purpose of life important? If we accept the premise that we are the product of an intelligent designer, then it follows that the designer had a purpose for all living things. According to the Bible, God put man in charge of the animals (Genesis 1:28) and entrusted the earth to man's protective care (Genesis 2:15; Psalm 115:16). As caretakers, however, humans were not to upset the balance of nature. Man's having the animals in subjection placed upon him a stewardship for which he would always be held accountable (Luke 12:48). As with humans (I also am dedicated to the human-human bond), I have come to view the life of animals as precious (Matthew 10:29). Does this mean I wouldn't harm an ant? The answer is that I would not harm an ant (or any other form of life) if the sole purpose for harming the ant is pleasure or thoughtless demonstration of superiority.

In the context of being a veterinarian, I view my role as a doctor as an extension of this stewardship. Although my training has led me to "specialize" in disorders of the urinary system, I am not a "body system racist." Rather,

I strive to provide the type of care for my patients that I would desire for myself. In addition, in my role as a university faculty member, I recognize that veterinary teaching hospitals not only are expected to use contemporary knowledge, but they also have the obligation to create and disseminate new knowledge about the causes, diagnosis, treatment, and prevention of various diseases. However, I am constantly on guard not to let the intellectual stimulation associated with scientific investigation override concern for my patients. In addition, I constantly remind myself to not let the desire for peer recognition or personal financial profit compromise their care and welfare. Despite our DVM, VMD, DMV, AHT, and PhD degrees, we are all members of a profession whose mission fosters the welfare of others. Our mission is to serve, not to be served. Therefore, the true importance of what we do should be measured in context of what it accomplishes on behalf of others, not just in light of what it does for us in terms of prestige or personal income.

The opportunity to contribute to the welfare of animals and their human companions in my role as an academic veterinarian has been a privilege and a richly rewarding experience. In fact, I have learned that the greatest reward for doing is the opportunity to do more.

Summary: Lessons I Have Learned

- I've learned – Not to let preoccupation with what I don't have crowd out my appreciation for what I do have.
- I've learned – It's often small, daily happenings that make life enjoyable.
- I've learned – Under the hard shell of others is usually someone who deserves to be appreciated and valued.
- I've learned – It is far better to say you won't do something than to say you will and not do it.
- I've learned – To ignore the facts does not change the facts.
- I've learned –The best veterinary teaching hospitals in the world should not only utilize contemporary knowledge, they should create it.[8]
- I've learned – The often quoted cliché, "To publish or perish," applies more to the survival of our patients than to the survival of careers of academicians employed by universities.[9]
- I've learned – Just because a thousand people say a foolish thing, it's still a foolish thing.
- I've learned – We must not let the pursuit of knowledge become sidelined by a scramble for funds, recognition, or prestige. To this end, there

is almost no limit to what we can accomplish, as long as we do not become preoccupied with who gets the credit.

- I've learned – We must strive to continually improve our knowledge and competence. To paraphrase the words of Dr. Donald G. Low, this will help us to practice 30 to 40 years of veterinary medicine in our professional lifetimes rather than repeat one year 30 to 40 times.[7]

- I've learned – Belief or unbelief does not alter the truth. Clinical impressions are inherently unreliable, generally conforming to our preconceived biases. However, strong preconceptions are not a substitute for objective evidence. We should use caution to not ignore data because it does not coincide with our beliefs. Rather than interpreting facts in light of preconceived conclusions, we must be alert to allow reproducible observations (facts) to lead us to reasonable conclusions.

- I've learned – Diagnoses are often a matter of opinion rather than a matter of fact. It is one thing to make a diagnosis and another thing to substantiate it. Just because a favorable outcome occurs in association with our treatment does not prove that our diagnosis was correct (or that our treatment was effective).

- I've learned – Waiting to pursue the diagnosis of the underlying cause of a disease until the patient has not responded to symptomatic shotgun therapy is like saying, "Ready! Fire! Aim!" Not only does this approach to diagnosis often result in use of drugs that miss the therapeutic target, it often results in iatrogenic damage to surrounding structures.

- I've learned – Hippocrates provided the following advice: "As to diseases, make a habit of two things – to help, or at least do no harm."[10] When confronted with situations in which therapeutic options are associated with significant risk to the patient, we must use caution to avoid the mindset of "don't just stand there, do something." Why? Because, although the psychological pressure imposed on veterinarians to do something is occasionally overwhelming, our desire to do something must be evaluated in light of the potential benefits and risks to the patient. There are times when it is in the patient's best interest to "don't just do something, stand there!"[10] We must not misplace emphasis on "what treatment to prescribe," when the fundamental question is "whether or not to prescribe."

- I've learned – Prognosis of disease requires judgment in the absence of certainty. Therefore, when making prognoses, we must remember that "almost right" is still wrong. For some patients, prognoses are life saving; for others, they are a death sentence.

- I've learned – Just because two events occur in consecutive order does not prove a cause-and-effect relationship. Unrelated coincidences commonly are associated with the treatment and subsequent clinical course of diseases. Therefore, we must use appropriate caution in interpreting uncontrolled empirical observations.

- I've learned – Diseases are often self-limiting. In fact, the severity of many disorders declines within a day or two. In this situation, any treatment may appear to be beneficial as long as it is not harmful.
- I've learned – One of the best ways for me to grow as a person is to surround myself and learn from people wiser than I am.
- I've learned – Recognition that I do not have all the answers allows me to learn from others.
- I've learned – We're all ignorant, only on different subjects.[2]
- I've learned – A smile has great face value.
- I've learned – Everyone I meet deserves to be greeted with a smile. S (smiling) M(makes) I(individual) L(lives) E(enjoyable)
- I've learned – Happiness is a by-product of doing things for others and not an end in itself.
- I've learned – A small deed done is greater than a great deed planned.
- I've learned – The opportunity of a lifetime only exists during the lifetime of the opportunity.
- I've learned – When I harbor bitterness, happiness will dock elsewhere.
- I've learned – To practice trusting others as I want them to trust me.
- I've learned – Being mild-mannered is not synonymous with being weak. It takes great strength to be mild during provocation.
- I've learned – We should keep our words both soft and tender, because tomorrow we may have to eat them.
- I've learned – The best defense against misrepresentation is fine conduct.
- I've learned – To avoid witticisms at the expense of others.
- I've learned – Most people classify wits either as half-, nit-, or dim-.
- I've learned – It makes others feel good all over when we tell them that their work has been well done.
- I've learned – When I make a choice, it's up to me to make it work.
- I've learned – Change is inevitable; progress is optional.
- I've learned – I can't choose what misfortunes may come my way, but I can choose how I will respond to them.
- I've learned – S/he who limps still walks.
- I've learned – Nothing steals happiness more than competitive comparison of ourselves with others.
- I've learned – The best things in life aren't things.
- I've learned – Very few rich men own their property. The property owns them.

- I've learned – The danger of acquiring the "apostrophe syndrome."
- I've learned – What we do for ourselves dies with us. It's what we unselfishly do for others that lives on.
- I've learned – To a friend's house the road is never long.
- I've learned – One of the greatest acts of kindness friends can give each other is always the truth.
- I've learned – Not to blame the messenger for the message.
- I've learned – A true friend is a person with whom I may be sincere; before him I may think aloud.
- I've learned – Appreciation lubricates the friction of close association.
- I've learned – There are only two reasons people will come to see me: because they want to or because they have to.
- I've learned – It is best to respond to the faults of others as gently as I do with my own.
- I've learned – A friend, not an apple, a day keeps the doctor away.
- I've learned – The only way to have a friend is to be one.
- I've learned – Empathy encompasses our capacity to appreciate and understand the other person's point of view, whether we agree with her/him or not.
- I've learned – Faithful friends are beyond price; their worth is more than money can buy.
- I've learned – To love and be loved brings the greatest happiness of existence.
- I've learned – Love can only be measured by the action it prompts.

References

1.   Webster's New World Dictionary of the American Language. 2nd ed. Springfield, MA: Merriam-Webster, 1970:1640.
2.   Seldes G. The great quotations. In: The Great Quotations. Secaucus, NJ: Citadel Press, 1983:283.
3.   Strauss MB. Familiar Medical Quotations. Boston: Little, Brown & Co, 1968:49.
4.   Osborne CA. The veterinarian's oath: are you keeping your promise? J Am Vet Med Assoc 1991;198:1906-1908.
5.   Osborne CA. What are veterinarians worth? J Am Vet Med Assoc 2001;219:302-303.
6.   Smith HW. The evolution of the kidney. In: Chasis H, Goldring W, eds. Homer William Smith: His Scientific and Literary Achievements. New York, NY: University Press, 1965:71-92.
7.   Osborne CA. Golden rules to nurture nephrologic logic. J Am Vet Med Assoc 2000;217:1622-1624.

8. Koltveit AJ. In appreciation of authors. J Am Vet Med Assoc 1976;168:574.
9. Osborne CA. Don't just do something – stand there: an exposition of Hippocrates' admonition "First do no Harm." Comp Cont Ed 1991;13:1248-1262.

Biography

Carl A. Osborne is a professor in the Veterinary Clinical Sciences Department at the University of Minnesota. He earned the DVM degree in 1964 from Purdue University and the PhD degree from the University of Minnesota in 1970. He is a charter diplomate and past president of the American College of Veterinary Internal Medicine. He has also served as president of the World Small Animal Veterinary Association and president of the American Society of Veterinary Nephrology and Urology. He is a part of the nephrology and urology team at the University of Minnesota, whose mission is "to enhance the quality and quantity of life of all creatures, great and small. We are committed to development of noninvasive methods that will consistently and safely prevent and cure diseases of the urinary system. Our mission encompasses compassionate utilization of contemporary science and selection of clinical teams to provide care that we would select for ourselves. We are dedicated to the welfare of our patients first and last," says Osborne. To this end, Osborne and his colleagues have been very active in nutritional research related to the urinary system of companion animals.

Osborne has authored or co-authored more than 1000 scientific articles and has written extensively about ethical issues frequently encountered by veterinarians. He has also given almost 600 scientific seminars throughout the world. Osborne's professional mission is to "devote my God-given energies, talents, and resources toward caring about others. By practicing the Golden Rule, I will teach students as I would want to be taught, and I will treat patients and their families as I would want to be treated. I will try to give others reason to smile, help them to cry, and provide them with a sound basis for hope. As a member of a health profession that abides by an ethical code, I am committed to a service rather than a profit orientation."

What Organizations Do I Join?

John Tait, BSc, DVM, MBA, CFP, ADR
Managing Partner, Ontario Veterinary Group,
Toronto, Ontario
Assistant Professor, Ontario Veterinary College,
Guelph, Ontario

> *The height of your accomplishments will equal
> the depth of your convictions.*
>
> — William F. Scolavino

As a member of any professional or local community, there are many options available for membership and participation. Each individual's career and leisure goals influence how organizational memberships are prioritized.

Professionally, your decision as to which organizations to affiliate yourself with or belong to is sometimes controlled for you. For instance, licensing bodies dictate that you must become a member in order to practice, and therefore such memberships are mandatory. However, many of the self-interest veterinary medical associations (VMAs) offer a variety of value-added services for both the individual veterinarian and the veterinary business entity; as membership is generally optional, it is at the discretion of the veterinarian whether to join or not.

The most prevalent and visible VMAs exist to support practitioners in all areas of practice; however, with the expansion of veterinary medicine to encompass a variety of alternate career paths (e.g., industry, management, and teaching/research), a variety of other VMAs have emerged, each dedicated to a specific career focus. Veterinary medical associations may also be categorized by their geographical presence, species orientation, and/or services they provide to their members. As a potential or current member, you will evaluate your membership based on the perceived value you obtain from membership fees (i.e., the return on your investment) and how the services or information available to you as a member meet your specific needs. A few examples of value-added services include access to continuing education (CE), job placement activity, management support and/or education, career support outside of practice, and access to current news and information relating to the profession.

In Canada, there is a national VMA and various provincial and regional VMAs. Nationally, the Canadian Veterinary Medical Association (CVMA) offers CE on both clinical and managerial issues in a variety of formats (including an annual conference), provides practice management support, represents national interests at international forums, disseminates information to the profession, and responds to current issues relevant to all Canadian veterinarians.

Various provincial VMAs often offer much more targeted services and benefits for their members, predominantly focusing on province-specific issues; however, some provincial VMAs have developed programs and expertise with relevance outside of their provincial boundaries, providing value to the entire profession. An example of this is the Ontario Veterinary Medical Association (OVMA), which is one of the most innovative VMAs in Canada. The OVMA contributes to the economic betterment of Canadian practitioners through research into practice management and economics. It has pioneered tools adopted in selected provinces, such as the Suggested Fee Guide, Associate Salary survey, and Veterinary Hospital Staff survey, and the OVMA continues to be a leader in developing resources for veterinarians, including such programs as the Farley Fund and consultancy program to monitor practice efficiency. Further, the OVMA hosts the country's largest and best-attended annual CE forum.

Other provincial VMAs also offer benefits and services specific to their members. Several self-interest VMAs are species rather than geography specific and, therefore, cross provincial as well as international borders. The most well known for companion animal practice is the American Animal Hospital Association (AAHA). AAHA consists of some 39,000 companion animal practice team members and 3,000 plus companion animal practices across North

America. Established in the early 1900s, AAHA was built around its standards for companion animal practice. Practices must qualify to be "accredited," meaning they must meet the highest standards of practice in the field of companion animal medicine in terms of their facilities, equipment, services, management practices, employee education, training, etc. The position statements of AAHA on issues affecting all aspects of the profession are recognized and widely endorsed on a global level. AAHA offers a number of affinity programs to members in both Canada and the United States to assist with numerous individual career planning and employment issues. It also offers the widest breadth of CE for companion animal practice teams in a variety of convenient formats and at various levels of application. Key to the branding effectiveness of AAHA is its efforts to educate and advertise to clients and to signal the importance of increased authenticity associated with its brand (e.g., AAHA accreditation) in a companion animal hospital.

Internationally, organizations including the American Association of Equine Practitioners (AAEP), American Association of Bovine Practitioners (AABP), and American Association of Feline Practitioners (AAFP) are leaders in their various species-specific fields, and they host their own member forums for CE as well as distribute current information to their members on a regular basis.

Veterinary medicine is also organized regionally or by the local community in most areas of the country. Participation in these organizations is often the most effective way to stay abreast of current community events, to plan and collaborate with local colleagues, and to share information or discuss issues of mutual concern.

More recently, practice management functions have become more organized into VMAs with this common purpose. Groups such as the Veterinary Practice Managers and Consultant's Association (VPMCA) and Veterinary Management Groups (VMG's) are "sole purpose" organizations dedicated to practice management issues.

The veterinary medicine profession has organized itself more globally in recent years as well. Large, multipurpose organizations such as the American Veterinary Medical Association (AVMA) are responsible for functions with a global reach, including the specialty colleges for various disciplines, the accreditation of veterinary schools, CE across species, liaising with other VMAs, and playing a role in the licensing of veterinarians.

Finally, some organizations have no membership fee but exist for the betterment of the profession and are supported with the aid of volunteers and sponsors. Resources such as the National Commission on Veterinary Economic Issues allow veterinarians to assess their business performance against their peers and access information to improve their practice's performance.

So where to start? Assess the value offered, examine the frequency and methodology or route of member contact, benefits offered, resources available, networking opportunities, current career needs, area of interest, and reference information from current members. Determine what membership will mean not only to you but to your practice or career path now and in the future; VMA membership provides an excellent stepping stone for giving something back to your professions (see later chapter on this topic in Section 8).

Biography

For Dr. Tait's biography, please see the Section 1 Introduction on page 3.

CHAPTER 1-6

Should I Buy, Join or Set Up My Own Practice?

Darrell Tracey, CA

Regional Professional Services Leader, West Coast

This is a question you may be asking yourselves as you prepare to embark on your career as a veterinarian. The choices may seem daunting, but the process is a lot easier if you focus on the right things.

There are many avenues that you could pursue as you establish you career. These are not mutually exclusive—as many of you will follow more than one of these paths during your professional lives. You may start in one place, make a turn in another direction for a few years, and make one or two more turns before it's time to retire. This is not uncommon, nor is it something to fear. In fact, it is to be embraced. These changes occur naturally as you gain experience in your profession. With experience comes confidence and, hopefully, increased income and new opportunities and challenges.

Most young professionals, such as you, aspire to purchase their own clinic/business at some point. It may be as a sole owner, as a partner with one or more colleagues or as part of a major business operation/chain of clinics.

Before we look at these options, there is another option that is very simple and may be attractive, at least initially. That is, employment in a clinic owned by someone else.

Advantages of employment:
- Simple
- No capital investment required up front
- No risk of business loss
- Regular pay cheque
- Business concerns are not yours
- Reduced liability

Disadvantages of employment:
- Very limited ability to deduct expenses from employment income
- No ownership in the business
- Your efforts build someone else's business—not your own
- Subject to marginal personal tax rates (more detail to follow).

Employment may be viable as you gain experience and strengthen your financial position after graduation. It may allow you to pay down student loans and help you decide what type of practice you would like to own in the future.

In anything other than an employment situation, you will be running your own business and have some important decisions to make. Two of these decisions are:

1. How independent do you want to be?
2. Do I incorporate?

Degree of Independence

Your choices are basically as follows:

(a) Work as an associate:
- You work as a subcontractor for one or more veterinarian clinics
- Your income is based on a contract for services and you invoice the entities to which you are providing your services (your customers)
- You register for GST/HST, charge and collect it from your customers
- You record all GST/HST you pay on your business expenditures
- You file GST/HST return
- Your income is, at best, partially based on profitability of the business—so you have less risk but also less upside potential
- You initially avoid the capital investment needed to start or purchase a practice—although you may have an opportunity to buy part or all of the practice at some point
- You are not really your own boss until that happens and you have to be able to work with the business owner

(b) Independent sole owner
- You set up and run your own clinic/business or buy an existing practice
- The significant capital outlay must be funded, often by debt—

which means you must qualify and be able to service that debt in addition to all ongoing business expenses (premises lease, equipment purchases or lease payments, leasehold improvements, inventory and supplies, staffing costs, advertising and promotion , etc)

- GST/HST and tax filings are the same as in (a) above
- You are your own boss so have complete independence

(c) Partner
- Here you run the business together with one or more colleagues as partners
- A partnership agreement governs the way you operate and how you share income, expenses, risks and rewards
- This can be good initially, as you share the start-up costs, operating costs and risks, etc.
- But the trade-off is a loss of complete autonomy—you lose sole decision-making power and share the upside with others
- Partners don't always agree on all aspects of the business, so there is potential for conflict.

So, you must weigh the pros and cons for each of these options to determine which is best for you—at a particular point in time. We often see young professionals start as an associate and progress to being an owner after a couple of years of experience. This happens either in the clinic in which they have been associates or by joining forces with colleagues or by purchasing a practice.

Incorporation

The first thing you need to know about incorporation is that it's simply an alternative way to operate your own business. In other words, everything you can do as an unincorporated, self-employed individual you can do as an incorporated practice. As a result, the three options described above regarding independence, apply equally to the incorporated veterinarian.

If that is the case, then why bother to incorporate?

Let's look at the main reasons to incorporate.

Income Tax Rates

When you incorporate, you create a separate and distinct taxpayer from yourself.

As you may work in any of the Canadian provinces or territories, I won't get into specific tax rates, since they vary among the jurisdictions. But the following comments will provide perspective on the tax benefits of incorporating in any jurisdiction in Canada.

The maximum marginal personal tax rate is in the range of 43% to 44% in most jurisdictions and is reached at taxable income levels in the range of $120,000 to $130,000.

In contrast, a Canadian Controlled Private Corporation (CCPC) carrying on an active business in Canada, such as a veterinary practice, is subject to a tax rate of only approximately 13 % or 14% on the first $500,000 of annual taxable income.

This is a dramatic difference of approximately 30% in tax rates on business income. (I will use 13% for corporate tax and 43% for personal tax for the remainder of this discussion).

WOW—30% less—almost a "no brainer", right? Well, not necessarily.

Let's briefly look at the Canadian tax system for incorporated professionals.

The corporation is a separate taxpayer and pays tax on its taxable income. The after- tax funds belong to the corporation. So, how do you get funds out of the corporation for personal use? There are basically two ways:

Salary

A salary is deductible to the corporation (so reduces tax at the rate of 13%) and is taxable to you at regular personal rates (maximum of 43%).

Dividends

A dividend is a distribution to shareholders of the corporation out of after-tax corporate funds. So the corporation has already paid tax at 13% and you then pay tax personally on dividends. However, the rate on dividends you receive is lower than on salaries—so you have to look at the combined tax for you and your corporation.

This can be a bit confusing but is valuable to understand as we look at factors to consider in determining the right time for you to incorporate.

- *Personal cash flow needs*

If you need all available cash from the business for personal use, the tax rate advantage of incorporating may be significantly reduced because you are taking all of the funds out and paying personal tax on them.

Our tax system is intended to be integrated so that the combined personal and corporate tax will be the same as if the income were earned directly by the individual. This is a key concept in the decision to incorporate—the 30% differential in rates is not a tax savings. It is only a deferral and only to the extent that you don't immediately take all funds out of the corporation, or to the extent you can otherwise reduce tax.

- *Family situation*

In most jurisdictions, your governing bodies will allow you to have some shares of your corporation held by family members who are not veterinarians. This allows you to split dividends with certain family members to spread income around and take advantage of lower personal tax rates. Since the rates are progressive, if you can allocate income to more than one person, less personal tax may be paid in total than if the income is all in one person's tax return. This may be a reason to incorporate sooner than would otherwise be the case. But you would need lower income adult family members in order to make this work. You should check the rules in the jurisdiction(s) in which you plan to practice.

- *Income level*

Since personal tax rates are progressively higher as income increases, the benefit of incorporating for tax reasons is likely not sufficient at lower income levels. With professional association dues, RRSPs, personal tax credits, possibly family dependent claims, student loan interest, possibly tuition credits carried forward, etc., your personal tax burden may be acceptable until your earning power increases. Remember that the maximum personal tax rate is not reached until you have taxable income of over

$120,000—net of some of the items I just mentioned.

- *Limited Liability*

When you run your practice in a corporation, creditors' claims are limited to the assets of the corporation, unless you personally guarantee the corporate debts. This means that your personal assets can be protected from business risks. If your practice/business is not incorporated, it is not a separate entity from you and your personal assets are available to satisfy creditor's claims. Of course, adequate professional insurance can mitigate this risk to some extent.

- *Cost-benefit analysis*

I recommend that you do a simple comparison of the initial costs of incorporation and the annual maintenance costs (company registration, financial statements and corporation income tax return, etc.) against the tax benefits of being incorporated. Again, the results of this analysis will change as your circumstances change and should support incorporation when the time is right.

For most professionals, the decision is not whether to incorporate but when.

Final Thoughts

You are at an exciting time in your professional careers. The future is yours to make of it what you will. Your professional choices are many.

I would like to leave you with one simple secret to success as you begin your professional journey:

Find a knowledgeable business advisor - and consult that person as a partner in your business.

Rely on that person for options and solutions on business matters, including the choice of other advisors for your team—a business lawyer, a small business banker, a capable, tax focused insurance advisor, and, at some point, a wealth management professional.

Your choice of a business advisor is one of the first and most important decisions you will make. If you don't know where to start, ask colleagues, professors, practicing veterinarians in the jurisdiction of your choice, or contact your college/governing body in the region.

Look for someone who focuses on professional clients, including veterinarians, so you know that they have experience handling the unique business and personal needs of those in your industry.

At MNP, we have a team of advisors dedicated to professionals like you, and we have offices from Campbell River on Vancouver Island to Montreal and about 60 other locations. Look at our professional niche team on our website and give one of us a call.

Leadership

John Tait, BSc, DVM, MBA, DFP, ADR
Managing Partner, Ontario Veterinary Group,
Toronto, Ontario
Assistant Professor, Ontario Veterinary College,
Guelph, Ontario

> *Leaders are visionaries with a poorly developed sense of fear*
> *and no concept of the odds against them.*
> *They make the impossible happen.*
>
> — Dr. Robert Jarvik

Veterinary practice is no different than most businesses in that its success or failure largely can be attributed to and is the responsibility of the identified leader. Leadership is identified in a number of ways, such as individual traits, behaviours, influence over others, and how an individual interacts with others. Two broad categories of leaders are "formal" and "informal." Formal leaders are leaders by virtue of their title or position; they have positions of power and thus, are able to influence others in an organization, regardless of what they actually contribute.

Informal leaders are viewed as much more effective leaders. They have innate abilities to influence the behaviour of others and abilities to have others follow them. Informal leaders tend to have a great deal of expertise in their area, volunteer and participate readily, and are very visible. They may not rank at the top in a larger organization, but by virtue of their personality and behavior, are more respected than some formal leaders. Therefore, informal leadership is a function of both the individual and the way the individual behaves.

Early in their careers, veterinarians quickly can emerge as either formal or informal leaders, depending on their approach to their positions within an organization or practice. Being an effective leader is different than being an effective manager. Ideally you would try and be both in a veterinary practice. However, management and managers generally are thought of as more "task-oriented" roles/positions, while leaders are all about human interaction. Managers tend to do the same thing over and over again, while leaders are the ones who innovate, create change, and grow an organization.

In the veterinary small-business world, distinct advantages exist to being thought of as a leader. Others whom you depend on to help you with your duties will be more committed to working with you. The workplace as a whole will be much less stressful and when times do become stressful, you will be better supported. Leaders are respected and become visible in a small profession, which can be advantageous when you are seeking new employment.

A set of leadership "traits" most often is identified when it comes to categorizing leaders. These traits include confident demeanour, enthusiasm with a sense of humour, and good organization. In addition, a leader is someone who is complimentary, can articulate a vision clearly, and also is a good manager. Combine these traits and behaviours into a single individual, and you have someone who can create an almost magical appeal for followers. More importantly, such an individual gets followers to set aside or de-prioritize their own interests for the good of the organization.

One of the challenges for newer graduate veterinarians is that you rarely have been placed into a leadership role and, therefore, have little experience directing others and resolving conflicts. Role confusion emerges and an incorrect path of behaviour is chosen, whereby leadership is confused with being "well liked" and "popular" as apposed to "respected" and "followed." Such behaviour is a "set up" for being over run, with friendships interfering with leadership roles. Positioning your behaviour too far to the other extreme also is not recommended as stern, non-approachable, and standoffish behaviour is thought of as being "pompous" or "arrogant."

What behaviours then can you practice to gain respect as a leader? Leaders are accessible and participate at all levels and they are able to provide clear direction on tasks and manage multi-tasking well. They are not afraid to ask questions or take advice from their subordinates or any other staff members. Leaders don't hog the glory, but give staff members some of the credit, particularly in front of the client. When reprimands are necessary, the leader does them in private. If an unpopular task needs to be performed, a leader should not be reluctant to assign it, and explain the reasoning why. Setting up a "me versus you" atmosphere, or an "it's not my job" type mentality, avoiding problems and confrontation, and focusing only on money and your own interests does not set a positive example of leadership behaviors.

There are six styles of leadership and these are coercive, authoritative, affiliative, democratic, pace-setting, and coaching. One of the biggest mistakes an individual can make is to try and apply one style to all situations. Good leaders will come to recognize that other members of the leadership team will have different but complementary styles that can be used advantageously in applicable situations.

The first leadership style is coercive, in which compliance is demanded and reflects a "do what I tell you" mood. This style may be effective in an emergency situation, or where you have to defend yourself or your organization quickly. It is not the most effective when attempting team building or interdependence and harmony. The second style is authoritative leadership, which reflects a "come with me" mood. It is effective in setting the tone for a large group where the leader would like everyone to engage in similar behaviours. It is not typically effective in a very small business setting where few individuals need to be rallied. The third leadership style is affiliative leadership. This leadership style reflects a "people come first" attitude and is meant to achieve harmony, enhance communication, and build bonds. This leadership style is effective in relieving stressful situations, particularly when a business is in disarray. It is not likely to be effective in a practice where there are fractions or cliques already formed and where opinions are polarized. The fourth leadership style is democratic, which attempts to achieve consensus and reflects a "what do you think" interactive mood. This leadership style depends on effective communication and collaborative skills, and is effective where consensus is needed and where the environment has been overly coercive. It will not succeed if the leader is inexperienced or their subordinates are powerful. The fifth leadership style is pace-setting leadership where high performance is the goal and the style reflects a "come with me" mood. Conscientious, driven individuals will engage in this leadership style, and it is effective where subordinates are skilled and where reward systems recognize extra effort. It is not likely to be effective in a smaller practice with unskilled subordinates. The sixth and final leadership style is a coaching style where the emphasis is on developing others for the future and the style reflects a "try this" mood. This leadership style is effective where subordinates embrace training and mentoring, and where there is minimum resistance to change. It is not particularly effective with inflexible individuals or in fractioned environments.

Establishing yourself as a leader takes time and some trial-and-error in different circumstances to get it right. Mentors can play a valuable role in providing modeling assistance in proper leadership behaviours and guidance in specific situations (see Chapter 1-2 titled Mentorship). Effective leadership also requires effective emotional intelligence, which is the ability to truly understand one's self and their relationships effectively. Emotional intelligence consists of four fundamental capabilities: self-awareness, self-management, social awareness, and social skill (see Chapter 8-6 titled Emotional Intelligence for Veterinary Professionals). Combining emotional intelligence with an astute choice of leadership styles will provide a solid foundation for an effective leader.

Additional Recommended Reading

Covey S. *Principle Centered Leadership*. Simon & Shuster, New York, NY, 1991.
The Feiner Points of Leadership. Feiner M. Warner Business Books; 2004.

Biography

For Dr. Tait's biography, please see the Section 1 Introduction on page 3.

The Gender Perspective in Veterinary Medicine: Will Feminizing the Profession Make It More Efficient?

Darren Osborne, MA
Director of Research, Ontario Veterinary
Medical Association,
Milton, Ontario

> *A person should not believe in an "ism," he should believe in himself. I quote John Lennon, "I don't believe in the Beatles, I believe in me."*
>
> — Ferris Bueller

Introduction

Using demographic survey data from Canada, it is clear that more similarities than differences exist between female-controlled and male-controlled practices. Female veterinarians outnumbered male veterinarians in 2005 and, if current trends continue, female veterinarians will account for 70% of the profession by 2020. What impact will this have on practice ownership? If female veterinarians are choosing to work fewer hours, what effect will these fewer hours have on the solo clinic, cooperation among clinics, and on-call hours?

This article explores the implications that changing demographics will have on veterinary medicine in Ontario.

The Feminization of Veterinary Medicine

Anyone who has walked the halls of a veterinary college in the last few years has probably noticed that the new veterinarians entering the profession are predominantly women. With female enrolment hovering around 75% for the last 10 years, it is easy to figure out that women soon will outnumber men in veterinary medicine.

Data collected by the Canadian Institute for Health Information shows that female Ontario Veterinary College (OVC) graduates have outnumbered their male counterparts since the early 1980s. Not only have female veterinarians outnumbered males for two decades, they have made up roughly three-quarters of the graduating class in each of the last 10 years. Figure 1 shows the percentage of the total licensed veterinarians in Ontario by gender. The percentage of female veterinarians steadily has increased from less than 5% 25 years ago to a forecasted 66% in 2015.

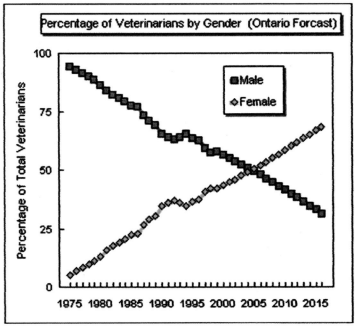

Figure 1 – Percentage of veterinarians by gender in Ontario during the last three decades with forecasts until 2015.

Gender Similarities in Practice Management Styles

With increasing feminization of the profession, it is important to determine if differences exist between the ways male and female veterinarians run their respective practices. Information from a study conducted in the United States (US) concluded that female veterinarians earn less than male veterinarians across the board. Reasons for lower pay included lower expectations, feeling satisfied with less and (no joke) women may make less savvy financial decisions and be less productive. With experience in thousands of practices across North America, I knew this was wrong—easy to say, but hard to prove. Well, here's proof that the US study was inaccurate when it comes to female veterinarians in Ontario.

As part of the Ontario Veterinary Medical Association (OVMA) Economic Survey, practices were flagged as either female- or male-controlled. An example of a female-controlled practice is one where female veterinarians hold sole ownership or the majority of ownership, and thus females make most decisions. If the practice manager was female, but the owner was male, the practice would be flagged as "male-controlled," recognizing that the owner of the practice inevitably controls hospital policy. If ownership was split 50:50 female to male, the practice was not classified as either female- or male-controlled.

Only practices that received in-field interviews were flagged, and only small-animal practices were considered. A large enough population of female-controlled mixed- and large-animal practices was unavailable to allow for comparison. Eighty-nine practices were studied and 29 were flagged as being "female-controlled."

Table 1 shows the differences, if any, between the average Ontario male or female-controlled practices. A 1% difference in full-time equivalent (FTE) net incomes was identified between the two groups (FTE refers to income earned per 2000 hours worked). The group with the higher income generally has more active clients per FTE, so one could argue they are more efficient. Conversely, it is also important to note that the group earning slightly more net income has less revenue per transaction and earns less per client. However, differences are slight and can be discounted since the results are generally accurate to +/- 4%, 19 times out of 20.

The group earning the higher net income achieves it with higher gross revenues. In this case, FTE gross revenues are a whopping 1% higher. Expenses do not fare as well. The group earning higher revenues does so at their peril. Expenses were way out of control—a staggering 2% higher than the group with the lower pay.

Fees are consistent with client-revenue numbers. The group with higher revenue per client and revenue per transaction had much higher fees (i.e., 2% higher for shoppable fees and 3% for non-shoppable fees).

Table 1
Comparing Female- and Male-Controlled Practices

	One	The Other	Difference
Full-Time Equivalent (FTE) Net Income	$124,046	$124,841	1%
Active Clients per FTE	$1,247	$1,293	4%
Revenue per Transaction	$82	$80	-3%
Revenue per Client	$318	$310	-2%
Revenue per FTE	$359,170	$363,755	1%
Drugs and Supplies	23.1%	24.6%	1%
Wages	19.3%	19.1%	0%
Specialists	0.1%	0.0%	0%
Rent	6.1%	6.0%	0%
Office	2.2%	2.3%	0%
Professional & Locum	0.6%	0.8%	0%
Bank Charges	1.7%	1.9%	0%
Depreciation	2.0%	2.2%	0%
Utilities	1.8%	2.0%	0%
Repair & Maintenance	1.3%	1.5%	0%
Laboratory	1.9%	2.2%	0%
Professional Dues	0.4%	0.3%	0%
Other	0.2%	0.1%	0%
Advertising	0.8%	0.9%	0%
Equipment Rental	0.4%	0.4%	0%
Bad Debt	0.2%	0.2%	0%
Vehicle	0.3%	0.2%	0%
Grooming Expense	0.3%	0.2%	0%
Continuing Education	0.4%	0.4%	0%
Insurance	0.5%	0.6%	0%
Total Expenses	63.6%	66.1%	2%
Shoppable Fee Index (elective, vaccine)	91	89	-2%
Nonshoppable Fee Index	93	91	-3%

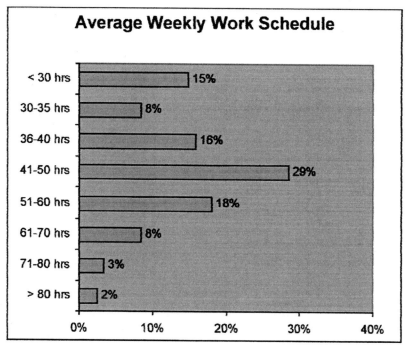

Figure 2 – Average hours worked per week for Ontario veterinarians.

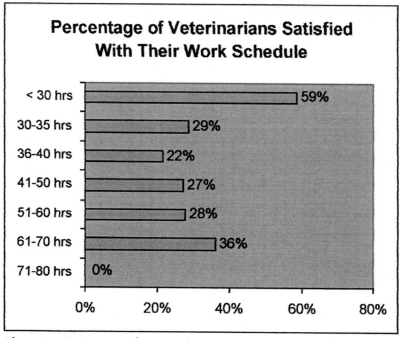

Figure 3 – Percentage of surveyed veterinarians in Ontario that were satisfied with the amount of hours worked.

So which group is which? To answer a question with a question— "Does it really matter?" No differences—I repeat, no differences exist between female-controlled and male-controlled practices. Women are just as savvy, just as productive, and can achieve work/life balance just as well (or as poorly) as their male peers.

Gender Lifestyle Patterns

In a recent survey conducted with veterinarians in Ontario, 68% indicated they would prefer to work fewer hours than they currently work. The results suggest that veterinarians in Ontario are working too much. The only subgroup satisfied with their workload was veterinarians who worked less than 30 hours per week. At the time of the survey, the majority (60%) of veterinarians in Ontario worked more than 40 hours per week (Figure 2). Thirteen percent consistently worked more than 60 hours per week, with 2% of these working more than 80 hours per week.

Assuming two weeks of holidays and two weeks of statutory holidays, 80 hours per week represents 3,840 hours per year worked. This is more than double the 1,735 annual hours that result from the 35-hour workweek experienced by individuals in most industries. As well as asking how many hours they worked, the survey asked veterinarians how many hours they would like to work. Comparing the hours actually worked with the ideal total shed light on how satisfied veterinarians are with their current work schedules.

Figure 3 shows that veterinarians working less than 30 hours per week were, by far, the most satisfied with their weekly workloads. Less than 30% of all other groups were satisfied with their current workloads. Thirty-six per cent of veterinarians were satisfied working 61-70 hours per week, but this figure only represented four veterinarians. Not surprisingly, no one was happy working 80 hours per week. Most (64%) veterinarians in the survey indicated that they would prefer to work fewer hours. When broken down by gender, it is clear that male veterinarians feel more overworked, since 69% indicated they would prefer to work fewer hours compared to 59% of female veterinarians.

When work schedule is examined by gender, the reason female veterinarians are more satisfied with their work schedule emerges (Figure 4). Twenty per cent of female veterinarians are working less than 30 hours per week and half (49%) are working 40 hours a week or less. This differs significantly from male veterinarians, among whom only 31% work 40 hours a week or less.

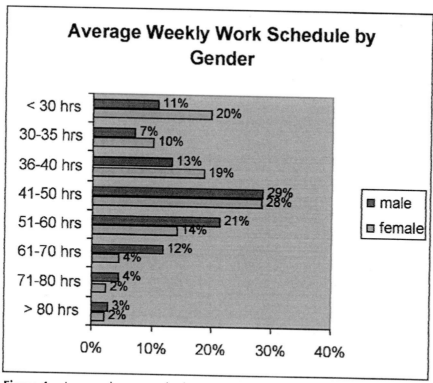

Figure 4 – Average hours worked per week based on gender for Ontario veterinarians.

Most veterinarians in the study reported that they would like to work less, but the only group that has made a significant move to achieving this goal is female veterinarians. This could explain why so much animosity exists regarding the fewer hours worked by female veterinarians; everyone wants to work less, but only female veterinarians have figured out how to do it.

Gender Ownership Patterns

No evidence in Ontario suggests that female veterinarians charge lower fees or earn less than males; however, evidence shows female veterinarians have been less apt to seek practice ownership. The difference is subtle, but significant, given the increasing percentage of female veterinarians entering the profession.

Going back 30 years in the OVMA database, one finds that female veterinarians generally have been slower to take on ownership. Also, fewer

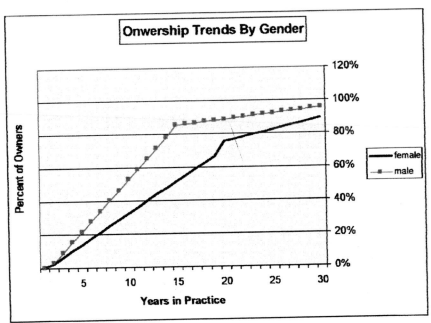

Figure 5 – Veterinary practice ownership in Ontario over 30 years in practice and based on gender.

female veterinarians choose ownership over salaried positions. Figure 5 shows the percentage of practice owners by gender and years in practice; this information examines the entire population of veterinarians in Ontario. For each year in practice, the graph shows the percentage of female- and male-practice owners. The bottom left of the graph shows no veterinary graduates buy or start a practice right out of school. After a few years, an increasing number of veterinarians become owners. This trend continues throughout 30 years of practice, at which point almost all veterinarians are owners.

Two distinct trends have been identified for female versus male ownership of veterinary practices. Historically, male veterinarians purchase practices sooner than their female counterparts. This is shown graphically by the steeper ownership curve for males. The right side of the graph shows that fewer females than males own practices. After 30 years in practice, 96% of male veterinarians are owners, while only 89% of female veterinarians are owners. The difference is only seven per cent, but with three-quarters of the profession being female by 2016, any decline in the number of veterinarians looking to purchase practices may diminish an already beleaguered demand for ownership.

Will Feminizing Make the Profession More Efficient?

It is clear that the profession will be predominantly female over the next two decades. We know that, from a management perspective, female-controlled practices are equal to male-controlled practices in every way. We see no reason to expect that this will change as the profession becomes feminized.

Two factors that vary by gender are hours worked and ownership patterns. While most veterinarians strive to work fewer hours, female veterinarians seem to find a way to actually do so. If this trend continues, we can expect that veterinarians will be looking for ways not to simply earn more money, but to maintain their incomes while working fewer hours. To realize this goal, some conspicuous changes may take place. Female-owned practices may start sharing on-call. As they do not appear to be in an expansionary mode, they may be more apt to agree on an on-call rotation in many areas. This ultimately could lead to a four-day-a-week practice in areas where less competition exists for clients. Data from Ontario shows that female veterinarians are slower to own practices and less likely to ever do so over their careers. The difference is slight but, nevertheless, it does exist. This could mean that the supply of practices will exceed demand in years to come, which ultimately would drive down the price of practices put up for sale.

Anecdotal reports from young female associates suggest that ownership trends will change as the profession becomes feminized. The suggestion is that female associates often do not enjoy negotiating with male owners for partnerships and ownerships of practices. Generational differences and varying expectations from the profession have driven a wedge between owners and female veterinarians looking to become owners. Many female associates report that they simply have walked away in disgust. When they look for other opportunities, they find that most practice partnership and ownership opportunities involve negotiating with males, so they simply back off. If this gender tension does exist, it suggests that partnership and ownership among female veterinarians will become more prevalent as the number of female owners increases. Ownership will start as a trickle and finish with a flood.

Note: this chapter is a compilation of previously published work (Osborne RD, OVMA Focus 2002; Vol 22,No 3:12; Osborne RD, OVMA Focus 2001; Vol 21,No 3:5) reprinted with permission by the Ontario Veterinary Medical Association.

Biography

Darren Osborne completed a Master's Degree in Economics from York University, Toronto, Canada in 1992. Since completing his degree, Darren has consulted for various Medical Associations across Canada with R. K. House and Associates Ltd. developing provincial fee guides and financial bench marking reports for dentists, physicians, and veterinarians. Since joining the OVMA in 1996, Darren has focused his attention on veterinary economic and market research both inside and outside of Canada. Darren has developed a practice benchmark report that includes a client survey along with a production and financial comparison and more recently has introduced a series of Real Life Stories that put names and faces on the data. Currently, Darren is providing economic research, articles, and fee guides to several veterinary associations in Canada and the United States.

When he is not bean-counting, Darren enjoys competitive fencing, golf, and endurance sports. On September 14, 2006, Darren cycled 261 km in one day to raise money for the Farley Foundation, a charity that helps disabled and seniors get emergency veterinary care.

CHAPTER 1-9

What Industry Can Do For You

Rob Bell, DVM, MBA
Ontario and Atlantic Canada
Bovine Area Sales Manager, Pfizer Animal Health

> *Begin with the end in mind.*
>
> — Stephen Covey

Introduction

If you question most new veterinary graduates, they will tell you that they feel confident entering practice from a scientific perspective, but they feel totally deficient from a business management point of view. Imagine their surprise when they quickly realize that their business skills will be as important as their technical skills in ensuring their success in veterinary practice, particularly if they will become practice owners. The veterinary schools are not to blame for this reality. To remain an accredited veterinary college, the curriculum must be packed with scientific and technical skills training. There is little time for developing business skills, even though there has been a recent push to enhance business management training. As a result, recent graduates enter practice keen on learning the business management aspects from their mentors, who in most cases have similarly learned by experience and not through formal education. It is therefore understandable how some poor management practices are perpetuated within the veterinary field.

Based upon this understanding, several business management studies have been undertaken in recent years to assess management deficiencies within veterinary practice. Of note is the recent 2004 Pfizer/American Veterinary Medical Association (AVMA) study, which surveyed management practices of over 2,650 United States (US) veterinarians representing all major species groups (i.e., companion animal, bovine, equine, and mixed practices).[1] The study identified eight important management practices categorized under three main management platforms that dramatically influenced veterinary net incomes, regardless of practice type (Table 1).

1.   Personnel Management
        • Employee development
        • Leadership

2.   Client Relations
        • Client development
        • Client retention
        • Client loyalty

3.   Financial Management
        • Business orientation
        • Negotiating skills
        • Frequency of financial data review

Table 1
Management Practices Dramatically Influencing Veterinary Net Income

Identified Management Practice	Income Differential	% Increase in Income
Business orientation	$47,070	62%
Frequency of financial review	$42,570	45%
Employee development practices	$34,470	45%
Negotiating skill	$31,210	3 9%
Client loyalty	$28,900	36%
Client retention practices	$15,560	17%
Leadership	$13,850	16%
New client development practices	$14,840	15%

Among other variables demonstrating significant positive correlations with income were such items as financial acumen, atmospherics (the physical attractiveness of the facility or vehicle), client service, client waiting time, sound judgment, acting confidently, relationship building, marketing, employee retention practices, and client-focused pricing. Following is a discussion of the eight leading business practices.

Business Orientation

Business orientation includes such behaviors as use of financial concepts to manage the practice and defining staff goals that are consistent with practice goals. Overall, veterinarians did not score high in business orientation, with men scoring higher than women. Table 2 provides the survey respondents' correlation between selected business orientation attributes and actual practice behaviour.

Frequency of Financial Data Review

This attribute assessed whether practice owners analyzed such information as revenue, profit or loss, and key performance indicators on a monthly,

Table 2
Percentage Indicating that Business Orientation Attributes Described Their Practice Very or Extremely Well

Business Orientation Attributes	Describes Very or Extremely Well
I define roles for staff that are consistent with practice goals.	46%
I link salary increases to practice productivity.	41%
I use financial concepts to manage my business.	38%
I use industry trends to better define clientele services.	28%

quarterly, or annual basis, or never. Those who reviewed a full menu of financial data on a monthly basis had significantly higher incomes than those who monitored their financial performance less frequently and/or monitored fewer data. While the majority of practice owners reviewed at least some of their financial data monthly or quarterly, those who didn't typically paid a high penalty in the form of lower incomes. Companion animal veterinarians were much more likely to review key performance indicators monthly or quarterly than were equine or food animal veterinarians.

The vast majority of practice owners tracked revenue increases or decreases (79%) and reviewed aged accounts receivables (77%) on a monthly basis; however, fewer (66%) measured production (i.e., revenues generated by individual veterinarians). Many practice management experts consider this an essential metric. Only 57% of owners track key performance indicators monthly, while barely half (52%) check profit or loss on a monthly basis.

Financial review frequency ranked second among the managerial variables in predicting personal incomes of veterinarians and owners, and it ranked sixth in the overall regression. There was an income variance of $42,570 between those who scored in the top third and those who scored in the bottom third.

Negotiating Skill

Negotiating skill is often associated with business success. The Pfizer/AVMA Business Practices Study utilized a battery of questions proven to measure competency in negotiating. Those who scored in the top third in negotiating skills earned $31,210 more than those in the bottom third. Interestingly, companion animal, equine, and food animal practitioners scored very similarly on this factor. In multiple regression analysis, negotiating skill was the controllable variable, with the strongest relationship to income among equine veterinarians. Some of the questions used to measure this factor are shown in Table 3.

Employee Development

Employee development is a combination of six activities, including regular written and oral performance evaluations, written job descriptions, well-defined performance expectations, a structured process for selecting new employees, and a leader who coaches. It is clear from the study that a large

Table 3
Attributes Important to Negotiating Skill

Attribute	Agree Strongly/Somewhat
I have discretion to adjust pricing for my services.	76%
In any competitive situation, I like to win.	69%
I'm a good negotiator.	56%
I enjoy trying to persuade others to my point of view.	54%

number of practices do not have written job descriptions or conduct annual performance evaluations. The strong relationship between human resources practices and income in this study is consistent with the findings of the 1998 Brakke Study, which found that out of a group of 19 standard business practices measured, the three with the highest relationship to income were employee management practices.[2] Equine and food animal veterinarians scored lower in employee development than companion animal veterinarians. This factor had one of the highest relationships to income in all types of veterinary practice, regardless of species focus.

Leadership

Leadership is a key factor in motivating others and includes such attributes as setting clear direction, challenging others to excel, and giving clear and constructive feedback. Women scored slightly higher than men in leadership (see Table 4).

Client Loyalty

Client loyalty included such items as "clients frequently recommend this practice to other potential clients" and "most clients will continue to use this practice." Food animal veterinarians scored slightly lower on this factor than companion animal and equine veterinarians.

Table 4
Percentage of Females Indicating That Leadership Attributes Described Their Own Behaviour Very or Extremely Well

Among Women:	Describes Very or Extremely Well
I stress the importance of other's contributions	70%
I challenge others to excel.	58%
I set clear performance expectations.	49%
I give clear and constructive feedback.	49%
I set a clear direction for others.	48%

Client Retention Practices

This factor included soliciting feedback, suggestions, and complaints from clients; monitoring client satisfaction; and determining why clients left the veterinary practice. As a whole, veterinarians scored low on this factor. Companion animal veterinarians rated somewhat higher than equine or food animal veterinarians.

New Client Development

New client development included such business practices as encouraging referrals, sending welcome letters to new clients, and offering incentives for client referrals. Companion animal veterinarians scored substantially higher overall in client development than equine or food animal veterinarians.

Other Relevant Veterinary Income Factors

There were certainly other factors that were identified as drivers of veterinary income, such as gender, hours worked per week, and practice location and type; but the management practices identified are actionable items for all veterinary practices. However, it is somewhat disconcerting that a similar study conducted in 1998 with US companion animal practices identified the need for similar management practices, yet the majority of companion animal practices had not implemented any changes within the six-year period between studies.[2] It is obvious that awareness of management practices is not enough to enact change. Veterinarians need assistance in developing the management tools required for management change and workshops to develop the skills necessary to implement change. That is where the pharmaceutical industry can be of assistance to practicing veterinarians.

Role of the Pharmaceutical Industry

The pharmaceutical industry has rationalized to a few large, sophisticated companies with highly developed management techniques, and they can be called upon to assist practicing veterinarians in improving their management practices. For example, Pfizer Animal Health, following the findings of the 2004 Pfizer/AVMA study, has developed management tools to assist practicing veterinarians in upgrading their management skills. The toolbox includes the following templates, which are available from your Pfizer Animal Health representative:

- Client survey handout
- Veterinary-related job description samples
- Veterinary-related performance evaluation samples
- Example key performance indicators

While this is a great start to assisting veterinarians in improving management practices, it is just the "tip of the iceberg" when it comes to what the pharmaceutical industry could provide to veterinary practitioners in the way of management assistance. Other actionable areas include:

- Development of a business vision and strategy
- Determination of penetration and compliance
- Improved sales and marketing skills
- Financial management training
- Inventory management
- New hire evaluation
- Personality profiling

While this list is not intended to be exhaustive, it does address some of the business needs within the veterinary profession. The following is a brief review of each of these management areas.

Development of a Business Vision and Strategy

The old theory in practice was: Keep busy, and the "nickels and dimes" will take care of themselves. This could not be any further from the truth. Practitioners need to take the time to manage their businesses, starting with the development of a business vision and strategy, and communicating this plan to all employees and business associates. As Steven Covey stated in *The 7 Habits of Highly Effective People*, "begin with the end in mind." The development and communication of a business vision and strategy is paramount to strong leadership—one of the key management parameters identified with increased net income in the Pfizer/AVMA study.

It is important for practitioners to recognize that they can exercise control over the destiny of their veterinary practices. Business schools have preached for years that strategy is either deliberate (i.e., under your direction) or emergent (i.e., will develop over time based upon your actions). Deliberate strategies are far more effective in taking your business where you want it to go. The basic business strategies are:

* Low cost
* Differentiated
* Niche
* Stuck in the middle

A low-cost strategy is by definition a "competition"-focused strategy; in other words, to be low in cost, you must know what the competitor is doing. Differentiated and niche strategies are "customer-focused" strategies, as they are only valuable if the customer sees benefit. A "stuck-in-the-middle" strategy is a common outcome of not developing a strategic direction, resulting in a business mixing all three strategies and trying to be "all things to all people." The latter invariably results in failure. One can easily recognize that the evolution of veterinary practice is driven by strategic direction. The movement toward species specialization and even within-species specialization is a differentiated, niche strategy. However, such a strategy cannot be assumed at low cost and be successful. You can tell when you have successfully developed and communicated a business vision and strategy, as a new culture will pervade the organization.

Pharmaceutical companies are proficient at developing and communicating a business vision and strategy, and veterinary practitioners can draw upon their expertise in developing their practice vision and strategy. For example, Pfizer Animal Health has led many veterinary clinics through a business development exercise that fosters business vision and strategy.

Determining Penetration and Compliance

While veterinarians understand the merits of a well-designed and implemented health protocol for animals, many do not know how well their recommendations are followed or, in some cases, how many animals are under their direct care. The result is lost veterinary revenue and high-risk disease situations for animals. Preventative medicine programs are truly win-win scenarios for veterinarians and their clients; however, in many cases, compliance is poor. It is important to measure compliance rates. To ensure optimal compliance, it is important to communicate the financial benefits of a preventative medicine program in addition to the scientific merits. This is particularly true in production animal medicine.

Pfizer Animal Health has developed a system to help veterinarians determine both penetration and compliance of their health protocols. Canada census data can be used to estimate regional animal populations, and annual product sales can be monitored to determine penetration and compliance based upon the at-risk population.

Improved Sales and Marketing Skills

Although most veterinarians do not like to admit it, they are in the sales and marketing business, whether it is the services being offered or the products dispensed. One only has to look at the poor compliance of preventative medicine programs that add value to clients and their animals, to understand that there is a significant opportunity for veterinarians to improve their skills in this area. Successful sales and marketing programs focus on customer needs. A recent survey of car owners regarding service satisfaction sheds some light on the attributes valued by customers (scale 1 to 4) (see Table 5).[3]

This survey begs the question of why many practices focus on low prices and believe a reminder system is all that is needed to ensure client retention and compliance with health prevention protocols. Fast action on complaints ranked second in importance, yet this is a situation often avoided in many practices. We are all consumers and know how we like to be treated by suppliers. All we need to do is transfer these learnings to our veterinary practices.

Pharmaceutical companies have well-developed sales and marketing training programs. Pfizer Animal Health has trained veterinary clinic staff on sales and marketing programs or, in other cases, had veterinarians attend internal training exercises. Feedback on both programs has been very positive.

Financial Management Training

Practitioners receive annual financial statements from their accountants to meet Revenue Canada requirements; however (and as the Pfizer/AVMA

Table 5
Satisfaction Ratings for Car Owners Having
Their Vehicle Serviced

Attribute	Importance Score
Done right the first time	3.83
Fast action on complaints	3.63
Prompt work	3.60
Able to do any job needed	3.56
Service available when needed	3.41
Courteous and friendly	3.41
Ready when promised	3.38
Perform only necessary work	3.37
Low prices	3.29
Clean up after service work	3.27
Convenient to home	2.52
Convenient to work	2.43
Courtesy car	2.37
Send out maintenance reminders	2.05

study has pointed out), not many practitioners review financial data on a monthly basis—a key factor in increasing net income. In many cases, veterinarians need to improve their basic understanding of standard financial statements, including:

- Income or profit and loss (P&L) statements
- Balance sheets

- Statements of changes in cash
- "Double Loop" accounting—emphasizing a "shared" understanding of financial statements. In other words—understand the story behind the numbers!

One of the best methods that I have encountered to improve the understanding and inter-relationships of these statements is through a game developed by Paradigm Learning, called *Zodiac, The Game of Business and Finance Strategy*. I have completed pilot project training of veterinarians on Zodiac with very positive feedback.

In developing monthly financial parameters to review, it is paramount to measure what matters; in other words, only measure what can be managed and correlated directly to financial outcomes. This process is known as developing key performance indicators (KPI). Pfizer developed examples of species-specific KPIs, which are available from your Pfizer Animal Health representative.

Inventory Management

One of the outcomes of improved financial review is an increased awareness of the financial importance of improved inventory management. Many practitioners take the view that low interest rates translate to a low priority for inventory management. However, this is misleading, as the carrying cost of inventory is only one financial parameter impacted by poor inventory management. Other important financial impacts include:

- Fiscal restraint on business opportunities, since capital is tied up in inventory
- High labour cost associated with shelving, storage, and returning excess inventory
- Increased inventory "shrink" through theft, damaged packaging, breakage, and outdated products
- And finally, excess inventory suffers from "the longer it sits, the harder it is to move" syndrome

Many industries have adopted sophisticated inventory management systems. For inventory management systems to be fully effective, bar-coding of all products is a prerequisite. Bar-coding enables "scan in, scan out" systems that link sales to inventory systems, including product reordering. However, many clinics struggle with computerized inventory management systems, as partial product dispensing and multiple locations of inventory (for example, mobile units) result in inaccurate inventory counts.

However, many clinics could currently benefit from establishing reorder points and reorder volumes for key products. Managing approximately 50 key products will reduce inventory costs in many clinics. A simple "kanban" system (i.e., a notification sign) can be utilized to trigger product orders once reorder points have been established. All products should be rotated on a "first in, first out" (FIFO) system; in other words, the oldest product is the first sold. If individual products are shelved in single file, a small sticker can be attached on the product container at a predetermined reorder point, and the reorder volume is printed on the sticker. This enables clinic staff to quickly identify which products need to be reordered and how many to order. For smaller items (e.g., pills) a predetermined number of pills is removed from the new pill container and placed in the previous pill container for the same product, and the lot number and expiration date is updated on the old container. Pills are dispensed from the new container, and the need to reorder is signaled by the empty container, at which time dispensing continues from the other container until a new order arrives. I have developed a spreadsheet that assists clinics in establishing reorder points and reorder volumes.

New Hire Evaluation

One of the keys to managing a successful business is getting the right person performing the right job. This process begins with hiring the right people. Utilizing newer situational interviewing techniques can be a very effective tool. During this process, potential candidates are interviewed based upon their actions and outcomes to past situations, and this has been proven to be very accurate in identifying personality traits and how potential employees will react in similar situations in the future.

Pharmaceutical companies have well-developed interview processes, and these systems can be readily adapted to veterinary clinic situations. Clinics have successfully used the Pfizer Animal Health Targeted Interview Selection guide to identify and hire new talent.

Personality Profiling

After personnel have been hired, it is important that all staff works in a harmonized environment to maximize practice effectiveness. There are multiple personality profile techniques available, and these can be used to assess differing personality traits within clinic staff. Once there is an understanding of varying personalities, work teams and job descriptions can be developed to utilize the staff most effectively. Personality profiling is also useful for staff members to understand why others react differently than they would in the work environment.

Pfizer Animal Health has performed personality profiling in numerous veterinary practices, and feedback has been very positive regarding the improvement in personnel interaction.

Summary

Your pharmaceutical companies can be much more than suppliers of products. They can become valued business partners. You can use the principles learned in strategy development to interact with your pharmaceutical suppliers. If they cannot add value to your business, buy their products based upon price and cost-benefit analysis. Meanwhile, work with your valued suppliers to improve your business.

References

1. Vol JO, Felsted KE, Cummings RF, Slocum JW, Cron WL, Ryan KG, Moosbrugger MC. Special report: Executive summary of the AVMA-Pfizer business practices study. J Am Vet Med Assoc 2005;226:212-218.
2. Cron W, Slocum J, et al. Executive Summary of the Brakke management and behavior study. J Am Vet Med Assoc 2000;217:332-338.
3. *Marketing Management Analysis, Planning, Implementation and Control.* Kotler P. ed. New Jersey: Prentice Hall, 1997.

Additional Recommended Reading

Production and Operations Management Manufacturing and Services. Chase R, Aquilano N, Jacobs R. Irwin McGraw-Hill; Boston; 1998.
The 7 Habits of Highly Effective People. Covey SR. Simon & Shuster; New York; 1990.
Getting to Yes; Negotiating Agreement Without Giving In. Fisher R, Usy W. Houghton Mifflin; Boston; 1981.
The Big Bang: The Evolution of Negotiation Research. Thompson L, Leonardelli GJ. Academy of Management Executive, Vol 18, No. 3, 2004.
Understanding Organizations. Handy C. Penguin Books; London; 1993.
The Strategy Process. Mintzberg H, Quinn JB, Voyer J. Prentice Hall; New Jersey; 1995.

Biography

Dr. Rob Bell grew up on a dairy farm in South Western Ontario and graduated with distinction from the Ontario Veterinary College in 1978. He entered private practice in St. Marys Ontario where he practiced for 25 years, 20 years as a practice owner; his primary emphasis in practice was bovine preventative medicine and farm management and economics. Rob's interest in management and economics was fueled during his five years as a member on Ault Foods Board of Directors, Canada's largest dairy processor, prior to its sale to Parmalat in 1997. This experience spurred him to complete his MBA from the University of Guelph in 2001 at which time he joined Pfizer Animal Health as a consultant and then on a full-time basis following the acquisition of Pharmacia in 2003.

Section 2

A PARADE OF PRACTITIONER PERSPECTIVES

Introduction

A major lifestyle question to consider is "Where do I want to live?" Veterinary medicine across the country and outside Canada offers varying experiences, types of practice and career opportunities, and lifestyle choices.

We asked representative practice owners from across the country to review their experiences and present their perspectives on their own unique region and career choices, as well as examine the issues surrounding leaving Canada for life in the United States. These are their stories.

John Tait, BSc, DVM, MBA, CFP, ADR Managing Partner,
Ontario Veterinary Group, Toronto,
Ontario Assistant Professor,
Ontario Veterinary College, Guelph, Ontario

For Dr. Tait's biography, please see the Section 1 Introduction on page 3.

CHAPTER 2-1

Professional Issues Unique to Female Veterinarians

Laurie Dunbar, DVM
Pierrefonds Animal Hospital, Montreal, Quebec

> *The question isn't who is going to let me,*
> *it's who is going to stop me.*
>
> — Ayn Rand

Introduction

Soon after graduating from the Ontario Veterinary College (OVC) in 1986, I interviewed for a job in a small animal practice near my hometown. I will always remember the interview because, although it was clear I was not going to be hired, the practice owner took the time to give me advice on how to make it in veterinary medicine as a woman. Despite the fact that he was a recent graduate himself, he felt confident that he could help me succeed in my career. He explained to me that female veterinarians did not inspire as much client confidence as their male counterparts and that I would have to work harder to get the same respect. I would have to focus on projecting a professional image, which meant that I should dress well at all times (a skirt would probably be best). As you can imagine, I was speechless. Our graduating class was an even split of equally competent men and women; moreover, I had lots of work experience and was extremely confident of my own abilities. How could this kind of attitude exist in the 1980s?

In the 20 years since that first interview, the status of professional women has improved in some but not all respects. I am certain that not one of you will share my interview experience. Not only would a conversation like that be considered discriminatory, but veterinary medicine has also evolved in many ways, both in sophistication and in the composition of its members. It is largely true that gender discrimination with regards to ability no longer occurs; however, issues remain that are particular to the female practitioner, which can create an unfavorable bias when it comes to hiring, and affect a woman's practice longevity. These issues often center around a woman's decision to become pregnant or adopt and raise a family. Today, female veterinarians who decide not to have children should enjoy the same status as their male counterparts, although, interestingly enough, when they are in hiring positions they tend to share the same bias towards women as their male colleagues. Society pays only lip service towards supporting women who choose to work less in order to raise children. In North American society, women and men are working more, not less, than in previous generations, and taking less vacation. Until this changes, there will be pressure on many veterinarians to be "super women." While that is exactly what many of them are, it is important to have a healthy balance. I have worked in several practices and had conversations with many women about this. I have found that while the details of working and home life are affected by the culture of each practice and social milieu of the community, the important issues facing women veterinarians today are universal.

Of note, I recently met up with the veterinarian who shared his words of wisdom with me as I embarked upon my career. We had a very lively and friendly discussion about our practices which are very similar (although mine is larger) and shared ideas for improvement. Neither of us was wearing a skirt!

Today's Families and Parenting

The challenges facing women veterinarians today are many—one of the greatest being the balancing of family life and career. There have been significant changes in family life in Canada, and Canada now has one of the highest proportions of working mothers with young children.[1] Although there has been a sharp increase recently in the number of employed women staying home to raise young children, the majority of women with children in Canada work outside the home.[2]

Canadian mothers tend to be more educated than they were two decades ago, and more women than men are graduating with university degrees. More than one-half of parents (men and women) with children under the age of 12 years have a post-secondary degree, certificate, or diploma. This means that the maternal age at the birth of the first child is also higher than ever before; almost one-half of women who gave birth in 2003 were aged 30 years or older.[2]

People today are much more likely to live and work outside the community in which they were born. Thus, children are often being raised without the help of extended family, placing a tremendous burden on working parents. The good news is that when today's working parents are home, they tend to spend more time with their children than did parents in previous generations. According to the *National Longitudinal Survey of Children and Youth,*children born to higher-income families (greater than $60,000 CD) tend to be more involved in recreational activities and are more likely to have healthy parents and a functional family unit.[3] Also, children born to mothers with post-secondary school education enjoy greater academic success than their classmates. However, the welcome addition of women in the workforce and the higher education level of today's parents have resulted in a declining birthrate. Human Resources Canada projects that there will be only six children under the age of six years per 100 Canadians by the year 2021, representing 26% of the total population, compared to 32% in 2004.[4]

Specific Challenges for Women in Veterinary Medicine

Veterinary medicine, like its sister professions, is clearly becoming dominated by women in terms of numbers. However, female veterinarians are more likely than their male counterparts to become part-time workers or to job share, because most of the responsibility for childcare and home management still falls to the woman. The challenge for the female veterinarian who wishes to have a family is to find a satisfactory balance between professional career and home life, without feeling resentful of choices made along the way. Compromises usually have to be made, and, despite the rise of women in the workplace, they are more often the ones to sacrifice career advancement, particularly while the children are dependent. Also, the average age of new parents is rising, and this is particularly true for those in the medical profession, where the age upon completion of training and therefore entering the workforce is generally higher than for those with other university degrees. As a result, some women may feel pressured to start a family early in their careers. Raising children, although a source of joy, is more time consuming than can be imagined and definitely requires significant financial outlay. For these reasons, new graduates who wish to specialize should consider doing so soon after completing their DVM or equivalent degree. I have met so many women who delayed internship or residency training and subsequently found that they had neither the time nor the money needed to pursue their dream, leading to a sense of frustration and regret. This can be especially true for women who have had children.

Establishing Relationships of Trust

Most new graduates are eager to bring ideas for change and improvement to a new job; however, implementation can require persistence and patience and can be quite frustrating. The period of time during which any new graduate will have the greatest influence in a practice (and therefore the ability to effect change) is during the first two to three years. The new graduate needs to invest a considerable amount of time and energy in order to establish a degree of trust and respect between him/herself and the practice owner. In my opinion, this is particularly true when the owner of the practice is male and the employee is a female. Although most practice owners look forward to having new graduates as a means to ensure the continuous evolution of their practice, some owners are resistant to new ideas. Usually the best strategy is to prove to the owners that the new measure will improve efficiency and be cost effective. During these first years, the new graduate probably has a heavy schedule, is trying to prove him/herself, and is working off student debt; starting a family at this time can be very stressful.

Maternity or Parental Leave

Once she has established herself within the practice, the new graduate who is planning to start a family should consider discussing with her employer the possibility of maternity leave. These discussions can sometimes be difficult. The majority of owners are open to them and appreciate the opportunity to plan in advance for the possible leave. However, from an employer's perspective, it is never desirable to lose a productive, practice-building veterinarian for any reason. The new graduate should not be hesitant to have this discussion; it will not affect job security, and it is important to be transparent. It is illegal to fire or refuse to rehire an employee because of a proposed or actual maternity leave. Although male veterinarians are legally allowed parental leave, most of them do not take it. As there are more young women veterinarians entering the workforce, practice owners will have to deal on a more frequent basis with the issue of maternity leave. This, without a doubt, has created a favorable bias toward the hiring of male veterinarians, which is one of the major barriers facing women veterinarians seeking employment.

We are fortunate to live in a country that values the family and understands the importance of caring for the newborn child. Canadian women enjoy generous maternity benefits compared to other countries around the world; Sweden, which allows 480 days of maternity/parental leave, being the notable exception.[5] Absence from work can take the form of maternity leave (taken by the mother), paternity leave (when taken by the father), and parental leave (which can be taken by either parent subdivided between both). Generally speaking, most Canadian provinces allow a maximum of 52 uninterrupted weeks (one year) of combined maternity and parental leave. The distribution of the maternity and parental leave is decided at the provincial level. In the case of the Federal government and the provinces of Manitoba, New Brunswick, Nunavut, and the Northwest Territories, a maximum of 17 weeks maternity leave and 37 weeks of parental leave are allowed but a combined total must not exceed 52 weeks. Manitoba and the Yukon allow the entire 54 weeks. British Columbia, Newfoundland, Ontario, and Prince Edward Island allow 17 weeks of maternity leave and 35 weeks of parental leave. In British Columbia, the parental leave can be extended to 37 weeks for the father; in Ontario 37 weeks are allowed for the father or for mother if pregnancy leave was not taken. In Alberta, maternity leave is 15 weeks and parental is 37. The provinces with the most generous maternity programs are Nova Scotia and Quebec; Nova Scotia allows 17 weeks for maternity leave and 52 weeks for parental leave.[6]

The Quebec government is very supportive of young families and, because of a lower-than-desired birthrate, has a generous maternity leave program. It is possible to have 18 weeks of maternity leave and 52 weeks parental leave for a combined total of 70 weeks or 490 days. Furthermore, Quebec recognizes the rights of the father entitling him to 5 weeks paternity leave in addition to a possible 52 weeks of parental leave.[7]

In Canada, the length of the maternity leave can depend on whether you are employed or self-employed. The self-employed veterinarian who is part of a group may be bound by a partnership agreement and have a limited length of maternity leave. Quebec has recently introduced a new program of maternity benefits, which is available to both the employee and to those who are self-employed; there are also specific benefits for fathers. Mothers may choose between two plans of maternity leave. The basic plan allows one to take a maximum number of benefit weeks at a lower percentage of a maximum average weekly income. The special plan allows a quicker return to work (10 weeks earlier) and a higher percentage of the same income.

Given the amount of time possible for the woman to be at home with her new child, one can understand the frustration of the employer. When full advantage is taken of preventive, maternity, and parental leave, it is possible in some provinces for a female veterinarian to be off work for a period exceeding two years. Nobody will argue that this is not in the very best interests of the child. Maternity/parental leave promotes breastfeeding that will ensure infant health and development, and a decreased incidence of disease both in childhood and during adulthood. As a result there are significant savings to the health care system. Contrary to popular opinion however, the leave following birth or adoption is not an extended vacation. The stress on the mother at this time can be multifactorial. She is sleep deprived and has little time to read veterinary journals. She is probably wondering how her colleagues like her replacement, how she will manage the return to work, and may be worried about keeping up to date scientifically. Thankfully the art of practicing veterinary medicine is about problem solving and client communication skills, which, once learned, are not easily forgotten. It is easy nowadays to keep abreast of new information using fantastic internet sites like Veterinary Information Network (VIN). Furthermore, the experience of caring for an infant will only improve the soft skills that the veterinarian will have at her disposal when she returns to work.

Preventive Leave

There are aspects to working in a veterinary facility that may pose health risks to the unborn fetus or to a child through breast milk. Modern hospitals with up-to-date scavenging systems, lead-enclosed radiography suites, negative-flow surgical and dental suites as well as treatment areas, should be safe environments in which to work. If the pregnant veterinarian has concerns about her environment, she must obtain a certificate from a medical doctor attesting that her working conditions pose a risk to herself or to her unborn child.[8] She may withdraw from work before receiving her medical certificate, with the understanding that she may be recalled to work if her request is denied. The veterinarian's doctor must in turn consult with a doctor designated by the Département de santé communautaire (in Quebec) or the Department of Public Health. This certificate grants the pregnant veterinarian the right to be reassigned to other functions in a safe part of the hospital. If she cannot be reassigned, or if the employer chooses to contest the request for reassignment, the health and safety department of the local government (in Quebec the Commision de la santé et de la sécurité du travail [CSST]) will decide (based on the advice of a doctor) whether there is a case for preventive leave or reassignment. The practice owner(s) may decide to have the hospital inspected with regard to safety hazards (e.g., levels of anesthetic gases, etc.) to ensure a safe environment for the practice team. The results may require that the pregnant veterinarian be off work for the entire pregnancy and the full, postpartum maternity/parental leave.[9]

It is a very personal decision to apply for preventive leave or to continue working. I know many women who have worked through their entire pregnancy and gone on to have a normal delivery of a healthy child. I have as many colleagues who have applied for and been granted preventive leave. In both instances, these women have returned to work with enthusiasm and dedication.

Return to Work Following Maternity Leave – Reintegration

Return to work following maternity leave can be emotionally and physically stressful for many reasons. It is not unusual for the veterinarian to feel that she has to regain the status she earned before the leave began. A smart practice owner will be supportive during this time and realize that the female practitioner will be an asset to the practice in the near future if not immediately. Many women return to work on a part-time basis and, while this is generally acceptable for the practice, for those women who have been very focused on career, working part-time can make them feel inadequate. It is important for all involved to realize that part-time practitioners can be as effective and involved in the practice as full-time practitioners, and they can remain on track to become a partner. Successfully raising a child is, arguably, the most enduring of any achievement; accepting this fact makes it easier to accept the compromises that are made in our children's best interests.

Return to Work Following Maternity Leave – Childcare

A significant challenge for working parents is finding satisfactory childcare. The federal government of Canada has recently introduced a Universal Child Care Benefit program. This program provides financial assistance directly to all families of children under the age of six, in the amount of $100.00 per month per child. The spending of the Child Care Benefit is at the complete discretion of the parents. It can be used as a contribution to daycare or homecare or, in the case of families with a stay at home parent, for preschool programs, occasional babysitting, or to purchase books.[10] Although any amount of financial assistance is welcome, the cost of good quality day-care in most provinces will far exceed this amount. For that reason, since 1977 Quebec has had a Universal Daycare Program, offering subsidized care to families for $7.00 per day per child. Understandably, there are waiting lists of up to several years for positions in these day cares. Application must be made as early as possible, usually before the birth of the child. Since this program has been in effect, there has been an increase (21%) in the proportion of working mothers in two-parent families, representing more than twice the increase in all other provinces. Although this has translated into more women resuming their careers, studies indicate that there has been an increase in the amount of depression experienced by parents of children in day care.[11] On the positive side, children in day care are well socialized, and some enjoy improved test scores and retention rates in school.[11] However, other studies have shown that negative behaviours in children increase as the amount of time they spend with their mother decreases.[12] The veterinarian parents with whom I have discussed this subject face the same dilemma: does one believe the studies for or against day care? It is a known fact that most professional parents are going to be more involved with their children socially and academically. The veterinarian has to choose the childcare option that makes sense for her lifestyle and support system.

No matter what the decision regarding childcare, gradual return to work is less stressful for the mother and child. If the option is home-care, it would be ideal to have the home-caregiver start to work prior to the mother going back to work, so that there can be a transition period with caregiver overlap. In the case of day care, consider taking the child to the day care facility for short periods, when you can both be there together and allow a period of adjustment. Finally, remember that children are very resilient and will survive the separation. Knowing this will allow a focused return to work, which is critical to successful practice reintegration. For this reason, it may be best to work part-time while children are young; once children enter the school system, childcare issues diminish, and there are more hours available during the day to focus on career.

Evening shifts can be a challenge for the veterinarian parent when children become school age, because of the child's homework responsibilities. I have found this period to be the most difficult and demanding of my time. Due to an ever-expanding body of knowledge, schoolwork must be supplemented at home. In Quebec, this is compounded by the fact that subjects are taught in two languages. Only when children are in high school do they become independent workers.

As veterinarians, we have a unique profession where our children can visit our workplace and enjoy seeing our patients. My children have been supportive of my career and have learned a degree of independence. Now that they are older, we communicate through e-mails when I am at work or conferences. They respect that in order for me to remain current in my profession, I must read and attend conferences. I hope that I will have taught them a good work ethic by example.

Healthy Balance

Balancing home life and career requires a supportive life partner, communication with colleagues and working partners, and creativity when it comes to time allocation, the most precious commodity. This is true for veterinarians in general, regardless of family situation. I have used many time-saving strategies to enable me to concentrate on my career and become a partner in my practice. Find a milkman who will deliver dairy and bread products to your door. Hire someone to clean your home and water your plants. Consider hiring a nanny to come to the house in order to save the time required to dress the children and drive them to day care—a huge time-saver most mornings. If the homework is out of control, hire a tutor. It is very liberating to realize that you need not be responsible for everything. Prioritization is the key to preventing burnout. A study on the length of veterinary careers found that women remain in practice on average 16 years, while men remain for 24 years (full-time equivalents).[13] Veterinary burnout is influenced by "high expectations and demands, perfectionism, and insecurity about their own abilities."[14] Develop outside interests that reduce your stress, lean on your family, cultivate friendships with people who do not place demands on you, and accept the reality that balance will require compromises. Pat your own back when you do a good job, and look at the big picture.

Setting Goals

It is important to set reasonable goals for yourself and to reevaluate those goals periodically. Failing to reach a goal is not the end of the world; if this happens, simply change your goal or change the time frame. Try not to be so focused on the goal that you don't enjoy getting there. I have consistently re-evaluated my own goals and measured my achievements every five years. This has been very successful for me and has allowed me to recognize my accomplishments. I turned down the prospect of a residency position in order to raise my children. This was a difficult decision to make, and I certainly had regrets initially. I set a new short-term goal to become a practice owner. Once I reached that goal, I set a new one, which was to ensure that this practice would be committed to the continuing education (CE) of its owners and staff. I regularly attended (and continue to do so) CE conferences in order to reach and maintain proficiency in my areas of interest (surgery and physical rehabilitation). I have built a rehabilitation practice and have completed the course work and training necessary to become a certified rehabilitation practitioner. I will write the examination when time allows, which has become my new short-term goal. The knowledge base in veterinary medicine is increasing to the point that it is no longer possible to have the same depth of understanding in all areas of practice. The general practitioner should develop an area of interest and focus his/her education in this area. In a group practice, this facilitates knowledge-sharing and creates an internal referral system. The challenge for the new graduate here is to determine in what area he or she is most interested. In my experience, veterinarians naturally gravitate toward the areas of their best skills. In my practice, my partners and I encourage and have a generous allowance for CE for our veterinarians, technicians, and staff. We are also committed to having students of all levels at our practice, so that we can contribute to our community and positively influence the upcoming generation. It is both revealing and validating to see your practice through the eyes of students.

Networking

It is extremely important to regularly attend major conferences. Local meetings are excellent for establishing a local network, whereas major international conferences foster a broader perspective to practice. It is easy to become set in a practice routine that can become frustrating. The importance of networking with other veterinarians cannot be overstated; it will garner new ideas as well as provide reassurance that colleagues are experiencing the same successes and failures. This is particularly true for the solo practitioner, but it also applies to those working within a group. Although not usually recommended for the new graduate who is at the peak of his/her knowledge, master classes and intensive short courses can be taken to learn a subject in depth.

Networking in the community in the form of volunteering also has immeasurable rewards. Volunteering in your community is not only good for the profile of your practice but it is also personally satisfying and stress relieving. It is very satisfying to coach a team or sit on a school governing board as it allows you to understand who your children are being influenced and surrounded by and also is personally enriching. Stepping outside your veterinary world is healthy and may help to prevent burnout, as long as you do not over-commit.

Summary

So why should a practice owner hire a female veterinarian? Many women make excellent practitioners, because they seem to have an inherent understanding of the human-animal bond. Pet owners' concerns for their sick animal are based on a nurturing relationship very similar to that of a parent-child relationship; women in general have an intuitive understanding of this, and it can be enhanced by their relationship with their own children. This can be very important in understanding the bond between a client and the child-substitute pet. Considering the focus on practice growth through recognizing and celebrating the human-animal bond, women have a prominent role to play in the modern, client-centered, veterinary practice. As our profession continues to evolve, practice structure must change not only to allow for women practitioners who are raising the next generation but also to encourage all its members in the pursuit of a healthy balance between working and personal lifes for all.

References

1. A New Generation of Canadian Families Raising Young Children. A New Look at Data from National Surveys. Human Resources Development Canada, Applied Research Branch. http://www.gov.mb.ca/healthychild/ecd/raising_young_children.pdf

2. Family Life: The Canadian Council of Social Development in *The Progress of Canada's Children and Youth;* 2006. www.ccsd.ca/pccy/2006/

3. Lipps, Garth, Yiptong-Avila, Jackie. From home to school- How Canadian children cope. Initial analysis using data from the second cycle of the school component of the National Longitudinal Survey of Children and Youth; Oct 14, 1999.

4. A New Generation of Canadian Families Raising Young Children –September 2003 http://www.sdc.gc.ca/en/cs/sp/sdc/pkrf/publications/research/2003-001330/page02.shtml

5. Foroohar R. The gender gap: Moms not wanted. Sweden bends over backward to help women work, but in ways that keep them out of the best jobs. Newsweek International Edition http://msnbc.msn.com/id/10682392/site/news

6. Work place Standards. IPM Management Training and Development Corporation 1984-2006. http://www.workplace.ca/laws/employstandard_comp.html

7. Emploi et Solidarité sociale Quebec, Quebec Parental Insurance Plan. http://www.hrsdc.gc.ca/en/ei/faq/faq_qpip.shtml

8. Government of Canada, Human Resources and Social Development Canada; Amendments to Part II of the Canada Labour Code (Bill C-12)- Frequently Asked Questions. www.hrsdc.gc.ca

9. Commision de la santé et de la sécurité du travail (CSST). http://www.csst.qc.ca/portail/fr/

10. Canada's Universal Child Care Plan; Government of Canada; June 29, 2006. http://www.universalchildcare.ca/en/faqs_benefit.shtml

11. Baker M. What can we learn from Quebec's Universal Childcare Program? C.D. Howe Institute e-brief; Feb. , 2006. http://www.cdhowe.org/pdf/ebrief_25_english.pdf#search=%22cdhowe%20institute%20what%20can%20we%20learn%20from%20Quebecs%20%20%20child%20care%20program%22

12. Child care linked to assertive, noncompliant, and aggressive behaviors *Vast Majority of Children Within Normal Range.* National Institute of Child Health and Human Development Early Childcare Research Network; July 16, 2003. http://www.nichd.nih.gov/new/releases/child_care.cfm

13. Heeath TJ. Length of veterinary working life. Aust Vet J. 1998l; 76 (7):478 481. http://www.ncbi.nlm.nih.gov/entrez/query.fcgi?cmd=Retrieve&db=PubMed&list_uids=9700402&dopt=Abstract

14. Stembert FM, Lipman LJ, Loomans JB. Veterinarian: a healthy profession? Tijdscher Diergeneeskd 2003;128:565-569. http://www.ncbi.nlm.nih.gov/entrez/query.fcgi?db=pubmed&cmd=Retrieve&dopt=AbstractPlus&list_uids=14535074&query_hl=2&itool=pubmed_docsum

Biography

Laurie Dunbar was born in Halifax, Nova Scotia, but she has lived in four other provinces and considers herself a true Canadian. She obtained a diploma in Animal Science from the Nova Scotia Agricultural College in 1980 and a BSc from the University of Guelph in 1984. She graduated from the Ontario Veterinary College with her DVM in 1986. Following graduation, she practiced small animal medicine and surgery at the Dartmouth Veterinary Hospital in Dartmouth, Nova Scotia. She moved to Montreal, Quebec in 1997 and joined the Hôpital Vétérinaire Côte St Luc. In 1991, she joined the Pierrefonds Animal Hospital, of which she became a part owner in 1996.

After having completed the first Canine Physical Therapy Short Course offered by the University of Tennessee in 2000, Dr. Dunbar began providing rehabilitation services for her patients. She has completed the course work for the Rehabilitation Practitioner Certification and a 40-hour externship at the Animal Wellness and Rehabilitation Centre in Raleigh, North Carolina (owned by Dr. Marcellin-Little, a pioneer in rehabilitation programs for companion animals). She is a member of the International Veterinary Academy of Pain Management and sits on a pharmaceutical advisory board concerning pain management.

In her spare time, she had two children who are now 15 and 12 years of age. She is Vice President of the West Island Lakers Basketball Association, which is a coed children's league with over 900 members. She is also a league coach and convener. She is working on her level one coaching certificate given by Basketball Quebec. Dr. Dunbar served on the governing board of her children's schools from 1998 to 2004, and on the Lester B. Person School Board Intercultural Advisory Board. She regularly gives talks at schools on basic science and is part of the mentoring program at the Université de Montréal Faculty of Veterinary Medicine.

2-2

Veterinary Medicine in the Province of Quebec

Laurie Dunbar, DVM
Pierrefonds Animal Hospital, Montreal, Quebec

> *Est Québécois qui veut l´être.*
> *(He who wants to be a Quebecer, is a Quebecer.)*
>
> — René Lévesque

Introduction

The new graduate has at his or her disposal all the tools needed to prevent, diagnose, and treat disease. Practicing in Quebec can present the new graduate with other challenges, such as learning a new language and adapting to cultural differences with respect to the clientele. Challenges and opportunities particular to Quebec will be discussed.

Geographic Considerations

Quebec is unique in many respects, primarily in that it is home to 90% of Canada's French-speaking people. Francophones make up approximately 80%

of the population of Quebec, compared to 8.2% of Quebec residents who declare English as their mother tongue. Of Quebec's Anglophones, 88% live in the Greater Montreal area.[1] Montreal, the province's largest city and the second largest in the country, is safe, vibrant, and culturally diverse. One of the largest French-speaking cities in the world, it has been ranked as the sixth best city in the world in which to live.[2] The city has a distinctly European feel, due to the architectural style and the fact that English is not the first language spoken.

While two-thirds of Montreal's residents are Francophones, the majority of residents are bilingual, speaking both French and English. There is a large number of immigrants, and almost one-third of the population are Allophones, whose mother tongue is neither French nor English.[1] Immigrants to Canada and Canadians who were educated in a French school system within Canada are required by law to register their children in the French school system. In order to attend school in the English school system, children must have at least one parent who has been educated in an English school within Canada. This program has been very successful in attracting immigrants from French-speaking countries. It has also played a role in ensuring that the French language and culture continue to thrive in Quebec, which not only has the country's lowest birth rate, but also is widely influenced by the surrounding American culture.

The most predominant ethnic groups in Montreal are Italian, Spanish, and Arabic, representing 6%, 2.9%, and 2.5% of the population, respectively.[1] Montreal is also home to large Jewish, Jamaican, and Haitian communities. Ethnic communities tend to be concentrated in certain areas of the city, which contributes to Montreal's colourful and diverse matrix.

One of the many positive aspects of Montreal's cultural diversity is a large number of fabulous restaurants, earning the city a well-deserved reputation as a mecca for food lovers. The city is also an entertainment and tourist destination. Summer in Montreal is hot, and the streets are filled with people. Outdoor cafes abound, and the nightlife is unparalleled. Bars are open until 3 AM, and there are after-hours clubs open from 3 until 11 AM. The city is host to many festivals and events that attract tourists from around the world. Festivals start in June and continue throughout the summer; the best known are the Just For Laughs Festival, the International Jazz Festival, and the Formula One Canadian Grand Prix.

Quebec is, in many respects, a liberal society and boasts some of the most generous social programs in the country. Individual rights are respected in a multicultural environment. Montreal is Gay-friendly, with a large Gay Village. It annually hosts one of North America's largest Gay pride festivals, drawing more than one million spectators and participants. Quebec couples are less traditional than in other parts of the country, with a much lower marriage rate as a result. In 2000, almost one-third (29%) of Quebec's children under the age of five years lived with common-law parents, as compared to 8% else-where in Canada.[1] Couples who do marry in Quebec are required by law to keep their surnames. Children, and pets for that matter, can be registered under the family name of the mother, the father, or a combination of both—making it sometimes difficult to keep track of to whom pets and children belong!

Most Montrealers are well versed on the political situation, and it is common to have passionate political discussion with families, friends, and even clients. Language issues and the constant specter of separation are frequent topics, making life in Quebec interesting! For those wishing to move to Quebec, it is helpful to learn about the local and provincial political scene.

Requirements for Veterinarians Wishing to Practice in Quebec

It is clear that a working knowledge of the French language is a requirement for a veterinarian wishing to practice in Quebec. This should not be a deterrent for those who are willing to learn the language or those whose French language skills are rudimentary. In Montreal, many residents speak at least two languages, and most Francophones can and will switch to English if they detect that you are not fluent in French. Although this is usually done out of politesse, it can make improving French skills a significant challenge. This is particularly true when working in certain areas of the city. Some parts of the city are predominantly English, where one can practice veterinary medicine almost exclusively in English. In my practice area, known as the West Island, the overwhelming majority of clients are bilingual. This is particularly true for younger clients, who can effortlessly switch from French to English and then sometimes to a third language. Outside of Montreal, clients are more likely to be unilingual Francophones, making it more important that a veterinarian be proficient in French when starting to practice in these areas.

French courses are available privately and at any of the community colleges or excellent universities throughout Quebec. Notably, Montreal is home to McGill University, Concordia University, L'Université du Québec a Montréal, and L'Université de Montréal. One can choose between intensive short courses taken during the day, or semester courses, which are sometimes held in the evening. Without a doubt, the best way to learn the language and become proficient is to take courses and then jump in with both feet, insisting on speaking in French to colleagues and friends, and asking that they correct gross errors.

One of the challenges faced by many new graduates is the ability to communicate confidently with clients. Admittedly, this can be an even greater challenge when trying to learn another language at the same time. With bilingual clients, it is possible to practice your French during a consultation and then recap in English at the end of the visit in order to ensure you have been understood, thus maintaining quality of care and increasing compliance. When I first began practicing in Quebec, I had high school-level French and had taken one semester of a conversational French course. I insisted on speaking French with my Francophone clients. I made many mistakes that resulted in laughter and, less often (thankfully), in derision from my clients. To this day, I remember telling a pet owner that his Airedale terrier was scratching due to the little sheep that were running all over its back! I owe a large part of my becoming bilingual to one of my partners who refused to speak to me in English for a period of one year. This forced me to learn the hard way, and I am grateful for it.

Not only is it personally enriching to learn a second language, it is also mandatory in Quebec. Vveterinarians must provide proof of a good working knowledge of the French language in order to be licensed. According to Section 35 of the Charter of the French Language:

> *"the candidate must have a knowledge of the official language appropriate to the practice of his profession. If not the person must obtain a certificate issued by the Office Québécoise de la langue française after succeeding to French examination."* [3]

The Ordre des médecins vétérinaires du Québec (OMVQ) allows a veterinarian three years to pass this examination. All written communication from the OMVQ is in French, including their monthly publication. Fortunately for the veterinarian who is not yet proficient in French, most, if not all, of the staff at the OMVQ is bilingual and can answer any questions in English. It is, however, both polite and helpful to at least say bonjour and merci at the beginning and end of such conversations; it is amazing how far this small gesture will go toward improving relationships. The Quebec association that is dedicated to the continuing education (CE) of its members, l'Académie de médecine vétérinaire du Québec (AMVQ), also communicates and publishes its monthly journal in French. However, guest speakers are from all over North America and sometimes Europe and, therefore, much of the CE content provided by the AMVQ is in English.

In Quebec, French is the legislated language of the workplace. Materials that are distributed to clients must be in both official languages. It can be a challenge to find a practice management software program that is bilingual and meets the practice's needs. The programs used by the majority of clinics and hospitals in Quebec allow the practitioner to identify the language of the client so that receipts and records are in French or English accordingly. Also, the language of the user is known, so that if one prefers, the computer language will be English.

Practice Demographics and Remuneration

Quebecers generally earn less money and pay more taxes than their counterparts in other provinces.[4] The result of this phenomenon may be less disposable income available for pet care. Studies have clearly shown that dog ownership in Quebec is on the decline, with dogs being owned by only one-fifth of the population. Cat ownership is on the rise in Quebec, primarily among Francophones.[5] This reflects what is seen in my practice, with the clientele roughly split between Francophones and Anglophones. Most of the large-breed dogs I see are owned by Anglophones, who also seem to be more likely to consider their pets as family members. There seems to be more resistance in the Francophone community to spending money on advanced veterinary procedures. The new graduate should prepare him/herself for this, as this is one of the major disappointments faced in veterinary practice in general, and for which veterinarians are usually poorly prepared. It takes some experience to be comfortable with the fact that some owners love their pets dearly but cannot spend the money, while others are not emotionally involved with their pet at all and are able to make very logical decisions about ending life or opting out of treatment. How our clients will respond to suggestions for treatment seems to be independent of education or financial status. In fact, the majority of my clients are both compliant and educated, and these decisions seem to be culturally driven.

In Quebec, a large number of people do not have a family doctor, and walk-in medical clinics are numerous and widely used. This pattern has spilled over into veterinary medicine; the result is that there has been a steady increase in the number of clients walking in without an appointment. Also, in many of the client families, both parents work outside of the home, making it essential to offer extended hours.

The new graduate seeking employment in Quebec can expect to make slightly less than his/her counterparts in some other provinces. However, housing prices are reasonable, and in Montreal they are much lower than those in Toronto or Vancouver. Quebec veterinarians, practice owners, and employees alike place a strong emphasis on quality of life, and this is reflected in new graduate attitudes. Of the 2005 graduates, 29% ranked their job as being very important; whereas, 42% ranked their leisure time as being very important. Most new graduates in Quebec will negotiate for quality-of-life conditions, such as vacation and schedule. Almost half (46%) of 2005 graduates surveyed enjoyed three weeks of vacation in their first year of employment.[6]

While the financial benefits of practicing in Quebec may be fewer than those in other high-population provinces, there are many non-financial benefits. Quebec is culturally diverse and socially vibrant. Quebec is a beautiful province with access to many outdoor activities. A short drive from Montreal will bring you to many ski resorts, including Mont Tremblant, one of the premier downhill and cross country ski resorts in the world. Throughout Quebec are many well-developed trails for cycling, and Montreal annually hosts the "Tour de l'île," a circuit around the island open to cyclists of all ages. Quebec is home to fantastic provincial parks for camping, canoeing, and hiking (although dogs are prohibited in all provincial parks run by the Quebec government).

Candidate Profile

For a veterinarian contemplating a career in Quebec, s/he should be an excellent communicator and preferably bilingual. At the very least, s/he should have a strong desire to learn French (or English, if French-speaking). The ideal candidate should be a leader, a motivator, and able to work well in a team. My practice works somewhat like the United Nations—there are at least four different languages spoken, and the conversation routinely switches from French to English and back to French. It is important that the candidate be able to work well in this environment. When hiring, my partners and I look for a veterinarian who wishes to develop an area of interest and actively pursue CE. Montreal clientele is made up of many families in which both parents work; therefore, many hospitals (including ours) are open seven days per week and offer consultation early in the morning until later in the evening. As a result, the candidate should expect to work evenings and weekends, with a heavier work schedule during heartworm season in the spring.

Summary

Veterinary medicine is a wonderful profession. However, the new graduate needs to pay as much attention to balancing his or her life as s/he did to succeeding in the program. This will ensure longevity in, and enjoyment of, practice. For those who are fortunate enough to be working and living in Quebec, many doors will have been opened as a result of learning a second language. Quebec culture supports family life and leisure time. What better province in which to start one's career!

References

1. Office of the Commissioner of Official Languages
   Youth Express: Statistics on official languages in Quebec. August 2004.
   www.ocol-clo.gc.ca/youth_jeunes/tools_outils/stat_can_qc.asp?Lang=English
2. Montreal. From Wikipedia, the free encyclopedia.
   http://en.wikipedia.org/wiki/Montreal
3. Office québécoise de la langue française; The charter of the French Language.
   http://www.olf.gouv.qc.ca/english/charter/index.html
4. Quebecers are being ripped off. The Gazette (Montreal) Editorial; April 24,
   2006.
   http://www.canada.com/montrealgazette/news/editorial/story.html?id=6394
   c81d-8781-4145-ae0f-5c37b0f2d77e&p=2
5. Sondage Léger Marketing Les chiens de mois en moins present Les chats de
   plus en plus populaires.; Le Rapporteur V18N2-Avril 2006:4-5.
6. Les Conditions de travail des médecins vétérinaires nouvellement diplômés au
   Québec. Le Rapporteur V18N1-février 2006:35-38.

Biography

For Dr. Dunbar's biography, please see Chapter 2-1 on page 108.

Veterinary Medicine in Canada's Atlantic Provinces

Steve Noonan, DVM
Formerly of Petworks Veterinary Hospital,
Dartmouth, Nova Scotia
Currently Practice Management Consultant,
Effectivet, Campbellville, Ontario

> *You can get everything in life you want, if you can just help enough other people get what they want.*
>
> — Zig Ziegler

Introduction

I have been asked to provide my personal perspective on the current state of veterinary medicine in Canada's Atlantic Provinces. When making this request of me, the book's authors asked me to take into consideration questions that would likely be on the minds of readers, including any issues unique to my chosen geographic area of work, the demographics of my clientele and coworkers/associates, professional challenges and opportunities (particularly in achieving professional satisfaction and work-life balance), and any "words of wisdom" that I might be able to impart to new colleagues entering our wonderful profession. Let me begin by saying, "Don't be afraid to look beyond your current personal and/or professional perspective." As a Southern Ontarian and graduate of the Ontario Veterinary College, the path to eventually finding my roots in Nova Scotia was anything but traditional. As the following narrative demonstrates, it was a decision upon which I have never looked back.

Nova Scotia

The Halifax Regional Municipality (HRM) where I practice is an amalgamated community of approximately 450,000 people. The largest portion of this population is centred in the two sister cities of Halifax, the capital of Nova Scotia, and Dartmouth, situated across the Halifax Harbour and surrounded by the "bedroom communities" of Bedford, Lower Sackville, and Cole Harbour. The smaller villages in HRM range from scenic coastal fishing villages, like Peggy's Cove (a short 45-minute commute from downtown Halifax) to the rolling hills and farmland of Meagher's Grant; however, nothing in HRM is farther than one hour from the city centre.

Throughout HRM, there are 33 veterinary facilities employing 83 veterinarians (as of April 2006). While there are a small number of veterinarians engaged in mixed-animal practice, the majority are small-animal practitioners. For a centre with a relatively small population, HRM boasts many of the features of a larger centre with an international airport, renowned orchestra, world-class cuisine, and hotels served by a hospitality industry on par with the best in the country. There are more than 10 universities and colleges, a large military presence, and the infrastructure necessary to support a capital city. The result is a stable economy in a beautiful, small city with short commuting distances. A historic waterfront with a seafaring history of over 400 years, combined with modern office towers and two giant bridges spanning the world's second deepest natural harbour, make downtown Halifax a delight for visitors and residents alike. A bustling tourism industry attests to the popularity of Halifax as a destination choice for many.

The veterinary clientele, like in many cities, ranges from upper to low income, but the stability of the economy in HRM is such that the majority of people are middle or upper-middle income earners. The local residents place a high value on their furry family members and are, for the most part, willing to make the necessary investments in maintaining the health of that human-animal bond.

New Brunswick, Newfoundland, and Prince Edward Island (PEI)

While my practice of veterinary medicine has been restricted to HRM, there are a number of lovely smaller cities and towns in Atlantic Canada that boast vibrant veterinary communities. In New Brunswick, the "hub city" of Moncton, the capital of Fredericton, and the industrial city of Saint John all have progressive veterinary facilities—as do the smaller Nova Scotia towns of Amherst, Truro, and Sydney.

In Newfoundland, the veterinary facilities are few and far between, reflecting the relatively small population that is scattered over such a large land mass. Many of those residing in Newfoundland are clustered close to the capital city of St. John's, which many islanders and visitors alike claim to be the friendliest city in Canada. It is also home to Memorial University and plays hosts to several very progressive veterinary hospitals.

Prince Edward Island has a population of just over 100,000—many of whom reside in the vicinity of their pretty capital city of Charlottetown, which has the largest number of small-animal practices and is home to the world-class Atlantic Veterinary College. The remainder of PEI is a pretty, rural, patchwork quilt of farmland interspersed with scenic villages and well served by an active mixed- and large-animal veterinary contingent.

A veterinary career in Atlantic Canada has many charms. The slower pace of life, short and easy commutes, and the friendliness of Atlantic Canadians—combined with an evolving veterinary medical profession that rivals the rest of the country—makes Atlantic Canada an enviable location to "hang one's shingle." This is the reason that many who come to visit never end up leaving (including myself)!

Challenges and Opportunities to Veterinary Professionals in HRM

As in any veterinary community, there are, have been, and always will be challenges to the success of practitioners from a lifestyle point of view, despite the progress that has been made over the last 10 to 15 years. One of the most significant challenges from a lifestyle perspective has been the recent formation of a freestanding, after-hours veterinary emergency hospital (the first of its kind in Atlantic Canada), which has eliminated after-hours on call for HRM companion animal veterinarians.

As a whole, the veterinary profession in HRM is one of the healthiest and most robust in the country according to Darren Osborne, economist for the Ontario Veterinary Medical Association. This is in large part due to regular economic surveys culminating in recommended fee guidelines. Begun in 1994, this ongoing initiative has greatly improved the economic, and subsequently the professional, success for Nova Scotia veterinarians and is beginning to be applied to other regions of Atlantic Canada as well. Based on the 2004 Nova Scotia Veterinary Medical Association Economic Survey, real incomes, when adjusted for the lower cost of living in Atlantic Canada, are the highest in the country.

It is my opinion that appropriate fees are the cornerstone to being able to provide the highest caliber of veterinary medicine. These fees not only provide suitable compensation to the veterinary employer and his/her staff (including helping to pay down the student debt that many of you are saddled with), but they also allow veterinarians to reinvest in their hospitals and continuing education (CE). Based on the ever-evolving advancements in medical technology, the purchase of modern medical equipment (which is often quite costly) is essential to meet the needs and demands of our clientele. Additionally, CE has become the bellwether of competency assurance and a must in this knowledge-based profession we have chosen. Running a full-service veterinary facility is costly; reduced fees not only result in service failure to your clientele, but may jeopardize the overall long-term health of the veterinary facility. As an example, if you reduce your fees by 10%, you need to increase your production by 50% to earn the same net income; if you reduce your fees by 20%, you need to increase your production by 200% to earn the same net income.[1] Based on this, it quickly becomes evident how fee structure can have a tremendous impact on professional and practice health!

My opinion is not shared by all, however. As in any community, there is a minority of veterinary practices whose business strategy can best be summarized as "low fees/high volume," with the goal being to attract a higher volume of work based on a low fee-for-service fee structure. The soundness of this philosophy has been challenged by virtually every economic survey conducted in this country over the last several years, with results placing veterinary fees 4th or 5th and well behind compassion, quality of facility, perceived professional knowledge, and location as issues clients deem most important in selecting veterinary care. From a professional's perspective, it begs the question: "Would you like to work harder for less money per hour?" There are practitioners who are willing to embrace this strategy, using as a defense their strong love for animals and the justification that they simply cannot say "no" to a sick pet regardless of the client's ability to pay for treatment. However, the ramifications of this approach go beyond the bounds of the veterinary-clientpatient relationship, impacting the practice staff and families of these veterinarians. The result: doctors that work so hard they rarely see their families, inadequate staff remuneration, and an inability to reinvest in their veterinary facility or themselves. This ultimately equates to high staff turnover, under-trained personnel, and burnout. In my opinion, this is wrong. One should not suffer in his or her personal life, or financially, because of a personal (or an employer's) love of animals dictating the provision of veterinary services to anyone regardless of the ability to pay. A better choice is to volunteer at the animal shelter and give aggressively to charity.

As mentioned earlier, lifelong learning through CE is a passion of my peers and mine and should be a lifelong passion for all veterinary professionals. The Nova Scotia Veterinary Medical Association dictates that members must participate in a minimum of 20 hours of CE per two years. While this is a good starting point, my personal opinion is that this commitment falls short of what is truly required, especially in our rapidly evolving niche of the medical profession. It is lifelong education that defines us as professionals and distinguishes us from other wage earners.

Finally, while the availability and access to specialty care have gained foothold in other parts of Canada, specialized care is in its infancy in the Atlantic provinces and is provided predominantly by the Atlantic Veterinary College in Charlottetown. This can result in travel times of up to four hours each way (much more if traveling from Newfoundland) to see a specialist in Atlantic Canada. Positive change is occurring, however; now a good number of visiting specialists are conducting specialty clinics throughout the year at various hospitals in HRM to better serve the needs of clients.

While there are challenges to the practice of veterinary medicine in the HRM, they are relatively minor and consistent with those in other parts of the country. Multiple opportunities exist each year for new graduates to find fulfillment in employment at one of the many quality veterinary hospitals in our region.

Conclusions

Like most who are part of the baby boomer generation, I was raised on a work ethic that embodied the "work harder, not necessarily smarter" philosophy. However, despite the 70-hour workweeks for the first eight or 10 years of my career (not to mention the attendant after-hours on-call), I have gotten smarter and created a good life/work balance for myself. Thanks in large part to an understanding and supportive wife (also a veterinarian), subsequent success in veterinary practice (secondary to the association with excellent business partners), and the formation of the emergency clinic, I have been able to recalibrate my work/life balance to a very enjoyable degree over the last 15 years.

Fortunately, it will not be necessary for newly graduated veterinarians to work the number of hours my generation did in the search for success, and most job opportunities now reflect this new reality. There are many employment and partnership opportunities in Atlantic Canada for dedicated veterinarians.

Partnership in a successful veterinary practice will be the wave of the future and the key to unlocking the formula for optimal life/work and professional/financial balance. Less emphasis should be placed on starting veterinary practices from "scratch." Personal egos will be put aside as veterinarians learn that cooperation and joint ventures are always superior to "solo-manship" (a new word!).

A satisfactory lifestyle has several components, depending on the individual. In my opinion, time spent with loved ones, the pursuit of one's hobbies, and personal health should be high on the list of priorities. Professional satisfaction and camaraderie amongst colleagues are close behind. Finally, financial success is important. As my partner's grandfather from a Nova Scotia fishing village used to say, "Talk is cheap! It takes money to buy rum!"

Novice veterinarians must intimately understand the direct correlation between the successful practice of veterinary medicine and fees in order to facilitate the lifestyle balance described above. Excellent medicine costs money—sometimes a lot of money—and there is no need to apologize for it. Veterinary fees are required to pay for overhead in a veterinary practice. This includes salaries, drugs and food, utilities, occupancy costs, and the list goes on. Some may say veterinary medicine is more expensive than its human counterpart, but they fail to see the relative value, especially when one considers that over 40% of every Harmonized Sales Tax (HST; or other tax dollar) collected in this country goes for human medical health care. When one considers that tens of billions are spent in this country each year on human health care versus the entire Canadian veterinary industry's gross annual sales of approximately one billion, it should be apparent that we are the dwarf.

Finally, my advice for new veterinarians:

- Be proud of our profession. Be professional in your appearance, behaviour, and demeanour. Be kind, compassionate, and empathetic. Let the love you have for animals show in your every action to your human and animal clients.
- Be thorough, explaining and documenting clearly everything you do for your patient and client. Be honest.
- Do not forget to charge appropriately for what you do. Most veterinary hospitals are lucky to earn 20 or 25 cents for every dollar the client pays; however, we must remember that it is from this 20% to 25% return on investment that the salary of the new veterinarian is derived.
- Participate in a lot of CE opportunities.
- Work harmoniously with staff and clients, utilizing excellent communication and interpersonal skills, enthusiasm, and a good work ethic.

- A stated and obvious desire to constantly improve is an endearing trait that I and many others admire as well.
- Become comfortable with charging an appropriate fee for the service provided. This, along with a strong desire to earn a salary while returning a profit to the owner, is a quality that must be possessed by one who aspires to be a partner. Go into every job opportunity with partnership in mind. While it may not always work out, you will learn enormously from the experience.

All of these are traits that are sought in a new veterinarian. An intelligent hospital owner will always be exceedingly willing to hire such an individual and consider him or her as a future partner. Individuals with the above skills cannot help but be successful wherever they choose to practice.

References

1. Osborne, D. OVMA Focus. 1999; Vol 18; No. 2.

Biography

Dr. Steve Noonan is a 1983 graduate of the Ontario Veterinary College, and, upon graduation, he and Dr. Diane Corlett, his wife and classmate, went for a 1-year job posting in Halifax. After 25 happy years in Nova Scotia, they returned to the Guelph area in 2008 to be closer to their families.

Dr. Noonan has served for many years on the boards and committees of various local, regional, and national veterinary self-interest groups. He has chaired or served on the veterinary economic committee in Nova Scotia since 1993. In 1990 Dr. Noonan, a passionate advocate of lifelong learning, and his colleaagues created a CE vehicle for veterinarians (the Nova Scotia Academy of Veterinary Medicine) to present topical issues in veterinary education at a time when CE opportunities were rare. He has served on the board of the Atlantic Provinces Veterinary Conference, an organization that, since 1999, hosts one of the largest (and best!) veterinary conferences in Canada. He was instrumental in forming a corporation of shareholders comprised of almost every veterinary hospital owner in the HRM, to create an emergency hospital in 1997; he served as the president of the board of directors for 7 years. He was co-founder and served 4 years as the president of the Atlantic Veterinary Management Group, a self-help cooperative of 12 privately owned veterinary hospitals.

Dr. Noonan's passion is to help create a veterinary environment where change and excellence are embraced and rewarded. He believes it is in this atmosphere where pets can receive the best veterinary care possible and veterinarians and their staff can be appreciated and rewarded for their commitment to this wonderful profession.

Dr. Noonan's hobbies are playing "horse Dad" to his equestrian-oriented family of Dr. Corlett and two teenage daughters at frequent horse shows; he also enjoys cooking for family and friends, playing guitar, biking, reading, and making regular trips to the gym. He also aspires to be a stand-up comic, award-winning karaoke singer, fluent French conversationalist, and world traveler.

CHAPTER $2-4$

A Female Practice Owner, Wife, and Mother from Prince Edward Island

Jane MacMillan-Bondt, DVM
Summerside Animal Hospital, Summerside, PEI

> *Don't wait for your ship to come in, swim out to it.*
>
> — Anonymous

My name is Dr. Jane MacMillan Bondt, and I am a small-animal veterinarian who has worked in the city of Summerside, Prince Edward Island (PEI), since 1985. I grew up in Charlottetown and was glad to be able to work on PEI after graduation from Ontario Veterinary College (OVC) in 1984.

With a population of 138,000, PEI has tourism, agriculture, and fishing as its primary industries. Summerside is a beautiful port city with about 15,000 people. Major employers are a Federal Tax Center, Prince County Hospital, Cavendish Farms, and the Space Industry. Famous Malpeque oysters are close by as well.

Currently, my professional activities are limited to my work at the Summerside Animal Hospital (SAH), of which I have been the owner since 1998. I was a member of the Council of the PEI Veterinary Medical Association (PEIVMA), but as a mother of four who also coaches synchronized swimming eight hours a week, I am presently finding my life busy enough. However, I do serve on the PEIVMA disciplinary board from time to time.

My career path was laid out officially in grade 11, when I, along with my parents, decided that veterinary medicine would be a good choice. I loved animals and enjoyed the sciences. I had wanted to be a "horse nurse" since I was four years old. My father is a medical specialist, and seeing how much he worked, I knew I did not want to pursue human medicine. Being from the city, I felt attending Nova Scotia Agricultural College would expand my knowledge of animals. They offered a pre-vet year in conjunction with the OVC. Shortly after graduation, I was offered a position in PEI. A year later, I was invited to run the first small-animal clinic in Summerside (with no opportunities to be on call; however, the neighboring mixed-animal practice would cover for me), and I have been in Summerside ever since.

Being the sole small animal practitioner for five years gave me the opportunity to "do what had to be done," including managing personnel and finances, handling challenging cases (as there was no referral center at that time), and reporting to my partners (who focused on the food-animal aspect of the practice). I quickly became an accountant, business manager, psychologist, and veterinarian all rolled into one. However, these challenges made me recognize my limitations. As I became busier, I had to rely on the services of others in the above professions and hire appropriate team members to take on some of these roles. (It is great to see that graduates of today have had at least some exposure to the business side of veterinary medicine.)

It is always hard as a mother and professional to balance your career and home life. I am in a position that I do have to work, and I am so thankful that I enjoy my work. I know I am a better person and mother because of it.

The clientele of the SAH includes about 2600 active clients. In most cases, they are pretty dedicated to their pets. Over the years, I have seen an improvement in the overall care and commitment shown toward their pets; however, about two-thirds of our clients have financial restriction concerning advanced care.

My professional challenges include the inability to work up cases due to financial constraints of the owners; a lack of consistent "different" cases to enable me to feel confident in handling them (e.g., I have only seen one gastric dilatation volvulus case since graduation!); restricted diagnostic tools (e.g., ultrasonography) due to their cost and my limited caseload; having to provide after-hour emergency service (the city of Summerside is not large enough to support an emergency clinic); and learning to manage/lead the hospital team, including engaging in the dynamics of creating an efficient and exciting workplace.

The professional opportunities are abundant. The Atlantic Veterinary College (AVC) is only an hour's drive from Summerside, so I can refer advanced cases to this facility if the owner is willing. The AVC also provides some continuing education (CE) programs, as does the Atlantic Province Veterinary Conference that is held in Halifax every year. The PEIVMA is a fairly small organization, so there are great opportunities to be involved. (There have been many CVMA presidents from PEI!) Being small in number, you get to know your colleagues well, and they are there for you when you need to call upon them for assistance (e.g., sharing emergency service, purchasing infrequently used drugs, etc.).

It has been very satisfying being part of this community for such a long time. I always see somebody I know while running an errand. I have elected in the last year to reduce my clinic hours to dedicate more time to my family (my youngest son has a learning disability). I was able to hire a recent AVC graduate, who has provided a lot of new information and energy and is able to provide more time for appointments and reduce the on-call emergencies. It has meant less income for me, however, because the practice has not grown significantly.

For anyone contemplating moving to this area to fill an opening, it is a great place to raise a family. The clients are friendly and understanding, and their pets are wonderful. The veterinary community is small, so it is easy to feel like you're part of a family. The AVC is an awesome referral center and very supportive.

Below is my advice to any veterinarian wanting to professionally be where I am today.

- Follow your dreams.
- Approach your work with honesty and with the best interests of the pets in mind (owners may not always be able to agree).
- Try to balance your work and your home life.
- Take time to take care of yourself. You need lots of energy and physical strength to "make it."
- Surround yourself with people who enjoy their positions.
- Take advantage of CE opportunities, as there is always new information to learn.
- Realize that you can't know or do it all, but commit yourself to doing your best in finding the answer or referring when necessary. Clients really appreciate that.
- Accept the fact that you are not going to save all your patients, and that's okay.

Practice ownership gives you the ability to be in "control," but it also means wearing many hats and delegating some responsibilities. Make sure that agreements are in writing and are lawyer approved. Hire the right people to fulfill your hospital's mission statement, and enjoy the journey.

Biography

Jane MacMillan-Bondt was born and raised in Charlottetown, PEI. From the time she was four years old she wanted to be a "horse nurse." She obtained her Doctor of Veterinary Medicine from the Ontario Veterinary College in 1984. In 1985 she joined the new, small animal practice in Summerside, eventually purchasing the Summerside Animal Hospital in 1998. She lives on a small, mixed farm in South Melville with her husband Phillip, four children, three horses, three dogs, and five cats. She enjoys swimming, cooking, and gardening, coaches synchronized swimming, and teaches church school.

Getting Started from the Perspective of a Toronto Multiple Practice Owner

Ian Sandler, DVM
Ontario Veterinary Group/
Rosedale Animal Hospital, Toronto, Ontario

> *I cannot believe that the purpose of life is to be happy. I think the purpose of life is to be useful, to be responsible, to be compassionate. It is, above all, to matter, to count, to stand for something, to have made some difference that you have lived at all.*
>
> — Leo Rosten

Introduction

As I reflect back on my veterinary career, I realize that I still have many things I wish to accomplish. For the last 12 years, I have practiced small animal veterinary medicine in large, urban settings (Detroit, Michigan, and Toronto). During this time, I have tried to ensure that both my professional and nonprofessional interests are always well balanced. The veterinary field requires years of training, dedication, and sacrifice. As health-care professionals, all of us are constantly bombarded by serious illness; but because we are also small business owners, we have to ensure that a pet emergency can be dealt with quickly, regardless if our staff is late or absent.

Unlike the veterinary profession's human counterparts, veterinarians often have to say good-bye to great pets (and clients) due to euthanasia or death. Pets have a shorter life span, and, therefore, members of our profession encounter death much more frequently. It is not uncommon for veterinarians to start to feel "burned out" after 10 to 15 years of practice. In this chapter, I will hopefully be able to give insight into some of the ways that I have tried to stay "balanced" while working in a busy, multi-person practice.

Tip no. 1: Find a Mentor

Upon graduation, I found two mentors in Detroit with whom I spent time. Both of these people were specialists. They were very supportive and allowed me to participate in hospital rounds on a routine basis. I spent many afternoons at their practices watching how they dealt with both difficult cases and the pet owners' responses. I have always believed in mentorship. As a student, I spent summers in Vancouver, Los Angeles, and Toronto at very busy and reputable practices. I developed lifelong friendships from those experiences. A mentor does not necessarily need to be a specialist. Any seasoned veterinarian can provide valuable insights into practice problems and their solutions. As a new graduate, do not be afraid to ask lots of questions. The first year or two involves a huge learning curve. A mentor can be very helpful during this maturation period.

Tip no. 2: Develop a Special Interest

When I graduated from the Ontario Veterinary College (OVC), I was intent on pursuing an internship and residency. When I did not match, I was caught a little "off guard." I did have a backup plan, but I was very disappointed at the time. I always had an interest in small animal oncology, so I was thankful when I started working in Detroit and found a board-certified oncologist with whom I could spend time, learning about and observing various chemotherapy treatments and protocols. From safety to dosing strategies, I became more and more comfortable with these types of cases. Specialization has become commonplace in many professions. While the role of the specialist has become very important to daily practice, there still is a need for practitioners to develop special interests.

As a part of a large veterinary group, we often refer to different people within our practice network. This serves both our clients and practice well.

For instance, I have never personally repaired a cruciate ligament, because orthopedic surgery is not a huge personal interest of mine, and our group practice has two people that do this procedure frequently. The reverse is also true; I often treat lymphoma patients for them.

Having a special interest will allow you to offer an additional level of service to your clients and allow you to stay focused above and beyond vaccinations and wellness programs.

Tip no. 3: Join Your Local Veterinary Association

When I returned to Toronto after practicing in Detroit, I wanted to meet some of my fellow colleagues. The Toronto Academy of Veterinary Medicine (TAVM) provided me with a great way to obtain continuing education (CE) and meet local veterinarians. Many urban centers have great associations, and these grass roots organizations are a wonderful way to network within your geographic location. (See also Chapter 1-5 titled What Organizations Do I Join?)

Tip no. 4: Get as Much CE as Possible

When I graduated, I remember a classmate saying that the practice he joined only encouraged CE for their veterinarians after two years of practice experience. While this may seem to make sense in theory, in practice I totally disagree with this concept. Lifelong learning should be a priority for all veterinarians, whether they are fresh out of school or not. The Doctor of Veterinary Medicine degree is one of the most comprehensive medical health science degrees available, but graduation from a top school does not make you competent. Years of practice and CE are key to developing lifelong skills and clinical intuition. Many of the first-year seminars that I attended focused on detailed cases that I was seeing in day-to-day practice. This helped to reinforce many of the treatment plans that I had introduced. I remember a seminar that I attended four months after graduation, where an internist was discussing a new treatment option that was never presented during class lectures or fourth-year rounds. This new treatment option was of immediate use for a patient I was treating. Attending a yearly international conference has also helped to provide me with a broader perspective and valuable training in a multitude of specialty areas. When I was a veterinary student, we only had three dental lectures and no wet labs. I am amazed at the number of dental procedures we do on a weekly basis. Many of these cases require dental tooth extraction (toothansia). Having advanced training in this area should be a goal of every new graduate. From dental radiology to advanced flap techniques, I recommend that dentistry be a priority for all new graduates. These are a few examples where CE has been crucial to my continued interest and understanding of small animal veterinary medicine.

Tip no. 5: Join Veterinary Information Network (VIN)

Many people now acquire their CE from a wide range of medias. Veterinary Information Network has been one of the most valuable tools for me since graduation. It provides endless chat groups, online programs, a huge reference search engine/library, and many other practical "goodies." I am able to post questions regarding difficult cases, and within 24 hours, internationally acclaimed specialists respond with multiple suggestions and recommendations. I also use the North American Veterinary Conference (NAVC) *Clinician's Brief* and the *Compendium of Veterinary Medicine* frequently for current concepts and information.

Tip no. 6: Work in a Multiperson Practice

Toronto is a very big and busy city. Like so many urban centers, there is a high density of small animal pet owners. Many of these clients are living "fast and furious" lives; both parents working with added responsibilities such as hockey practices and ballet recitals. People expect a great deal from veterinarians, and they expect it quickly. The ability to practice with other veterinarians has been crucial to my development—and sanity! There is not a day that goes by that I do not consult with one of my four practice colleagues. This removes some day-to-day stress, as I know I always have adequate backup. When I returned to Toronto in 1995, having two experienced practitioners in the "room" next to me helped to push me ahead in a way that never would have happened if I were alone. From performing large dog spays to major dental procedures, I was able to learn multiple ways of attacking a medical or surgical case through experience.

Working with many people has also allowed me to delegate many tasks. Knowing that when I'm away my clients are well taken care of allows me to "let go" and focus on other interests while away from work.

The fact that I work in a multiple-person practice correlates directly with my next few tips.

Tip no. 7: Don't Underestimate the Importance of Time Off

My family and friends are a major part of my life. I have always been driven; but since starting a family, some of my priorities have changed. We travel often and try to spend time together. My wife works full-time, so it is important that we stay connected by spending time with the kids, friends, family, or just with each other.

I play guitar in a band, canoe at our cottage whenever possible, play golf regularly in the summer, and love to cook (when it's not heartworm season!). If it were not for great partners and associates, my life would be very different. The need for time off to maintain an appropriate and personal balance is essential to keeping a healthy mind and body. This may not be as vital in a small, rural town, but in downtown Toronto it is crucial.

During my first few years of practice, I did the work of two associates. My bosses at the time (who are now my partners) were always extremely flexible and understanding when I needed time off to re-energize. Don't underestimate how stressful practice can be, especially during your first two to three years.

Tip no. 8: Volunteer Your Time

Whether it is a veterinary or non-veterinary group, be prepared to give back to your profession and/or community. When I joined the TAVM, I also became active on the board. The old saying that 80% of the work is usually done by 20% of the people is true. Participation in veterinary professional associations should be important to all of us, because by being involved we can help plan and implement programs that hopefully benefit all veterinarians. The Ontario Veterinary Medical Association (OVMA) fee guide is an excellent example of how a few board members directly impacted the health of the veterinary profession in this province for many years to come.

As the TAVM president, and with the aid of some pharmaceutical representatives, I along with the board helped to reorganize our local golf tournament. The funds raised were donated to University of Guelph's Pet Trust fund. When my tenure on the TAVM board ended, I offered to sit on the Pet Trust board. I have now served as part of the board for the last several years and have been proud to have helped facilitate OVC purchasing a multimillion-dollar MRI machine and allocating hundreds of thousands of dollars in clinical research grants, including many Doctor of Veterinary Science (DVSc) projects. I feel very privileged to have helped out in whatever way possible to see these visions come to fruition. (See also Chapter 8-8, Giving Something Back.)

Tip no. 9: Meet Your Local Pharmaceutical and Industry Representatives

As a student at OVC, I helped to organize the final year Industry Day. This was a great opportunity to meet many of the country's veterinary pharmaceutical and industry leaders. Over the last 12 years, I have felt that these relationships have kept me in touch with many of the latest treatments and equipment. I have also helped manage these relationships for our group practice since its inception, and this has allowed us to benefit from special CE and training for our staff. The pharmaceutical and medical industry can play a vital role in helping your practice develop innovative strategies to not only grow but also to increase efficiency.

Tip no. 10: Get Involved in Teaching

Over the last few years, I have started lecturing to the first-year technician students across Ontario. I have enjoyed this new challenge and endeavour. As a veterinarian in downtown Toronto, it is essential to help train and retain excellent technicians. These individuals play a large role in all veterinary practices and, as we move toward high-density scheduling, they will become more and more involved in client communication and education. From administration and maintenance of anesthesia to the treatment of critical care patients, veterinary technicians are an essential part of every practice's success. By getting involved with the technician colleges, I am more aware of the students' concerns and interests. I enjoy providing students with the chance to gain knowledge regarding these interests, especially when they are in subject areas that are barely covered during class lecture time (such as oncology). Industry's sponsorship has been an important part of my ability to deliver these lectures.

Tip no. 11: Try Something Different

Several years ago, a client forwarded my name to a segment producer at CTV's Canada AM. I went in for an on-air interview, and within two weeks I was appearing on national morning television. These segments have continued on an intermittent basis, but they also opened the door to a whole new pastime for me—public media exposure and interaction. I enjoy the opportunity to help educate the public on veterinary health issues. This has led to the opportunity to write articles for *Maclean's Magazine* and *Reader's Digest*. I enjoy speaking to schoolchildren and giving seminars to clients. All of these projects help to increase awareness and understanding of veterinary medicine and animal health for the general public.

Tip no. 12: Never Say "Never" and Always be Prepared for Change

When I look back on my first year of practice, I was very disappointed that I was not matched into an internship program. Yet, as a direct result of that failure, I was able to find lifelong friends, colleagues, and partners in Toronto. I would never have become involved in the Ontario Veterinary Group nor had the opportunity to get involved in the profession the way that I have. I now look back at not matching as the best thing that ever happened to me. Being flexible can be difficult, especially if you have had a game plan set for several years. But never dismiss an opportunity when it knocks at your door. Remember to enjoy the ride and not always focus on the "task ahead."

Summary

The next decade looks bright for small animal practice in Toronto. The demographics reveal that many of the clientele are willing to pay for and therefore expect the highest level of veterinary care. Our staff and associates are the lifeline to our business. At Rosedale Animal Hospital, we hired our first associate four years ago and a second one last summer. These newer graduates are extremely dedicated and hard working. They have all the attributes of great leaders—being kind and caring, yet still tough—and they always focus on client care and satisfaction without alienating the staff. They are also dedicated to CE and lifelong learning. Working with them is such a pleasure. Rarely (if ever) do they bring their personal issues into the hospital.

As our hospital and practice group continues to grow, I look forward to many of the challenges that lie ahead. From changes to vaccination protocols, to new advances in oncology and dental care, the next stage of my career will hopefully continue to bring me a feeling of satisfaction, accomplishment, and continued learning. Regardless of what path or direction I find myself headed in, it would be unlikely that I leave clinical practice and all the varied challenges that it brings.

Biography

Dr. Ian Sandler graduated from the Ontario Veterinary College at the University of Guelph in 1994. After graduation, he practiced for one year at a busy 24-hour small animal hospital in Detroit, Michigan. In 1995, Dr. Sandler returned to Toronto and joined the Secord Animal Hospital as an associate. He is now a partner in the Ontario Veterinary Group (currently featured on "City Vets" on Animal Planet) and is practicing at the Rosedale Animal Hospital in Toronto.

Dr. Sandler's special interests in veterinary medicine include oncology and internal medicine and he has a long history of volunteer involvement, including: as a panel member at the Merial Conference on Vaccine Associated Feline Sarcomas, Toronto 2002; President of the Toronto Academy of Veterinary Medicine, 1997; past Chairperson for the Toronto Canadian Guide Dogs for the Blind; member of the Records Accreditation Committee of the College of Veterinarians of Ontario; and he currently serves on the executive board of Pet Trust, which is the research and fundraising arm of the Ontario Veterinary College. Dr. Sandler appears on CTV's Canada AM as the animal expert and has written articles for many publications including Dog Sport magazine, Maclean's, Readers Digest, and City Dog Magazine.

CHAPTER 2-6

A Locum Veterinarian in Calgary

Laura Hunt, BA, DVM
Calgary, Alberta

> *Never continue in a job you don't enjoy. If you're happy in what you're doing, you'll like yourself, you'll have inner peace. And if you have that, along with physical health, you will have had more success than you could possibly have imagined.*
>
> — Johnny Carson

My name is Laura Hunt, and I graduated from Ontario Veterinary College (OVC) in 1983. Although I had started my post-secondary education at the Nova Scotia Agricultural College and intended to have a career in food animal production, I found myself working in a small animal practice in rural Nova Scotia as a summer student the year before my graduation—and I thoroughly enjoyed the experience! As a result, the following June I worked as a new veterinarian at a companion animal clinic in Calgary instead of attending my graduation at the University of Guelph.

Since 1983, I have made Calgary my home. After two years as an employee at one practice, I became a locum doctor and spent the next 18 years working at many clinics in the city and surrounding area. I developed a special interest in dermatology and became quite popular as one of the few veterinarians who would willingly walk into an examination room with an itchy, smelly dog and an anxious or exasperated owner!

After 20 years of practice as a small animal clinician, I felt that I had accomplished the goals I had set as a new graduate – to work as a competent clinician and contribute to the well-being of dogs, cats, and their owners in Calgary. During these years I also discovered that there was more to life than veterinary medicine, as fulfilling as it might be. I developed a great interest in the arts and the study of history, which I wished to pursue further. As well, my family was a priority and I wanted to spend more time with my son while he was still living at home. In 2001 my husband's career in the oil and gas industry was amply rewarded and we became independently wealthy. Although I still enjoyed veterinary medicine, I was able to retire in 2003 and focus on other very important aspects of my life: health, relationships with family and friends, altruism, and hobbies such as travel. In 2004, my husband also retired and we now enjoy a new stage in our lives together.

Calgary is a remarkable city of one million people and growing. There are plenty of stories and myths about its wealth, opportunities, and vices. City boundaries push outward in every direction, houses seem to appear in fields overnight, and road construction is as unavoidable as rush-hour traffic jams. The cost of living is high, while available housing is in short supply. Skilled labor is also scarce, and keeping trained staff in Calgary veterinary clinics is a constant concern for most owners. But with these growing pains come some wonderful advantages. Calgary has several large parks, an extensive bike and walking trail system, and accessible wilderness in the nearby mountains. Local art and culture are thriving, and there is a huge variety of restaurants and entertainment venues.

The phenomenal growth of the oil and gas industry in Alberta has generated a great deal of wealth and attracted many well-educated people. A concerted effort over the last decade to build a diversified economy has been successful, and, as a result, there are a wide variety of socioeconomic backgrounds. Many residents have come from other parts of Canada, so people are generally outgoing and welcome newcomers into their communities and circles of friends. Pets are present in all of these layers, meaning that veterinarians will encounter a wide range of attitudes and capabilities regarding animal care.

Calgary has a very attractive professional environment for veterinarians. The local Calgary Academy of Veterinary Medicine is a strong, dynamic group that provides excellent continuing education and networking opportunities. The University of Calgary is presently building a veterinary college that is scheduled to open in 2008.

With the growth of this city, a new feature in Calgary is the establishment of two very large referral centers. These hospitals are open 24 hours a day and take referrals as well as emergency cases. Most of their veterinarians are board-certified specialists whose areas of expertise include a wide range of disciplines and diagnostic procedures. This has changed the practice of veterinary medicine for many small animal clinicians in Calgary and throughout southern and central Alberta. General practitioners are becoming more like human family physicians. They are continuing to be on the front line in terms of seeing new cases and doing initial workups; but, unlike days gone by when that primary doctor diagnosed and treated the pet to the best of his or her ability, many of these patients are referred, as there are now more referral options for challenging or complicated cases. Alberta is a wealthy province and more and more often, owners have the financial resources to follow through with more extensive workups and treatments.

While this new scenario is wonderful for the pets involved, it leaves the general practitioner with the role of a supportive caregiver rather than a primary role. Unless a clinician has pursued an interest to become equally proficient, the option of transferring a pet to a specialist must be given. This new environment has decreased the variety of work that is done, as well as potential sources of income. On the other hand, having accessible specialists allows clinicians to be involved and encourages learning through cases that might otherwise have been euthanized. As well, there are still a large number of pet owners who cannot afford referrals, and their pets will remain within the general practitioner's care.

There are currently 67 small animal clinics in Calgary and approximately 200 veterinarians, of which 20 are locums. Many of these clinics are one- and two-person practices, and with the constant development of new communities, many established clinics are expanding or new clinics are being opened. This scenario creates an ideal environment for veterinarians seeking full- or part-time employment and for locum veterinarians. Not only is there a demand for locums during scheduled vacations and parental leaves of absence, but it is also often possible to cobble together a permanent, regular schedule by filling in at several clinics one or two days per week to allow scheduled weekly days off for permanent staff.

After so many years of locum practice, I have discovered that a successful locum veterinarian requires several important skills and attitudes. First and foremost is technical competence and confidence. This is required not only for the obvious reason of successfully diagnosing and treating the pets that arrive in the examination room, but it is also an important way to earn the respect of the clinic's professional and support staff. Walking into a clinic for the first time is a challenge, and there is little time to get to know your coworkers before you are thrown into action as a team leader. While new graduates have a great deal of technical skills, it takes time in the field with a good mentor before one can be ready to jump into a new working environment on a regular basis, especially in a one-person practice. And there is nothing worse than hearing an animal health technician say to you, "Are you sure? Dr. So-and-So never does that!"

A locum vet must be flexible. While one of the benefits of locum work is the ability to have some control over where and when one works, there is a much greater demand for locums in the summer and when children are out of school. As well, the length of time and the hours may be beyond your control, especially when first getting established in the veterinary community. It is therefore important to have your own schedule in mind, but to sometimes compromise on the timing details. Calgary clinics presently have a great demand for locums, and there are many opportunities to set up a schedule you are happy with. It always takes time, however, to train these vets to plan ahead!

Flexibility is also crucial when dealing with the wide range of owners who bring their sick pets to you. A locum vet works in a variety of neighborhoods, and while there are very affluent areas in this city with owners who have no economic constraints regarding their pet's medical care, there are plenty of working poor who simply cannot afford extensive workups and treatments. Telling clients what you have diagnosed and giving them options with regard to treatment may not lead to an ideal outcome, but it may provide a reasonable quality of life for a pet that would otherwise be euthanized due to its owner's lack of funds. While it is very challenging to work with a limited budget, it is especially rewarding when there is a happy ending.

One area in which flexibility is not recommended is with regard to your standard of practice. It is important to visit a potential contracting clinic before starting as a locum so that you can get a feel for the level of service offered and decide if you and the practice are a good fit. For example, what equipment is present? What kinds of protocols are used for cases? What textbooks, journals, and other resources are available? Are extra, unnecessary services done to generate more income? What are you expected to deliver in terms of hours and caseload? Is the primary goal of the practice to be a successful business or to provide the best possible medicine for the patients at various costs? It can be difficult to answer all these questions through first impressions, so sometimes it is helpful to do a short contract before beginning a long-term commitment at a practice.

I have also discovered that a locum vet must be able to communicate very well. This skill is essential, because a locum doesn't have time to gradually get to know the routines of a clinic or the thought processes and idiosyncrasies of each staff member. As well, a locum is often not present long enough or frequently enough to follow cases through from start to finish. Therefore, it is crucial to be able to speak clearly and concisely to both clinic staff and owners, and to write clear and often extensive notes so that another vet who must continue a case knows what your thought processes were, what the diagnostic findings were, and what treatments were instigated. Even if you return to this case at a later date, despite your best intentions you will have forgotten details and need to read your records (legible handwriting so that others can read your notes is also essential!).

Another type of record keeping is important to a locum veterinarian: business records. A locum is self-employed, and, as such, must keep track of all income (with receipts) and expenses (with bills). If income exceeds $30,000 a year, a GST number is required. Many locums hire an accountant or other knowledgeable professional to give advice and prepare income tax returns. This expense should be factored into your yearly budget. The high demand for locums in Calgary allows vets to charge a premium for their services—several hundred dollars per day. But while this daily take-home pay is higher than a regular employee's pay, locum vets receive no holiday pay or a guaranteed number of workweeks per year. Sick days are at your own expense; benefits are nonexistent; and you must pay for continuing education yourself. Your schedule may be quite erratic, especially when getting established in the veterinary community.

As a locum, you provide technical leadership, but you are quite limited in influencing the management of a practice. As a temporary worker, or someone who has no investment in the clinic, you must accept the people you work with and the physical aspects of the practice. At times, a locum must be very sensitive and diplomatic and know which issues are acceptable to tackle and which ones must be left alone.

One of the biggest rewards I found during my time as a locum in Calgary was the constant chance to learn from other clinicians and their styles of practice. New surgical techniques, diagnostic approaches, treatment options, and numerous tricks of the trade have kept me stimulated and interested in my career as a small animal veterinarian. Due to the large number of clinics and veterinarians in Calgary, it is possible for locum veterinarians to find good mentors and others who share similar practice standards and ethics.

Another reward has been meeting so many other veterinarians and getting to know them quite well. Several have become good friends, and we share a strong bond from having worked together. There are many recent graduates and young veterinarians in Calgary, as well as many older, experienced clinicians. The result is a great balance between new ideas and ambitions, and mentors with expertise and wisdom.

Calgary is filled with opportunities for a satisfying personal life, and the veterinary community is vibrant and fast-paced. New graduates have plenty of opportunities to find jobs and work with experienced practitioners. Although I would not recommend locum work as an immediate career path for a new graduate, it is certainly a very viable and rewarding option after just a few years of practice. The presence of referral centers provides a valuable source of knowledge and employment opportunities for those who graduate with more advanced qualifications. As well, the University of Calgary's veterinary college will also provide employment in an academic setting. Looking back on my career here in Calgary, I have very few regrets and would recommend this city to a new graduate.

Biography

While growing up in Nova Scotia, my dream was always to have a career in veterinary medicine. I began my post-secondary education at the Nova Scotia Agricultural College and after one year there, transferred directly to the Ontario Veterinary College. Although I had planned to work in food animal production, I found small animal medicine more interesting and stimulating. And so, in May, 1983, my dream was realized when I moved to Calgary as a new graduate to work as a small animal clinician. After two years as an employee, I began locum work and had a special interest in dermatology. In 1991 I enrolled as a part-time student in the history program at the University of Calgary and graduated with a bachelor of arts in 2003.

Balance between professional and personal life has always been a priority for me. As a locum I often worked on a part-time basis and was able to volunteer in numerous organizations, including the Pet Access League Society, Alberta Mentor Foundation for Youth, Crowfoot Minor Soccer Association, and St. Andrew's Anglican Church.

I now live on an acreage near Calgary with my husband, 14-year-old son, two cats, and a Tibetan terrier. Current hobbies include hiking, running, yoga, collecting Canadian works of art, and travel.

CHAPTER 2-7

Food-Animal Practice

William Armstrong, BSc, DVM
Upper Canada Veterinary Services, Winchester, Ontario

> *Perfect freedom is reserved for the man who lives by his own work and in that work does what he wants to do.*
>
> — Robin George Collingwood

My name is Dr. William Armstrong (Ontario Veterinary College [OVC] '83) and I am a large-animal veterinarian. I have worked in Dundas County, just south of Ottawa, Ontario since graduation. This area is close to the area where I grew up, but more importantly, I chose this area because it has a high concentration of dairy cattle. Winchester village (population ~2000) is in a primarily agricultural area, but is within commuting distance of Ottawa, which helps support the local economy.

I started my career as a mixed-practice associate, doing everything from dogs and cats to sheep, goats, horses, and cattle. Even though I was approached to buy in as a partner at another eastern Ontario practice, I decided that geographically, I would be better off starting my own practice in Winchester. In 1984, I started Dundas Veterinary Services and my wife, a small-animal veterinarian, joined me the following year. We worked hard, on-call 24/7, paying our bills, starting our family, and growing the practice. In 1988, we took on our first partner and in 1995 bought out a retiring neighbouring veterinarian, who subsequently worked for us at his own pace. Over 18 years, we grew from just the two of us, with one staff member, to a group practice. We encompass three animal hospitals and two veterinary offices with 10 veterinarians and 30 staff! Practicing in a large, multi-veterinarian, food-animal practice provided me with the opportunity to develop more advanced skills in nutrition, milking-equipment evaluation, and herd-health management.

In 2002, we sold the practice, looking forward to a change of pace and different professional challenges. I worked with colleagues at a neighbouring large practice, until 2005, when we opened a new mixed practice near our home. We enjoy the slower pace, dealing with local community members, whom we have come to know and respect over the last 23 years.

My wife and I have three children. Our eldest daughter is part of the OVC 2010 class, enjoying her first steps into our profession. We both now have the time to drive our youngest son to soccer and middle daughter to riding lessons and horse shows. Making time to be with your family is extremely important. In large-animal practice, you often get called out at meal times or from a soccer game. In a multiple-veterinarian practice, scheduling personal time is often easier; however, as a solo practitioner, you have much more freedom and don't have to be compromising constantly on issues that are important to you. You only have to answer to yourself and your clients. My clients call me on my cell phone when they need advice or have emergencies after hours, so I still have a lot of freedom to go where I want. I have a good working relationship with another practice in the area for the times when I am truly not available.

One of the most important things I learned over the years is how to listen. You can't just go on to a farm and start telling people to change things, without first finding out what is important to your client. Some clients want to learn, and will challenge you by asking lots of questions. Others are happy with the way things are with their herds and what may be important to you is of no concern for them. Over 15 years ago, before many veterinarians were doing comprehensive herd-health programs, computer records seemed the way to go. So we started advising on reproduction, mastitis prevention, and young stock management. I remember each month writing a report for each of the 18 herds we had on the program. I charged by the head at each monthly visit and many herds showed tremendous gains. About a year later, one of my clients sent me a very heartfelt letter thanking me for all my help, but to remind me it was his herd and he did not want anyone to tell him which cows to cull!

This was a wakeup call, and I listened. I discontinued the structured, formal herd-health program, and developed a more customized approach to herd health—based on the individual farmer's preferences. The practice then took off and never looked back. We did what clients wanted done and helped them when and where they wanted it. It was only one year later that the Eastern Ontario Soil and Crop Improvement Association gave me an award for my contribution to agriculture in our area. Having been chosen by my clients for this award was a very humbling experience.

When working as a large-animal practitioner, it is very important to establish trust. The best way to do this is to work hard for your clients, don't be afraid to get dirty and assist in catching that cow's head if necessary. Keep your hands out of your pockets; maintain a professional demeanour (e.g., no chewing gum, no off-colour jokes), arrive clean, and be courteous. Speak their language and explain what is happening, so your clients can understand. They are your equals, don't talk down to them. Once you have gained their trust and respect, they will confide in you and accept your advice and suggestions much more readily. Over the years, many of these people will become good friends, but remember even good friends need to separate business from pleasure. As a colleague recently said to me, "*Don't party with your clients, go away to party.*" It helps maintain a much better professional and business relationship.

To be successful as a solo practitioner, you need to respect your client's time and they need to respect yours. Book your work ahead and make exact time appointments for herd-health visits; then if something comes up, let your client know right away that you will be late. Believe me, busy farmers will appreciate this consideration. Do not expect clients to call you for the next herd appointment; rather, book it before you leave the farm and keep the appointment. I've never had a client say they didn't want to have a follow-up visit that I recommended.

Many times as a large-animal veterinarian, I have found that farmers don't want to listen or change the ways they and their families have always done things. Be patient and wait for that "teaching moment." It may be when you are dehorning calves and, out of the blue, they ask about booking the herd vaccination that they didn't want to do last year. It may be while you are treating their third case of mastitis and they ask for a prevention program. Don't try to fix too many issues in one visit. If you wait for the clients to decide something is an issue, they will listen more to your advice. They will tell their friends and will remember for years how you fixed the problem. If you try to preach at the clients about something they weren't worried about, they will resent your "interference."

After having associates that did horse work for 18 years, I found it a challenge to get back into equine practice with new clients. It was a good reminder to keep up with more fields than just your area of specialty, because you never know when a career change in direction will present itself. In any new situation, don't be afraid to ask advice from colleagues, call in a specialist if needed, and use your veterinary laboratories to aid in diagnostics. I find this to be especially useful in my new solo practice, where I feel less familiar with some equine cases.

Even without a change in practice focus, continuing education (CE) is essential. Take advantage of every learning opportunity, whether formal or informal. I set a goal of learning at least one useful thing to bring back to my practice from every CE event. I make a note on a summary page during each talk at a conference of things I intend to implement when I go home. This page will be a "to-do" list on my desk that I can refer to easily when I get back to the practice. Share new information with clients by writing newsletters and articles in local newspapers. Clients do read these and will ask questions, if they are interested. This is a great way to get to know people, especially when you are just getting started in a community.

One of the best ways to get to know people in the farm community is to volunteer as a 4-H leader. This helps with your public speaking skills, as well as gaining you respect in the community. What better way to get known and have fun with young people? I have been asked to do presentations in Ontario and New York State and could never have stood in front of a group without the practice and confidence I gained leading 4-H Club meetings.

One of the many recent challenges in food-animal practice is bovine spongiform encephalopathy (BSE). This disease clearly has separated farmers into two groups, those who value their cows as individuals (the way people value their horses or pets) and those who look at their cows only from the economic perspective. In these latter herds, the individual cow is a disposable commodity. Changing the farmer's beliefs and showing them the value of herd health is challenging, but rewarding, when you see the herd's profitability and health improving.

Another recent challenge is facing the biosecurity issue; as veterinarians we always needed to set a good example by being clean when we arrive on the farm, changing coveralls and disinfecting equipment between farms. As herds get bigger, clients need advice on animal movement, housing, and buying decisions. Writing Standard Operating Procedures (SOPs) for farmers on these issues, as well as treatment decisions, continues to be an opportunity.

I always have mentored new graduates, as well as foreign-trained veterinarians studying to seek licensure in Canada. This mentoring experience helps keep your skills current, your enthusiasm for your profession fresh, and gives you a great sense of pride when you see these colleagues move into their own exciting career.

Make sure you join your local, provincial, and national veterinary associations. During meetings, you will meet many colleagues and learn new information—often during coffee breaks, rather than at the lectures!! Don't be afraid to ask for other veterinarians' opinions or advice. It is the best way to learn the craft of veterinary medicine. Networking with colleagues often makes your career more enjoyable and can lead to new opportunities over your professional life.

In summary, a career in large-animal practice can be very satisfying. Always remember to be humble, learn each day, and be able to reflect and wind down during those drives between farm calls. Take pleasure in the many client friends you will make, and pride in the animal-care advances your actions will bring. Always try to do the right thing, even if it isn't the easiest thing. Don't forget to take the time to enjoy your profession and your life every day.

Biography

Dr. William J. Armstrong graduated with a BSc in Biology in 1979. He received his Doctor of Veterinary Medicine degree from the Ontario Veterinary College in 1983, with an award in Large-Animal Surgery. He worked as an associate for one year before opening Dundas Veterinary Services in Winchester, Ontario in 1984 with his wife, Dr. Michele Dutnall. He has been a member of the Central Canada Veterinary Association for 15 years, having served as president, treasurer, and conference convener over that time. He also was a 4-H leader for 20 years. In his spare time, he is a passionate woodworker, who loves to build. After selling his practice in 2002 and working as an associate for a few years, he started Upper Canada Veterinary Services in 2005. He and his wife have three teenage children and share their home and life with two dogs, two cats, and five horses.

CHAPTER 2-8

Life as an Intern and Resident

John Tait, BSc, DVM, MBA, CFP, ADR
Managing Partner, Ontario Veterinary Group,
Toronto, Ontario;
Assistant Professor, Ontario Veterinary College,
Guelph, Ontario

Danielle Richardson, DVM
Faculty (Small Animal Internal Medicine),
Ontario Veterinary College,
Guelph, Ontario

> *The important thing is this: to be able at any moment to sacrifice what we are for what we would become.*
>
> — Charles Du Bos

A certain quotient of each graduating class will seek more formal continuing education in the form of an internship or residency. Graduates will generally pursue these positions as a means to an end (e.g., becoming Board-certified specialists) but also as a way to acquire advanced clinical training in a general or specific clinical area.

An internship generally lasts one year and is most often undertaken either immediately upon graduation or within a few years of graduation. Internships are intensive, supervised clinical experiences. Interns will usually

135

rotate through broad areas of medicine and surgery, including emergency and critical care, and they will often have an opportunity to spend some time on specific areas of interest.

Internships may occur in private practices or institutions and will cover all varieties of species. However, a word of caution: there are no real criteria for establishing an internship. While most are offered through the veterinary colleges, some internships are offered through private practices. With no overseeing regulatory body, applicants assume the risk that the internship will be supervised and mentored by qualified individuals interested in mentoring. Internships that lead to residencies and have higher levels of credibility are achieved through the "matching process." This process involves an interested individual applying to the internship-matching program, which includes ranking or prioritizing the practices and/or schools/institutions that are preferred for the internship. In turn, the registered private practices and institutions offering internships submit their list of prioritized or ranked applicants. A computerized matching program then correlates the rankings of applicant and host and matches the candidates. While institutions and private practices differ in their specific criteria when ranking intern candidates, the criteria generally revolve around grades/relative class standing, letters of reference, and strength of application (e.g., résumé, background information, etc.). Previous employment in private practice can also be an asset, as it provides the candidate with experience in handling routine and emergency cases, as well as providing a frame of reference for dealing with referring practitioners. Letters of reference should be from faculty appointees who are well aware of the applicant's qualifications and ability to thrive in an internship. All of these are required as part of the candidate application process.

Individuals successfully completing an internship may then apply for resident positions or enter practice or another career path. Salaries for interns tend to be below half that offered to entry-level practitioners in private practices. Internship hopefuls should be aware that the lost salary or opportunity cost from doing an internship versus going into private practice is not recaptured following the internship when entering private practice. In other words, the incremental salary following the completion of an internship is only marginally higher than those with the same level of experience who have not completed an internship. Those considering an internship should also investigate potential positions to ensure they will receive adequate mentorship and training, a viable caseload, and sufficient hands-on experience to justify the internship salary. They should have assurance that the position is not merely a general practice position with a reduced salary and no opportunity for advanced training. Internships represent a lifestyle change and sacrifice for a year; applicants should be convinced that the desired outcome at the end of the year will be realized.

Interns and residents leaving Canada for other countries will be considered visitors for educational purposes, and hosting institutions outside Canada will generally handle the immigration issues.

Residency positions follow internships, and they tend to be much more competitive than internships, as there are fewer of them available each year. Residencies will focus on a specific clinical area or discipline (e.g., internal medicine–small animal, internal medicine–food-producing animals, ophthalmology, dermatology, neurology, etc.) rather than the broader areas of medicine and surgery combined. Residencies will be multiple years in length and set the stage for Board qualification in a specialty area. It is possible to enter some residencies without completing an internship and having the equivalent experience in another setting.

In Canada, traditional residencies may be replaced by degree programs such as the Doctor of Veterinary Science program, wherein a postgraduate degree is completed concurrently or as part of the clinical residency. These programs usually involve research and are often three or four years versus the traditional two-year clinical residency alone. Residencies will also include some traditional lecture-format coursework.

If you are considering an internship and residency, investigate the host institution or practice, review the areas of specialty and the resources they have, and ask for references from former interns or residents. Make sure that the internship or residency you are considering will meet your expectations and help you to achieve your long-term goals. In some cases, spending some time at the host institution(s) prior to making a decision will help ensure that the right decision for you is ultimately made.

Biographies

For Dr. Tait's biography, please see the Section I Introduction on page 3.

Dr. Danielle Richardson graduated from the OVC in 2002. Following three years in private practice, she returned to OVC in 2005 to do an internship in small animal medicine and surgery followed by a residency in small animal medicine. Danielle is currently a faculty member in small animal medicine at the Ontario Veterinary College.

CHAPTER 2-9

Veterinary Emergency Medicine

Jen Lebel, DVM
Practice Manager
Mississauga–Oakville Veterinary Emergency Hospital,
Oakville, Ontario

> *Change in all things is sweet.*
>
> — Aristotle

"Doctor LeBel to the treatment room, STAT." The receptionist has rushed into the treatment room with an injured dog, and the client is following behind, yelling, "Kirby was hit by the neighbour's truck. Save her. Do everything possible. Somebody do something. Please help her!!!" The support staff looks to you for immediate instruction, while the owner is crying and is draped over her injured dog, who is lying on the treatment room examination table.

Does the above scenario ignite feelings of excitement, fear, or both?

Life as an emergency veterinarian is constantly variable and unpredictable, filled with ups, downs, and on some days flips all around. In the above real-life scenario, you are expected to deal with the injured patient, the support staff, and the distraught client. You are expected to be the strong leader and professional veterinarian, educated to react and take charge of the situation. This is not unlike a typical situation that an emergency veterinarian would deal with on a regular basis.

Why Choose Emergency Medicine?

The idea of emergency medicine brings about mixed emotions, as it is an area of medicine where a moment can mean the difference between life and death. For some veterinarians, this represents an exciting challenge; yet for others, it sparks feelings of fear and panic that can bring a large amount of stress to the practitioner.

In emergency medicine, as with everything in life, pros and cons are associated with this career choice. Depending on your interests and your personality, the scale can tip either way.

Pros: Reasons to Choose a Career as an ER Veterinarian

Emergency medicine comes with a variety of joys and freedoms in both clinical and emotional ways. When owners look into your eyes and thank you for saving the life of their beloved pet, that emotional rush is indescribable. Even more rewarding is when a patient recovers and is wagging its tail, acting like nothing happened, even when it has just gone through a life-saving procedure. These emotions are the ones that are unforgettable and remind the emergency veterinarian why he or she has accepted the difficulties of the position.

Clinically, you have the ability to perform treatments and procedures where you see immediate results, and this lets you fulfill the "fire engine" medicine component of your veterinary training. In one emergency shift, you will likely see and treat more sick animals than a regular veterinarian will usually see in a week. Emergency veterinarians tend to master skills that many other veterinarians do not get to perform on a regular basis. The routine emergency treatments and diagnostic tests are the opposite of what is performed at a regular clinic. Performing life-saving treatments becomes the norm, and the skills learned will help you deal with many clinical cases in the future.

Lifestyle perks include fewer hours worked and a higher-than-average wage with the possibility of more free time to enjoy other activities or locum work. It is usually easier to schedule time off by rotating the schedule with the other emergency veterinarians within the practice. Negotiating vacation time is usually related to finding other veterinarians to fill your shifts versus having to find a locum or being unable to take time off during busy peak times (e.g., heartworm season).

Cons: Points That May Cause Reconsideration

On the flip side, you have those moments when you are placed in the realm of serious doubt regarding your decisions and treatment actions. What happens when you are unable to save the pet? You ask, *Was it my fault? If I did this differently, would that family have their pet?* Unless you work in a very large referral hospital, you are a solo practitioner in a multi-practitioner setting. Emergencies do not stop or spread themselves out because you are alone. This can be very difficult and stressful day in and out.

Shift work can be tiring over the long term. Shifts can be stressful and very long, where you can be on the clinic floor with no breaks for more than 14 hours straight. Generally, emergency veterinarians have long overnight shifts, and, depending on the clinic, the workload can be overwhelming at times. In the end, the shift work is what usually prevents emergency veterinarians from continuing long term in this field.

Depending on what your social life consists of, melding into our society's social world can be difficult, as emergency veterinarians work when other people are not working. This can be difficult with friends and family, as shift work includes holidays, weekends, and overnights. In the future, this will likely be less of a factor as other work environments are changing, including expanded hours, with very few people working a traditional 9 to 5 job anymore. However, working Christmas Day always causes a little drop in spirit, especially after you have been doing it year in and year out!

Challenges

Veterinarians do not always recognize the different challenges they will face when they embark on entering the field of emergency medicine. Usually, the biggest worry or expected challenge is the type of patients seen as emergencies. What is most important to remember is that although the emergency patient is stressful and challenging, the biggest challenge is and always will be with the clients.

Of utmost importance is building the client-patient-veterinary relationship in an emergency setting in a very limited amount of time. To instill trust and develop a rapport while a pet is potentially dying is very difficult. Also, when a pet is seriously ill but not in a life-threatening state, it can be even more difficult to express that your recommendations are in the best interest of the pet, especially when substantial costs are involved. It is important to remember that every client walking through the emergency room door is in some sort of duress. Clients will be rude, argumentative, and accusatory regardless of what you say or do. On the flip side, many will be kind and appreciative; but the reality is that not everyone deals with stress in an appropriate way.

As an emergency veterinarian, you need to separate out the personal attacks and accusations. The clients usually will calm down if you maintain your honesty and composure. Do not expect to get a thank you when you save the life of a patient, and be prepared for those same clients to complain about an insignificant issue even after you have saved their pet's life. Sadly, many clients do not realize how close their pet has come to passing away, and in the end you often need to draw your satisfaction from within yourself.

The illusion of many veterinary students is that they are going to be working with animals. The reality hits when you graduate and you really understand that the pet owner and not the actual patient is your biggest challenge. In a large referral center, where technicians perform a lot of the procedures, you usually spend 75% of your time with clients, 20% with the support staff, and 5% with the actual patient. This ratio is usually different in regular emergency practices; but in the end, regardless of the practice where you work, you will be spending a minimum of 50% of your time with the clients.

Another people-rather-than-patient challenge in emergency medicine is when a client uses the emergency hospital against the regular veterinarian in an inappropriate manner. Clients do not know you personally and will use your words as ammunition. Nothing is worse than when a colleague calls and is wondering why you said a certain statement to a client about the referring veterinarian. It is amazing to hear what clients say and how they can change your words. They do not realize that the different veterinarians will speak to each other. It is shocking when you find out what people say and do when they are upset and distraught, especially when they are looking at someone to blame in an effort to cover the cost of the bills.

What Does It Mean To Be a Good Emergency Veterinarian?

Veterinarians who enjoy emergency medicine are flexible and can juggle multiple tasks at any one time. Successful emergency veterinarians have confidence and excellent problem-solving skills. They maintain their composure in high-stress situations and can succeed as leaders during these times.

A lot of what an emergency clinician does is not written in textbooks. You need to be able to problem solve and take the basic principles you have learned during your veterinary education and combine them with your career experiences—both of which can be variable depending on past educational and career paths. Many situations I have seen only once. These scenarios do not have any written "how-to" instructions. Emergency medicine is an area where you need to take the clinical signs along with the problem and develop a solution immediately, exemplifying the "art of veterinary medicine."

As a new graduate, you need to be work ready and have a good amount of experience acquired from your years of schooling to be adequate as an emergency veterinarian. Did you have an externship where you were able to make big choices with your mentor? Were there times you felt you could take care of that case on your own?

The last year of veterinary school is when you gain experience and put everything together; however, clinical rotations only provide you a few weeks in emergency medicine, so it is extremely important to spend your elective weeks at emergency clinics if you are seriously considering this career path. At the larger emergency hospitals, newer graduates are given back-up veterinary roles, since it is very difficult to expect a new graduate to practice at the level of a full-time referral emergency veterinarian. Having at least 6 months of regular practice is also highly recommended and will make you a better emergency veterinarian in the long term. You will better understand the referral veterinarian's role in treating chronic medical conditions and the pet owner's perspective, thereby allowing you to become more understanding when owners start complaining about past veterinary care or when the referral veterinarian questions why you did or did not do something. Diplomacy is a very important skill for any emergency veterinarian—sadly, I have worked with many good veterinarians, but due to their lack of diplomacy or ability to build rapport with clients, they were unable to continue as emergency veterinarians.

What Else is Out There in the "Emergency World" When You Want More?

When you love emergency medicine, but the lifestyle or shift work is no longer acceptable to you, or you have reached a level where you want to do more, what is out there? One can choose to go back to school to gain a speciality in Emergency and Critical Care, or the realm of management can be considered.

When I was presented with this crossroads in my career, I decided to pursue management in the emergency veterinary setting. As the practice manager of a large emergency practice in a referral center, I have been working toward improving regular veterinarian communication, improving the level of patient care, and ensuring that our clinic strives to be the best emergency hospital in the area. I work extensively on human resources and communication.

Overall, emergency medicine has provided me with a career path that is filled with excitement, life-saving procedures, and a list of experiences that can already fill a lifetime.

Biography

Dr. Jennifer LeBel graduated from the Ontario Veterinary College in 2001 and has been practicing strictly emergency medicine for over 6 years. The path of emergency medicine was not always what she had aspired to do. Only after her summer clinical externship and the 4th-year rotation in emergency medicine did this career path become clear. The concept of being the mixed-animal veterinarian of her childhood dreams was very quickly replaced with the realization that herd health and regular appointments did not provide enough variability and led to a too-predictable workday. Upon graduation, she initially joined a 24-hour practice and then moved to regular practice for 6 months before realizing the true passion of her interests really was in emergency medicine.

Over the past 7 years, Dr. LeBel has worked at a number of emergency hospitals in Southern Ontario before starting at the Mississauga Oakville Veterinary Emergency Hospital as a full-time emergency veterinarian. She continued in this role until she decided to take on management of the emergency practice. At this time, Dr. LeBel is the practice manager of the emergency hospital, and she manages over 60 staff members.

CHAPTER 2-10

Veterinary Medicine Beyond the Books

Rob Ashburner, BSc, DVM
West King Animal Hospital,
Vancouver, British Columbia

> *To find out what one is fitted to do and to secure an opportunity to do it, is the key to happiness.*
>
> — John Dewey

One of the many challenges facing you as a recent graduate is determining your future career path in a profession as diverse as veterinary medicine. And believe me, this is a challenge that you are likely to face more than once throughout your career. I'm reminded of this daily, especially when I ponder the many twists and turns that my own career took over the years. Where I find myself now is definitely not part of a master plan that I consciously mapped out upon graduation, but one that evolved as I—like most veterinarians—took advantage of opportunities and challenges that came my way.

I grew up at a time and in a place where everyone finished high school and automatically went to university. I went to the local university, the University of Calgary, and as I had always loved the natural sciences, I registered in Zoology. Upon completion of my Bachelor of Science degree, I applied to

Veterinary Medicine; however, despite a number of attempts, I did not even get an interview, as I did not have the required marks.

I then obtained a job with the National Parks and worked as a Park Warden for a number of years. The job offered many opportunities to do a variety of things, including being involved in the National Parks fledgling bear management program, which at the time involved primarily trapping and relocating problem grizzly bears.

Eight years after graduating from university (and after taking many additional courses to improve my marks), I again applied to veterinary college and was accepted at the Western College of Veterinary Medicine. I entered veterinary school with the intention of becoming a wildlife veterinarian. When I graduated, there were no jobs for veterinarians in a wildlife field or in my hometown of Calgary, so I took advantage of a job opportunity in Vancouver, British Columbia (BC), and I moved my young family and started my first job as a veterinarian. Over the ensuing years, my career has changed from employee veterinarian to a partner in a large practice, and, currently, to owning my own single-person practice. During this time, I also did all of the veterinary work for the animal care facility at Simon Fraser University for a number of years. I very much enjoy veterinary practice, but I have many other interests outside of work. I generally work 45 to 50 hours per week in the weeks that I work, and I try to take at least eight weeks of holidays during the year. Yes, I have had to conscientiously limit my hours (and my income); but without doing this, it would not have allowed me to do so many other things outside of veterinary medicine and achieve what I consider a proper work-life balance.

Veterinary medicine is a dynamic and exciting profession, and the numerous opportunities within the profession are not always immediately obvious, nor are they something written down anywhere. A number of the most interesting opportunities result from veterinarians being open to seeing new ways of doing things and acting upon them in order to "mold" or personalize their careers into unique professions that work for them. Never forget to look for and take advantage of these opportunities. The most common stereotype of a veterinarian is the image of a person (until recently, male) looking like a human doctor, but treating pets; or a person in coveralls in a rural setting, treating farm animals. This is just one aspect of our profession. As graduating veterinary students today know, there is a much broader scope of possible career paths open to them, and new opportunities seem to become available all of the time. However, statistics show us that most of this year's graduates will pursue one of the stereotypical roles. While there is nothing wrong with this (and indeed, that is how I started out), I urge you to spend a little time considering some of the unique career opportunities you will encounter as you move out into the working world and through your career.

I am presently a companion animal practitioner in Vancouver. I have raised my family in Vancouver, and I thoroughly enjoy calling it home. I would consider myself successful. I have always made it a priority to provide high-quality medical care to my patients and to give their owners "good value for their money." At the same time, I have always tried to make my family the number one priority. In order to do this, I feel that there are three things that one must always remember: adequate income; working a reasonable number of hours; and a recognition (or admission) that there are other veterinarians who can take over for you and do a good job of treating your patients and servicing your clients in your absence. British Columbia pet owners are well educated and have high expectations. They know what they want when it comes to service and care for their animals. As veterinarians, we must meet these expectations to retain clients and build goodwill.

Adequate Income

I hesitate to put this first, as it implies that it is the most important. Although there are many other factors besides income to consider, the reality is that unless you have a benevolent benefactor, you need to generate an adequate income so that you can first and foremost provide good-quality health care to your patients and, secondly, provide adequately for yourself and your family. One of the myths that still haunts the profession and is often perpetuated by veterinarians of my generation, is that veterinarians do not make a reasonable income. The extension of that myth (perhaps perpetuated by the likes of James Herriot) is that a good veterinarian works for the benefit of the animals, and consequently, economics take a back seat. In reality, nothing could be further from the truth. This has been shown in a number of studies and is echoed in the "mantra" of the National Commission on Veterinary Economic Issues (NCVEI), which states, *A successful veterinary practice requires a sound economic base.*

Working a Reasonable Number of Hours

This is often strongly related to income, as in some cases, veterinarians will work longer hours to make up for lower per-hour revenue generation.

However, if one implements the first point, that fees charged must be adequate to ensure a reasonable income, this should help in finding the right balance with number of hours worked. To this end, the various provincial veterinary associations and the Canadian Veterinary Medical Association (CVMA) have generated economic data that will help veterinarians in implementing appropriate fee guides for services offered.

One of the biggest challenges for a private practitioner in working a reasonable number of hours is the responsibility we assume in providing after-hours emergency care for our patients. This can be a significant challenge. In my own case, I have the fortune of being located near an emergency facility to which I refer all of my after-hour calls; however, for those veterinarians without access to this type of facility, being on call can represent a significant number of hours. Many creative solutions do exist, however (e.g., shared on call with neighbouring practices), to mitigate the impact of these extra professional responsibilities.

Coverage While You Are Away

That brings us to the third point. Many practitioners fall into the "trap" of believing that they are indispensable; that only they can service their client's and patient's needs adequately. Veterinarians must acknowledge that any other competent veterinarian will do as good a job as they will (at times possibly better), although in all likelihood, it will be done differently—and you must also train your clients and those who work for you to accept this as well.

Alternate Career Paths

Thus far, I have only addressed private clinical practice, in large part because that is the area in which I work and am the most familiar. However, the above three principles apply equally to all fields of veterinary medicine. In reality, all veterinarians—be they in research, academia, or public practice—must be concerned with ensuring that there is a sound economic base to support the work they do. If there isn't, how can they have a viable career? The researcher must remain on the cutting edge and be creative to successfully obtain funding. Veterinarians in academia are constantly looking for novel ways to obtain additional funding to meet the required needs of providing research and education for an increasingly diverse profession. Public health veterinarians point to the severe economic impact that a major disease outbreak would have as justification for the public to support careers in public health, epidemiology, disease prevention, and meat hygiene, and for the government to recognize the overall societal value of veterinary medicine and so invest in the infrastructure that provides the tools for potential veterinarians to be successful in their chosen careers.

My Career Path

As stated previously, I currently work in a practice in BC in the greater Vancouver area. While the style of practice does not differ much from other areas of the country, Western Canada certainly has some unique features to offer. The outdoor opportunities for an active lifestyle are numerous, with access to water, mountains, and a generally temperate climate. While this area averages more rainfall than other geographic areas, which can be an inconvenience at times, the diversity offered in Western Canada is more than worth it.

I have also been fortunate to be extensively involved in organized veterinary medicine, having recently completed a term as President of the CVMA. I would encourage newer graduates to get involved and become part of the future direction of the profession. The opportunity to travel, experience diversity within the profession, network with others (including learning about new issues with a national and international perspective), and have a national presence is in many ways just as rewarding as practice. It is often the younger generation that drives change, so get involved!

Summary

The main message that I hope any new graduate will take from all of this is that you should not spend a great deal of time and energy worrying about how your new career will "end up." Your career will evolve as opportunities arise, as long as you are able and willing to take advantage of them. You are entering a profession that is full of potential. There are a great many options to pursue, as long as you remain flexible and open to change. In this way, you will be able to customize your career into something that fits your particular lifestyle and expectations. Do not be complacent and settle for something that does not feel right for you. Take advantage of the opportunities, rise to the challenges, and your career will develop into something you can be really proud of and enjoy.

Biography

Dr. Rob Ashburner graduated in 1984 from the Western College of Veterinary Medicine and headed to BC to begin his career in a small animal veterinary practice. He has remained in BC's lower mainland ever since, and he became practice owner of West King Animal Hospital in 1989, a small animal veterinary practice that he continues to own today. He has been very active in volunteer veterinary medicine and is a past president of both the BCVMA and CVMA.

CHAPTER $2-11$

Practicing and Living in the United States

John Tait, BSc, DVM, MBA, CFP, ADR
Managing Partner, Ontario Veterinary Group,
Toronto, Ontario
Assistant Professor, Ontario Veterinary College,
Guelph, Ontario

> There is no security on this earth . . . only opportunity.
>
> — Douglas MacArthur

When the North American Free Trade Agreement (NAFTA) was ratified a number of years ago, it eliminated or reduced the barriers for naturalized Canadian and United States (US) citizens from various professions, including veterinary medicine, to cross the border. Since that time, movement of veterinarians has been ongoing between Canada and the US, as many opportunities have been available for practitioners on both sides of the border.

The standards of practice and structure of practice in the US are generally the same as in Canada. Practices operate as proprietorships, partnerships, groups, and corporate entities on both sides of the border; however, the "corporatization" of veterinary medicine is more prevalent in the US than in Canada. Graduates from accredited Canadian schools are well recognized and actively recruited in the US.

The issue of Canadians working in the US is not as simple as showing up and crossing the border. Entry of any non-US citizen is controlled by policies set by the United States Immigration and Naturalization Service (INS). While NAFTA has made it possible to enter the US with less "red tape," it does not preclude requiring that entering veterinarians have a work visa.

According to NAFTA, different forms of visas and residency status classifications are available for Canadians entering the US. Most veterinarians initially enter on a work visa that has a one-year duration from the time issued. You'll require proof of your identity by way of a Canadian long-form birth certificate (available from Provincial Ministries of Documents and Records), a copy of your Doctor of Veterinary Medicine degree, a confirmed job offer, and money to pay the fee for the one-year visa (typically less than $100 USD). The entry-level or one-year visa limits a veterinarian entering the country to the specific job position for which they have been hired, meaning that one cannot change jobs while in the US during this year without having a new visa issued.

As the visa approaches expiration, it can be renewed in most cases; however, the short-term work visa situation in the US is reflective of any perceived threats and subject to change. Therefore, it is highly advisable that anyone in the US on a one-year visa checks with the INS or an immigration lawyer with respect to current criteria and renewal requirements. Longer-term visas also are possible. The institution (if a university) usually handles immigration procedures for those entering the US for internships and residencies. If a veterinarian decides to reside in the US on a permanent basis, s/he can apply for permanent resident status—the so named "green card," which allows the veterinarian to move freely about the country and change job positions. The Canadian with a spouse or a parent who is a naturalized US citizen will be "fast tracked" toward permanent resident status. Procedural steps for achieving permanent residency status include health and tuberculosis screening, fingerprinting, and a direct meeting with the INS, among others. The task of achieving permanent resident status is best accomplished with the assistance of a lawyer aware of current requirements.

Upon leaving Canada, it is a good idea to inform the Canada Customs and Revenue Agency that you are now a "non-resident." If you maintain ownership of assets (e.g., house), it appears to the government you are still a resident, and you risk being taxed by governments on both sides of the border. The recommendation is that you divest any assets that reflect residency; however, assets such as investments and retirement funds are safe. The Canadian government will place a withholding tax on the growth of investments held by non-residents.

The taxation rules and immigration standards are somewhat of a moving target. Check with knowledgeable sources including the INS, veterinary regulatory body for the particular state you are entering, and the Canada Customs and Regulatory Agency for current details. Accountants and lawyers with international portfolios also have accurate current information.

Employees of US-based veterinary practices will notice some differences in the capitalist and regulatory systems compared to Canada. Veterinarians in the US generally require a Drug Enforcement Agency license, as well as a state license, to practice and dispense narcotics. The National Board Examination generally is accepted now everywhere in the US to qualify for practice; however, some states may have state-specific entry examinations. Practice styles, operating standards, economics and management, and staff roles are basically the same.

Taxation for consumers, in general, is somewhat different, with taxes on income generally less in the US. Additionally, consumption taxes and prices for major consumer goods (such as cars and electronics) are lower. However, capital gains/inheritance taxes, business-owner remittances to the government, post-secondary education costs, and health-care costs are higher in the US than in Canada.

If you plan to remain in the US, your Canadian provincial health-care coverage will cover you for a few months after you leave Canada, depending on the Province. It is best to confirm this coverage prior to leaving. United States-based health care is driven largely by private, for-profit insurance companies, with a number of different policies that have varying rates of coverage and user co-pay rules. These policies may or may not permit flexibility in choosing a physician. Check out any potential plans thoroughly, including the amount you as an individual must pay, the presence of any capitation on the policy (covers to a certain lifetime amount and that is it), and the ease in which it can be cancelled by the provider. Personal disability-insurance policies and life-insurance policies will follow individuals around, regardless of where they live. They will pay out benefits only in the currency of the country in which they were issued.

Due to the private nature of the banking system, the cost of borrowing money for everything from mortgages to business loans can be up to two percentage points higher in the US. The interest payments on a mortgage are tax deductible above a certain limit.

The US has its own version of retirement plans called "401Ks" or "Individual Retirement Accounts" (IRAs). If you are a US resident and have no taxable income in Canadian dollars, you are not eligible to contribute to your Canadian RRSP.

Veterinary practice incomes and values for practices compare quite favourably with those in Canada, regardless of experience level. The cost of living in the US is variable, depending on the region. In many geographic areas, the salaries for associate veterinarians have not matched the escalation in the cost of living, thereby reducing the purchasing power of a salary. Check on the relative cost of living before agreeing to a salary. Budget your cost of living against your income to ensure that your expenses are not higher than your income.

The exchange rate between the US and Canadian dollar can help Canadian graduates who are earning in US dollars, but have debts in Canadian dollars. However, do not convert a US-dollar salary into Canadian dollars for remuneration comparison purposes. A $60,000 per year US-dollar salary, if living in the US, and a $60,000 Canadian-dollar salary if living in Canada, are essentially the same. Assuming the $60,000 US-dollar salary is really near $70,000 Canadian and, therefore, "better" than a $60,000 Canadian-dollar salary may not be the case. The veterinarian receiving the US-dollar salary also is living and spending money (US-dollar currency) in the US. The exchange rate only comes into play when using US dollars to pay expenses in Canadian-dollar currency.

For veterinarians returning to Canada from the US, it is again a good idea to let the Canada Customs and Revenue Agency know you are back, so you won't risk taxation issues that affect non-residents.

Biography

For Dr. Tait's biography, please see the Section 1 Introduction on page 3.

Section 3

ON THE HUNT:

Job-Seeking Strategies

Introduction

Congratulations on taking a proactive approach to succeeding in your veterinary career! This section provides you with the crucial building blocks that you need to ensure you are on the right track in your job search. It offers vital support and tools that will enable you to secure your position and plan for your future growth as a leader in this dynamic profession.

As the executive director of Career Professionals of Canada, I was thrilled to write a forward to this important section on the working life of veterinary professionals. I know firsthand the importance that knowledge and clarity play in the job search process. Often, I encounter professionals who have great dreams, but they do not know how to attain them. A structured approach to the job search makes all the difference. In my experience, job seekers who keep up with the latest advances in résumé, interview, and negotiation strategies attain more fulfilling jobs—and they get them more quickly.

For graduates, the competition for appropriate jobs can be tight. Embarking on a job search for the first critical position in your career does not have to be daunting. Preparation, practice, and persistence are key factors to gaining confidence. The successful candidate will take these three factors very seriously.

First, prepare yourself well. Arm yourself with all the knowledge that you can—this book is a great start! Learn as much about your industry and the kinds of positions you might be targeting. Find out what you need to know in order to compete in the market. The better you prepare yourself in advance, the more likely you are to address your next employer's or business partner's requirements.

Next, practice delivering your message. Learn to present your value with comfort and ease. As a graduate, in addition to a valuable degree in veterinary medicine, you bring with you a unique wealth of knowledge, skills, expertise, and talents. To secure the right position, you need to know how to present and articulate this information in a clear and concise manner. For the best results in your job search, present your value consistently and effectively in your résumé and cover letter, during your employment interviews, and in your networking efforts. By creating and delivering a consistent value proposition, you will greatly improve the way your colleagues perceive you.

Finally, persist in the search. Your job search process is a job in itself. Allocate appropriate time and energy to it. If you do it well, you will reap many rewards. Your job search process is a valuable exercise, but it can sometimes become routine. The secret to keeping focused is to break down the process into manageable steps that you can achieve every day. As you take these steps, you will feel that you are taking positive action in the search.

Now, and throughout your career, concentrate your efforts on applying for jobs that you really want. If you are not comfortable with the direction that you are going, take a step back and revisit your personal and professional goals. You will be far more satisfied with your search if you know that it is taking you where you want to go.

Everybody needs help from time to time. An experienced career practitioner can help you with your job search. If you are having difficulty identifying, finding, or securing the right role, consider taking advantage of this type of service, which is readily available for professionals.

Your commitment and focus in these early stages of understanding, uncovering, and securing the position of your dreams will determine your future. Read this section with zeal and dedication. Use the strategies put forward. With serious attention, you will develop and execute a plan to heighten your chances of long-term career and business success!

Sharon Graham, CRS, CIS, CPRW, CEIP
Executive Director, Career Professionals of Canada
Principal Consultant, Graham Management Group

Sharon Graham is a professional résumé writer, employment interview strategist, and author of Best Canadian Résumés. She is executive director of Career Professionals of Canada (www. CareerProCanada.ca) and services job seekers through her consulting firm, Graham Management Group (www. Graham Management.com).

CHAPTER 3-1

Types of Private Practices

John Tait, BSc, DVM, MBA, CFP, ADR
Managing Partner, Ontario Veterinary Group,
Toronto, Ontario
Assistant Professor, Ontario Veterinary College,
Guelph, Ontario

> *I try to learn from the past, but plan for the future by focusing exclusively on the present. That's where the fun is.*
>
> — Donald Trump

Veterinary practices exist in a perfectly competitive marketplace where, according to economic theory, each practice is generally a substitute for another based on the fact that they all deliver essentially the same services and sell roughly the same products.

At a macro level, this may be true; but at a more micro level (besides location, facility differences, operating variances in hours, fees, and equipment), there are some basic differences in styles of practice that will affect your experience. All have advantages and disadvantages.

Practice styles can be subdivided according to how they schedule, staff themselves, assign staff responsibilities, set fees, view customer service, apply business acumen (including reporting, marketing, and training), and what demographic of clients they attract. There is no right or wrong about which style and philosophy of practice are best. Different styles offer experience and expertise in different areas; however, these differences can bring certain drawbacks and cautions.

At one end of the spectrum are practices based on higher volume and lower fees; they trade lower fees for processing a high volume of patients and clients daily. These are not client-centered or "high-density" practices that leverage their staff to provide a more efficient system. Instead, these are practices that shorten appointment times; often have minimally trained technical or professional staff beyond the veterinarians; have less in the way of advanced diagnostic equipment; experience a higher turnover of staff and clients; are more focused on elective surgery and vaccinations; have little in the way of marketing; have no dedicated management; and frequently, but not exclusively, service demographic areas near or below average-per-family income levels. A high volume of patients passing through the hospital per day with minimal technical support and downtime, forces the veterinarian to become better versed at basic technical skills, elective surgery time per procedure, basic laboratory work, and focused communications. The sacrifice in this type of practice environment is often personal burnout. There is no opportunity to develop a relationship with clients, receive much mentoring, obtain exposure to a high level of business acumen, and pursue in-depth case workups or use more intricate diagnostic equipment.

In contrast, the hospitals that emphasize progressive and consummate business principles, focusing intently on the client transaction and the movement of the "case" through the hospital, are typically larger practices with multiple veterinarians, trained staff at all positions, central or dedicated management, information technology (IT) systems with wide applications in the practice, a strong equipment base from which to practice, a wide range of services and diagnostics, internal support manuals and references for employees, and elaborate and broad marketing. These practices are often located in demographic areas at or above average-per-capita family income levels. These hospitals usually offer excellent mentoring, a chance to learn from colleagues and coworkers, a more moderate pace, challenging cases from a wide spectrum of clinical material (with some using larger client bases and/or their diversity to practice in niche areas), a chance to learn current business practices, efficient reporting of productivity, more opportunity to develop a relationship with clients, and more depth in managing cases.

In larger practices where staff is leveraged more and continuity of case care may not always be possible (due to the multi-veterinarian dynamic), it may still be a challenge to develop a relationship with clients. Furthermore, since technicians are often responsible for much of the routine patient care, laboratory sampling and analysis, surgical preparation, and anesthesia and recovery, these practices may not be the ideal location to refine one's technical skills and speed, if that is a goal.

Somewhere in the middle of these two practice philosophies is a practice that has coined the term "bond centered" or "relationship centered." These practices cross all demographics and are focused primarily on the veterinarian as a visible primary caregiver and the person or persons the practice is built around. These practices are not generally very large multi-veterinarian practices, but they are practices that focus on personalized customer care and personality—traits that are not always possible in the larger practices.

Client-based relationships, mentoring, communication, customer service, and potential for broad access to clinical material are special priorities for the bond-centered practice. These practices can still offer exposure to a high-impact amount of technical experience, as they don't manage their operations to the extreme that a true high-volume/low-fee practice does.

Within the veterinary practice, leadership from the top sets the philosophy of the practice; as an associate entering a practice, it is difficult to change that philosophy and style of practice. Any style of practice can be current and progressive in its technique, can be committed to training, be innovative, and try to maintain a culture of celebration and success.

Regardless of the style of practice, I would take the time to assess and evaluate a practice's acceptance of and resistance to change. In time, a practice that operates with any particular style will be challenged by change of some sort. The practice's ability to respond to change, rather than ignore it or react to it, will dictate how effective that style is in sustaining itself over time. While there are a great deal of progressive practices out there, there are also a number that are stale and have become tired, stuck in routines, stubborn, complacent, or set in their ways. They have not "kept up." Practices that have, for instance, too centralized a control that rests with one individual who is micromanaging will not likely keep up to changing times, so their "style" eventually becomes inefficient.

Practices signal their ability to deal successfully with change, and you'll be able to read the signs when you visit or work there. If they are willing to take some risk, stretch themselves and make decisions in the face of uncertain information, communicate openly among each other, share authority around the practice, and not procrastinate on tough decisions, then they are likely to be a practice that accepts and even takes on change and will continue to successfully deliver their style of practice into the future.

Biography

For Dr. John Tait's biography, please see the Section 1 Introduction on page3.

Résumés and Cover Letters

Heather Erskine, RN, BA, CPRW, CRS, CIS
Vice-President, Erskine Associates, Inc.,
London, Ontario

> *Résumés are the only part of the job search where you have 100% control . . . so don't treat them casually.*
>
> — Jay Block

Introduction

This chapter introduces strategies to empower your career-related communications. You will learn how to write impressive résumés, targeted cover letters, e-mail correspondence, and "thank you" notes. Structural guidelines, strategic tips, and sample résumés are included to help you present your specific job-related actions in a measurable, results-oriented, and timely way—enabling you to demonstrate your transferable skills and accomplishments succinctly and powerfully.

The content in this chapter follows the standards of Career Professionals of Canada (CPC) and Professional Association of Résumé Writers and Career Coaches (PARW) and features the **Combination Format** of résumés. This format showcases prospective value by combining the best of the old Chronological (work responsibilities) and Functional (listing of skills and achievements) styles of résumés.

Writing Impressive Résumés

It is important to understand the concept of **transferable skills** before starting the writing process. Transferable skills are the skills that propelled you to achieve in the past, and are key indicators of how you will perform in the future. Determining your most valuable transferable skills is a four-step process. First, review your past accomplishments to determine your transferable skills. Second, analyze the type of position you are seeking. Third, calculate the skills that the position requires. Finally, establish a link, or a **fit** to connect what you have to offer with the position requirements.

Uncovering transferable skills requires analysis of past roles and achievements to determine the skills you have used to perform well. You need to uncover your **specific actions** and then analyze **how** you carried them out. In so doing, you'll find a theme beginning to surface—maybe you have been a keen team player, maybe you are an effective communicator, maybe your surgical abilities are strong. Determining your transferable skills is the underpinning of your **value proposition** (i.e., your unique employer-targeted marketing message). The way to uncover your skills will be clearer after you read the section entitled "Career History."

In the following pages, step-by-step writing guidelines will cover the five key résumé sections: **Headline** (replacing the Objective), **Profile Summary**, **Education**, **Career History**, and **Related Activities**. Although the first two sections (i.e., Headline and Profile Summary) appear at the top of the résumé, they are *written at the end of the process*, because only then is it clear what your transferable skills are and which ones you want to display at the top of your résumé. Hence, the Headline and Profile Summary sections will be covered after the sections on Education, Career History, and Related Activities.

Education
New graduates (less than two years out of school) place the Education section ahead of the Career History section, whereas experienced professionals (out of school for more than two years) place the Education section *under* the Career History section.

Bullet marks typically are not used in the Education section—they are reserved for Career History accomplishments. However, if you achieved a place on the Dean's List or won a scholarship, these accomplishments are set apart with bullet marks. If you have received several awards, you might want to add a sixth section to your résumé entitled "**Awards**."

List your degrees in reverse chronological order (periods are not used in this section). Place the name of the school first, and underline it, but don't

Example of a Typical Education Section

EDUCATION

<u>University of Guelph, Ontario Veterinary College</u> – Guelph, ON

Candidate for Doctor of Veterinary Medicine (DVM)   2006

   • *OVC Deans Access Bursary (2005-2006)*

<u>University of Guelph</u> – Guelph, ON

**Honours Bachelor of Science: Nutritional
and Nutraceutical Sciences**

   • *Deans Honour List*   2002

---

bold it. Line up the dates with the far right margin. Reserve bold print for your degree earned. Remember, your résumé serves as your key marketing tool and bolding your degrees serves to showcase "you."

Education statements commonly are formatted with a number 5-font space between entries.

Career History

An impact player is someone who can quickly improve the economics of a company. An impact player is someone who can bring in customers, energize the sales force, restructure an underperforming department, speed up the innovation process. . . An impact player also is someone who will do the necessary but noxious tasks no one else wants to do.

— Jeffrey J. Fox

The term "Career History" can be used interchangeably with "Employment History" or "Work History." For consistency, the term "Career History" is used in this chapter.

Employers want to see **achievements**, **accomplishments**, and **results**. Your goal, therefore, is to demonstrate these qualities in each Career History impact statement. One very helpful tool to guide you through this process, is the "**SMART**" guide. The SMART Guide is an effective way to quantify your experience.[1] **Skills** need to be **S**pecific, **M**easurable, **A**ction-oriented, **R**esults-oriented, and **T**ime-based in order to have impact. Imagine placing the following "ruler" under each bullet you write; asking yourself if your statement measures up.

| Specific | Measurable | Action-oriented | Results-oriented | Time-based |

Career History Example and SMART Assessment

Biologist
• Performed literature review

SMART? ➤ NO
This statement is neither specific nor measurable. More importantly, it does not define the "action," or the skills, used during this "role." As well, we don't know the results or the time frame. Clearly, the biologist's transferable skills do not show through. It was revised as follows:

Biologist
Worked in the field **for six weeks** to collect and summarize data:
• **Reviewed and summaried literature on population and habitat modeling** for a large aquatic-systems consulting project: **presented findings to management,** who used the information to make **significant protocol changes.**

SMART? ➤ YES
Now the *specifics* around both the role and the event are evident: the *action* is spelled out and *measurable*. (**Reviewed and summarized literature on population and habitat modeling from a large aquatic-systems consulting project**). The *results* (**presented findings to management**, who used the information to make **significant protocol changes**) are now backed up with evidence. The *time frame* is clear (**six weeks**).

Use bullet marks to set off your Career History impact statements, as they add white space and create a focal point, while showcasing achievements, accomplishments, and results. Place periods at the end of each bulleted impact statement. To gain impact, place your job responsibilities directly under your position title in one "unbulleted" statement (Role Descriptor). Using the SMART guide, you then can showcase your specific and measurable accomplishments in bulleted statements directly under your Role Descriptor, as shown in the following example:

Example of a Career History Entry Containing a Role Descriptor and a SMART Impact Statement

Emergency/ICU Veterinary Extern

Shadowed Dr. Lyle James, and read related information two hours each evening **(Note: role descriptor)**:

* Assessed patients (TPR, blood pressure, oxygen saturation, and attitude) and documented results, administered and facilitated (with guidance) a broad range of treatments to critically ill patients, and restrained patients for emergency veterinary procedures: acquired understanding of small animal emergency diagnostics, treatment, and intensive care medicine. **(Note: SMART impact statement)**

Note that the colon in the previous and following examples serves to introduce "results."

Career History "Power Play:" Add the company or the clinic's "**Bottom Line**" information under each job listing to empower your entries. Use a number 10-italicized font and set the *line spacing* at number 10.

Targeted Career History "Impact Statements"
Now that you are sure that your Career History impact statements are SMART, the next thing to do is determine whether or not they are **targeted**. In other words, you want to be sure that your statements are mapped to the employer's needs. How you determine which of your transferable skills to showcase depends on the job you are targeting. Read the job posting carefully to assess the skills your potential employer is seeking.

Example of a Career History Entry Utilizing the Company Descriptor

(Notice how the Company Descriptor "sets the stage")

CAREER HISTORY

Emergency Pet Care, Centerville, Ontario Summer 2005

Emergency Pet Care *is a small- animal, emergency veterinary practice, providing high quality medical and expanded surgical services 24hours a day, seven-days a week.*

Emergency/ICU Veterinary Extern

Shadowed Dr. Lyle James, and read related information two hours each evening:

- Assessed patients (TPR, blood pressure, oxygen saturation, and attitude) and documented results, administered and facilitated (with guidance) a broad range of treatments to critically ill patients, and restrained patients for emergency veterinary procedures: acquired understanding of small-animal emergency diagnostics, treatment, and intensive-care medicine.

See the following Job Posting and two related Career History impact statements that demonstrate the process. By assigning each of the key skills a number, and then matching the numbers to the demonstrated skills in an impact statement, it is easy to see what message this statement delivers. This employer is looking for the following skills: Communication[1] / Teaming [2] / Analysis/Problem-Solving [3] / Empathy [4] / Confidence to Work Alone [5] / Technical Expertise [6] / Diagnostic Skills [7] / Ability to Produce Results [8] / Health Promotion and Education [9] / Ability to Build and Nurture Key Relationships [10] / Keenness to Learn [11].

Job Posting
Full-time veterinarian required for a small hospital in Northville. We offer a full-service approach to pet care, with emphasis on Health Promotion and Education [4] [9]. Applicants should have strong communication [1], diagnos-

tic [7], medical, and surgical abilities, [6] as well as team spirit [2] and sound problem-solving skills [3]. We cherish our clients and work together with them to achieve results [8] [10]. We fully support and encourage CE. [11] Four veterinarians rotate through a 24-hour on-call schedule, which operates seven-days a week [5]. If you have a passion for people and pets, and a commitment to excellence in veterinary care, send your résumé to Northville Animal Hospital, Box 123, Northville, ON, A1B 2C3.

Impact Statement (created to target the skills highlighted above)
Improved clinic's image [8], during a summer internship, by working with the clinic staff [2, 10] to provide excellent customer service [1, 3, 9, 10], health promotion [9] (designed an educational poster highlighting the importance of immunization [1, 3, 5, 8, 9]), and compassionate pet care [4, 7, 8].

A closer look at the preceding statement suggests that technical expertise [6], diagnostics [7], and keenness to learn [11] have not been demonstrated. Thus, a second impact statement, highlighting these skills, follows:

* Studied with Mr. Andy Durham [11]: performed lameness examination, radiograph interpretation, nerve block and ultrasound [6] [7]; assisted with surgical and medical colic case diagnostic and treatment regimes [6] [7]: gained extensive experience in equine ambulatory medicine, including dentistry, vaccination, and pre-purchase examination.

Note that *not every impact statement needs to showcase every skill.*

Related Activities

This type of information attracts others to you and can be the single reason someone calls you for an interview. My motto is "Use what you have to, to get in the door."

— Wendy Enelow

The section entitled "Related Activities" is placed at the end of the résumé. It is meant to complete your Value Proposition. Focus only on those activities that round out your Value Proposition. Often job postings highlight activities available in the region. If so, it is most appropriate to document your passion for related sports or activities. As in the other sections, keep the items in this list parallel in structure. Do not use either bullet points or periods in this section.

Example of Related Activities

Advanced Computer Skills: *Microsoft Office Word, Excel, Access, Outlook, PowerPoint*

Sports: Golf, Weight/Cardiovascular Training, Mountain Biking, Scuba Diving, Snowboarding

Or—

Exchange Student in Switzerland; *Humane Society* Volunteer; Tennis Club Vice President; 6 Handicap in Golf; Fluency in English, French, and Spanish

Or—

Grade 10 Royal Conservatory of Music in piano

Member of Provincial Women's Softball Team (1990 to 2004): qualified for Nationals in 2001 and declared Ontario Champions in 1991: **Captain** (1999 – 2004) and **MVP** (1999 – 2001)

Captain and MVP of senior girl's volleyball team (1997)

Profile Summary (Your Value Proposition)

To effectively market yourself to your employer, you must deliver a unique, powerful, and consistent message. This message is called a "Value Proposition." It should concisely answer the employer's question: "Why should we hire you?" Well-written Profile Statements promote this message and draw the reader in. A solid Value Proposition is the foundation of a marketable résumé. It enables you to promote your very best features, clearly and consistently.

— Sharon Graham

Most North American recruiters spend an average of 10-to-15 seconds screening each résumé. If they can't see a reason to hire you in that first "glance," they toss the résumé aside! To capture recruiter attention, and showcase your transferable skills up front and centre, I recommend using a section called

Profile Summary. The Profile Summary outlines specific transferable skills, which link to the employer's needs, and forms the basis for the "back-up" information outlined in your Career History.

Having completed the Education, Career History, and Related Activities sections, you can now create a Profile Summary (also called "Summary of Qualifications," "Core Strengths," or "Career Summary") to market your Value Proposition developed in the completed three sections. Profile Summaries describe the key skills, abilities, knowledge, and qualifications that match your targeted position requirements. The Profile Summary is placed directly *under the Headline* section. For maximum impact, reserve bullet marks for highlighting your Career History accomplishments (impact statements). Periods are not used in Profile Summaries, because they typically do not form grammatically correct sentences. Profile Summaries usually follow one of three formats: a succinct paragraph outlining transferable skills, three-to-four targeted statements, or a list of skills (see examples). Except for the bulleted skill list, *bullet marks are not used in this section.*

Profile Summaries address the employer's needs up front. They not only grab the recruiter's attention, but also begin to identify your Value Proposition, while showcasing **whom** you are and **how** (transferable skills) you have come to be who you are. I recommend that you create a long list of transferable skills, drawing on only those skills that specifically match employer needs, each time you send out a résumé. This section of your résumé may change each time you apply for a new position.

Preparing a Profile Summary will not only define your value, but also empower you (during your interview) to respond in a succinct and focused way to the most commonly asked interview question, *"Why should we hire you?"* A good answer to that question depends on an accurate and targeted description of your skills.

Three Examples of Profile Summaries

PROFILE SUMMARY

A dedicated, client-focused, and team-oriented individual with outstanding communication skills and sound technical expertise. Proven ability to work with individuals from a wide variety of backgrounds and function well within a team environment. Exceptional capacity to multitask and prioritize tasks, in addition to taking initiative and motivating team members to provide quality patient care.

SUMMARY OF QUALIFICATIONS *(Note: different title but similar message)*

Committed to excellence in veterinary care and ready to take ownership in a friendly and thriving practice

Confident to diagnose, practice internal medicine, perform general surgeries, and work alone due to comprehensive training and sound summer experience

Highly attentive to patient and client needs and eager to foster harmonious relations with associates, colleagues, and all support staff

Innovative, enthusiastic, and keen to try new ideas and services

CORE STRENGTHS (Note: different title and format but similar message)

Clinical Experience
Soft-Tissue and Orthopedic Surgery Principals and Practices of Veterinary Medicine Health Promotion and Education Delegation of Support and Office Staff

Soft Skills
Commitment
Inquisitiveness
Passion for Animals
Empathy and Sensitivity

Profile Summaries showcase potential **value**. According to Jay Block,[2] **value** is made up of three components: **skills**, **qualifications**, and **intangibles**. **Skills** are those benefits that help the employer achieve his/her goals. **Qualifications**, he says, *"encompass specific training and preparation, including academic achievement, credentialing, certifications, and licenses..."* **Intangibles** are neither skills nor qualifications—they include such things as bringing a good reputation in your field to your next job, or carrying forward a client list to your next job. Collectively, skills, qualifications, and intangibles, or **Core Strengths**, are outlined in Profile Summaries.

Core strengths are difficult to assess. One useful tool to help you identify your core strengths is the **Profile Summary Writing Guide**. Note that you write the key reason you should be hired in the top box. Your goal here is to capture the recruiter's attention and to show a "fit" between what you can offer and what the employer needs. After you have the recruiter's attention, you want to break down that first "attention grabber," with two to four sub-statements that will not only spell out the skills, qualifications, or intangibles you own, but also back up your opening statement. The answers to these four questions should form the basis for your Profile Summary.

Profile Summary Writing Guide

Why should the company hire me?

Committed to excellence in veterinary care

What valuable skills, abilities, qualifications, and credentials can I offer?

Confident to diagnose, practice internal medicine, perform general surgeries and work alone

How can I show that I bring more to the job than expected—in other words, add more value?

Highly attentive to patient and client needs and eager to foster harmonious relations ...

How can I show that I bring more to the job than expected—in other words, add more value?

Innovative, enthusiastic and keen to try new ideas and services

Headline

The goal [in a Headline] is to capture the recruiter's attention and to show a "fit" between what your client can offer and what the employer needs. Back up what you say in the Headline throughout the résumé.

— Sharon Graham, *CRS Certification Guide*

The term "Objective" is no longer used in résumés because most employers see it as self-serving. Instead, the term **Headline** is used to promise value to future employers. Headlines often are put in boxes to capture the reader's attention. A Headline is the last section of the résumé to be written.

Examples of Typical Headlines

GRADUATING VETERINARIAN

SUPERIOR CLIENT RELATIONS, TEAMING, AND INTERPERSONAL SKILLS

SURGICAL AND MEDICAL EXPERTISE

GRADUATING VETERINARIAN

ENTHUSIASTIC / ORGANIZED / OUTGOING / TEAM-ORIENTED

ABLE TO WORK WELL WITH OTHERS / CONFIDENT TO WORK ALONE

EXPERIENCED VETERINARIAN

MIXED-ANIMAL PRACTITIONER SPECIALIZING IN
LARGE-ANIMAL MEDICINE AND SURGERY

SUPERIOR CLIENT RELATIONS, TEAMING, AND INTERPERSONAL SKILLS

Headlines emphasize potential value by summarizing skills and accomplishments. Just as newspaper headlines draw you in, so do Headlines in résumés. Writing a Headline is the *last task* in résumé-writing. Developing a Headline takes time. Brainstorm to identify your skills. Each time you jot down a skill, ask yourself, *"How would this skill benefit the company?"* This question forces you to get more and more specific. What you say in the Headline has to "fit" with the employer's needs. As with Profile Statements, Headlines change depending on your target company's needs.

When it comes to first impressions, you are like an actor stepping out on centre stage. Your objective is to receive rave reviews, have your audience love you, and leave behind a positive impression.

— Linda Schnabel

Targeted Cover Letters

The key strategy in all types of career-related correspondence is to *map your skills to the employer's needs*. If you are short on related job experience, link your university experience or volunteer roles to your targeted job. Cover letters should be situation-specific, showcasing the fit between experience and/or qualifications and the specific targeted position requirements. Although you will see references to "generic cover letters," they really do not have a place in focused job searches. What does work, however, is to create a generic list of skills, with short descriptors (relating to education or work experience) accompanying each skill. You can draw from this list each time you research a new position. You may need to spin the skills a bit, to make them fit. As Katherine Hansen says in her book, *Dynamic Cover Letters Revised,* "You weren't a waitress, you were a customer-service specialist."[3]

Note that it is strategic to research potential employers not only for their required skill sets, but also for language and style. If they, for example, refer to 5,000,000 USD as $5M US, then use that same style in your résumé and cover letter so that you can start to "connect" at the outset. Just as active listening benefits from "mirroring," so does a strategic job search.

Steps to Writing a Targeted Cover Letter

1. **Hook the reader** by establishing a connection. Give the employer a reason to keep reading and stay aligned with your Value Proposition (identified on your résumé).

2. **Create a succinct, targeted, and clear one-page document** by using short paragraphs, sentences less than three lines long, bullet points to highlight skills and accomplishments, and lots of white space to enhance your message. Map your skills to the company's needs.

3. **Initiate Action/Close the Sale**: never assume anything! If you are writing to request an interview, say so! Tell your reader when you will call (no more than one week in the future) to confirm receipt of your docu-

ments and coordinate an interview time (and then follow through with that call!). Thank them for their time.

4. **Include an enclosure line** to indicate everything you have sent with your cover letter, such as résumés, transcripts, or portfolios. This line directly follows your typed name.

5. **Review your letter asking yourself, after each point you've made, "So what?"** If you can't answer this question, the point probably shouldn't be included.

6. **Think about the following question**: Does this letter show my passion for the job or is it simply "generic?" Try to give the reader a snapshot of you.

7. **Proofread your letter**, and then send it to a friend for a second edit, asking them to pay particular attention to grammatical and spelling mistakes.

What Not to Include in a Cover Letter:

1. **Do not repeat** what is in your résumé. Rather, compliment the message with "back up" information.

2. **Do not simply list out** the target company's products or services—unless doing so demonstrates your value.

3. **Do not overstate**. Provide just enough information to give your audience a sense for your scope of experience and key selling points. Try to discuss only those personal attributes that relate to the job. Your goal, when writing your cover letter, is simply to entice your readers to read your résumé. *Less is more!*

Read through your cover letter, keeping the following questions in mind:

1. Does the cover letter support your Value Proposition, first introduced in your résumé? Do you believe your targeted employer can see and feel your value? Do you back up your Value Proposition with "evidence" (e.g., examples from previous jobs)?

2. Does the letter describe how previous employers/professors/teammates/classmates have benefited from your performance?

3. Have you helped your employers to make money, save money, save time, make work easier, solve problems, be more competitive, build re-

lationships, expand business, attract new customers, and retain existing customers?

4. Is your cover letter politically/culturally correct? Sarah Shergill poignantly points out, in an article entitled *"Job and Career Resources for Global Job-Seekers,"* that different cultures have different rules, customs, values, priorities, protocol, and religious or societal influences on business practices.[4] Enlist a peer to screen your cover letter for evidence of cultural insensitivity.

5. Is your letter grammatically correct? Did you use two spaces (rather than one) between each sentence (preferred in formal writing)?

6. Does your letter include the date, recipient's name, title, company/clinic name, a position reference title or number, if appropriate, and an inside address?

7. Have you included only the personal information that is related to the job, as unrelated personal information takes away from the point of the cover letter?

See an example of an effective résumé and cover letter package, which brought forth an interview, on the following pages. Adam was responding to the job posting for Kawartha Animal Clinic. He highlighted what he saw as the "necessary skills" to showcase in his résumé and cover letter, *before* starting the writing process. Note that Adam's Value Proposition, first introduced in his résumé, is obvious in his cover letter.

Kawartha Animal Clinic is striving for excellence and looking for an experienced, enthusiastic, progressive full-time or part-time veterinarian. Our clinic is lovely—spacious and well equipped—and the support team is wonderful. We are located in the beautiful Kawartha Lakes region, so you can play while you practice. Contact Dr. Peter Martin: **p.martin.vet-clinic@vetcom.net**.

ADAM B. HAZELTON

123 4th Street • Centretown • Ontario • CANADA • A1B 2C3
PHONE: (321) 987-6543 or (321) 345-6789
EMAIL: abhazelton@vetschool.ca

March 21, 2006

Dr. Peter Martin Kawartha Animal Clinic
P. O. Box 222 Kawartha Lake, ON K1W 2L3, CANADA

Re: Full-Time Veterinary Position at the *Kawartha Animal Clinic*

Dear Dr. Martin: *(Note: hook the reader)*

Graduating from Veterinary College has allowed me to follow my dreams and provide high quality, compassionate medical and surgical care for companion animals and their families. *Note: Create a succinct, targeted, and easy to read one-page document)*

My experience has been both relevant and comprehensive, preparing me to use my strong communication and technical skills to promote health and wellness in a companion-animal practice. I feel confident that my most recent externship, in particular, has paved the way for me to carry out a holistic approach to veterinary medicine: diagnosing, treating, and caring for sick animals, while educating and supporting their family members. I am an avid learner, always looking for ways to expand my own awareness; and I expect to continue to seek out new knowledge and techniques. I was thrilled to read that your clinic strives for excellence, on an ongoing basis.

Past performance evaluations have stressed, in addition to my excellent technical skills, my sound team skills and my ability to listen effectively. As well, my evaluations have recognized my ability to form positive and enduring relationships with veterinary assistants and support staff. I look forward to using these skills as I practice veterinary medicine.

(Note: Initiate action/close the sale)
I am excited about the possibility of moving to the Kawartha Lakes region, as I am an avid sports enthusiast with a passion for fishing and canoeing. Thank you very much for taking the time to consider my application. I will call you next week to set up an interview.

Best regards,

Adam B. Hazelton

Enclosure: Résumé *(Note: Include an enclosure statement)*

ADAM B. HAZELTON

123 4th Street • Centretown • Ontario • CANADA • A1B 2C3
PHONE: (321) 987-6543 or (321) 345-6789
EMAIL: abhazelton@vetschool.ca

GRADUATING VETERINARIAN
Committed to the continued development of veterinary knowledge, skills, and abilities through academic and experiential learning

---

SKILLS SUMMARY

A dedicated, client-focused, and team-oriented individual with outstanding communication skills and sound technical expertise. Proven ability to work with individuals from a wide variety of backgrounds and function well within a team environment. Exceptional capacity to multitask and prioritize tasks in addition to taking initiative and motivating team members to provide quality patient care.

EDUCATION

University of Guelph, Ontario Veterinary College – Guelph, ON
Candidate for Doctor of Veterinary Medicine   2006

- *OVC Deans Access Bursary* (2005-2006)
- *Mary I. Whitelock Bursary* (2005-2006)
- *OVC Class of 1952 Bursary* (2004-2005)

Honours Bachelor of Science:
Nutritional and Nutraceutical Sciences   2002

- Dean's Honour List

RELEVANT WORK EXPERIENCE

Centretown Veterinary Clinic – Centretown, ON   Summer 2005

Centretown Veterinary Clinic is a private mixed-animal practice with three full-time veterinarians: Dr. Jim Smith, Dr. Paul Jones, and Dr. Mary Roberts

ADAM B. HAZELTON Page 1

Extern

Assisted veterinarians and addressed clients' emotional and financial concerns:

- Provided primary patient care, medicated, and monitored patients; performed routine spay/neuter and surgical procedures; administered anesthesia and monitored patients; completed in-house laboratory procedures; and inserted intravenous catheters: developed a keen sense of confidence and competence.
- Gained valuable experience forming differential diagnosis lists and using diagnostic tests to rule disease in/out to form treatment plans for a variety of species.

High View Animal Hospital – Centretown, ON   Summer 2003
Highview Animal Hospital is a small-animal emergency veterinary practice providing high quality medical and expanded surgical services 24-hours a day, seven-days a week.

Emergency/ICU Veterinary Assistant

Supervisor: Dr. Lyle James

- Assessed patients (TPR, blood pressure, oxygen saturation, and attitude) and documented results, administered and facilitated a broad range of treatments to critically ill patients under the guidance of emergency veterinarians and specialists, and restrained critically ill patients for emergency veterinary procedures: acquired understanding of small-animal emergency diagnostics, treatment, and intensive-care medicine.

Ontario Veterinary College – Guelph, ON   Summer 2002
The oldest veterinary college in Canada and the United States, OVC has been educating veterinarians since 1862

Research Assistant: Pathobiology Department

Assisted Dr. Bryce Cortney with an investigation into the cause of epizootic catarrhal gastroenteritis (ECG) within commercially farmed mink:

- Collected blood samples and administered a trial vaccination program for West Nile Virus within a population of northern owls affected with the virus: gained valuable experience and expertise in animal handling, research, and disease protocol.
- Traveled to 11 mink farms throughout Ontario: collected and compiled pertinent research data, and presented the findings in a *Power-Point* presentation to Dr. Cortney and four other faculty members.

ADAM B. HAZELTON Page 2

- Participated in the Summer Student Leadership Program in OVC: created four teams of five veterinary students who each managed one section of the first year Orientation Program.

<u>Centretown Zoo</u> – Centretown, ON   1997 – 1998

Centretown Zoo is Canada's oldest private zoo, established in 1919, and is home to over 300 creatures, including many famous Hollywood celebrity animal actors.

Animal Care Attendant

Cared for animals in assigned section, cleaned exhibits and holding areas, and observed animals for signs of illness, indifference, or injury.

<u>Mainstreet Animal Hospital</u> – Centretown, ON   1996 – 2000
Mainstreet Animal Hospital is a small, private veterinary practice with one full-time veterinarian: Dr. Paul Sow

Veterinary Assistant

Assisted with the care and treatment of sick and injured animals; performed routine lab procedure tests on blood and fecal samples; and engaged in customer service (answered phones, scheduled appointments, and prepared invoices):

- Received recognition, from supervisor, for ability to both problem-solve effectively and establish sound rapport with clients.

PROFESSIONAL AFFILIATIONS

Member: *Ontario Veterinary Medical Association* (OVMA) and *Canadian Veterinary Medical Association* (CVMA), 2002 to present, and *Veterinary Emergency and Critical Care Society* (VECCS), 2004 to present

CONTINUING EDUCATION

Western Veterinary Conference – 2006 • *Iams Nutritional Symposium* – 2006 *Hill's Veterinary Nutritional Advocate Tutorial* – 2005 • *OVMA Conference* – 2004, 2005, 2006

PERSONAL INTERESTS

Sports Enthusiast: hockey, cycling, jogging, canoeing, camping, and fishing
Passions: travel, continuing education, and personal finance

E-Mail Correspondence

If a company posting requires "just résumés—no cover letters," a covering e-mail note must still be written. A targeted e-mail note is your chance to impress the hiring manager, because most job applicants do not bother to do so. By using the following guidelines, you can compose an effective e-mail note:

1. Type an appropriate error-free subject in the "subject" line.
2. Start the note with "Hello" rather than "Dear."
3. Keep the note brief. Write three short paragraphs to introduce yourself, show your fit with the advertised position, and identify your plan for follow-up.
4. Keep symbols or unusual fonts out of the text, as the recipient's computer may not accept these variations, causing the message to be incomplete.
5. Put the letter through Spell Check.

Thank You Notes

Sending follow-up "Thank You" letters to individuals with whom you have interviewed is a *must*. Like cover letters, each "Thank You" letter should be customized to the recipient and purpose of the meeting, and it should be sent within 24 hours of the interview. The jury is still out on whether or not the letter should be typed or handwritten. If it is handwritten, the writing should be legible, with a succinct and error-free message. If you connected in a personal way during your interview, ensure that you remind the interviewer of the connection in your note. For example, "What a coincidence— seeing my cousin in the picture on your desk! I had no idea that you had played football with him in college." Thank You notes should end on a positive note, emphasizing interest in the position and showing appreciation for the time spent during the interview process. Mention can be made of key skills or accomplishments that were not addressed in the interview.

Example of an E-mail Note

Hello Dr. Jones:

(Note: Describe how you found the posting)
I saw your advertisement for a small-animal practice Veterinarian on *Monster.com.* After reviewing the position description, I feel confident that I not only have the skills and experience you are looking for, but also am flexible with regard to working at night or on weekends.

(Note: Introduce your "fit")
I have been recognized for my strong customer focus, clinical excellence, and teamwork. In particular, I am passionate about Health Promotion and Education and I was happy to see that your clinic wants to do more in this area. I also am excited about your in-house biochemistry, endoscopy, radiography, ultrasonography, pulse oximetry, and high-speed dental unit, given my desire for fast and accurate results. I look forward to meeting with you to hear more about your practice.

(Note: describe your follow-up plan and thank them)
Thank you very much for your consideration of my application. I will call you towards the end of next week to set up an interview.

Best regards,

Isobel Andrews, Candidate for DVM 2007

Attachment: Résumé

Example of a Typical "Thank You" Note

February 06, 2007

Dr. James Andrews
Pet Paradise
123 4th Street Toronto, ON
A1B 2C3, CANADA

Dear Dr. Andrews:

(Note: Express your sincere appreciation)
Thank you for spending so much time with me on Thursday. I feel that I now have good insight into your practice. I also appreciate having had dinner with you, Scott, and Ryan at *Chimes*. I felt very relaxed talking with the three of you over dinner and I learned a lot.

(Note: Re-emphasize your qualifications)
My proven communication, medical, and surgical skills, in combination with my strong academic record and sense of humour, position me to succeed at *Pet Paradise*. I think it would be a great place for me to start my career.

(Note: Reiterate your appreciation and end on a positive note)
Thank you very much, once again, for a wonderful experience. I look forward to meeting with you again in the near future.

Best Regards,

Joe Smith

Structural Considerations

Packaging is critical to any endeavor...Good packaging also means high quality and attention to detail...No matter how strong your employment credentials, they are useless if your resume is sloppy, disorganized, or cumbersome.

— Jay Block

Active versus *Passive* Verbs

Verbs are either active (e.g., • **Advanced** three positions in two years) or passive (e.g., • **Promoted** three times in two years). Active verbs describe actions performed by the speaker and passive verbs describe actions performed by someone other than the speaker. If you read, for example, that someone was **"asked** to lead a project of ten....," your first question might be, "Did he actually do it or was he simply asked to do it?" If, on the other hand, you read: "**Lead** a team of ten..." you know that he (not anyone else) did, in fact, lead that team. Résumés and cover letters are key marketing tools, with the intent of showcasing accomplishments; thus, they benefit from the use of the "active voice."

Alignment

Full justification (where the print is pulled to each side margin) is not popular for résumés and cover letters. Reading such text is very tiring. The goal in résumé writing is to help the reader, in every possible way. For that reason, résumés and cover letters are "left aligned."

Bullet Marks

Typically, bullet marks only are used to showcase accomplishments. If bullet marks are placed elsewhere, the résumé becomes too "busy" and accomplishments tend to fade.

Commas

Use commas to separate items in a list. Be consistent with the use of commas before "and": either way (using serial commas before "and" or not using them) is correct; but mixing styles is wrong. The most important thing is to be consistent.

Font

A serif style font, such as **Times New Roman** (**TNR**), is preferred. Serif fonts have been proven to be 30% easier to read (on printed materials). Generally, in résumés, number 14 or number 12 TNR is used for Titles, and number 11 TNR is used for everything else but "Company Descriptors" and Educational "add-ons" where number 10 TNR (italicized) is used. Typically, in cover letters, number 12 font is used throughout.

Margins and Spacing

Résumé and cover letter margins need to be a minimum of <u>1 inch </u>around the sides and bottom, and 0.5 inch at the top. Spaces are required between entries on résumés, but they can use up a lot of room. Using <u>number 5 Font spaces </u>between Educational and Career History entries save space, while still giving the feeling of extra white space.

Numerals

Write out the numerals "zero" to "nine" and use the numbers for "10" and higher. Some résumé writers use numbers throughout to save space. Consistency is the key.

Modifiers

Modifiers (words, phrases, or clauses which describe other words, phrases, or clauses) should be placed as close as possible to the word or words they modify to prevent ambiguous interpretations and assumptions. If they are misplaced, they are called "Misplaced Modifiers."

Examples of Misplaced Modifiers include the following:

- Won the "Monthly Bonus Pool" for three consecutive months based on monthly sales revenues. (**Wrong**)
- Won the "Monthly Bonus Pool", based on monthly sales revenues, for three consecutive months. (**Correct**)
- Working there for five years, my peers grew to depend on me. (**Wrong**)
- Working there for five years, I gained considerable respect from my peers. (**Correct**)

Parallelism

All statements should be parallel in structure. In other words, all introductory words or phrases should have the *same grammatical function*. If impact statements are not parallel, the problem is called Faulty Parallelism (≠). Parallel structure also is required in lists or series. All items in the series must be parallel:

Examples of parallelism include the following:

- *Advised* clients regarding immunization protocol (*Advised* is a verb)

- *Skilled* (≠) in anesthesia induction (*Skilled* is an adjective therefore represents faulty parallelism)
- Revised in parallel structure:
- *Advised* clients regarding immunization protocol …
- *Performed* anesthesia induction …

Parallelism in a List

Gained valuable experience *forming* differential diagnosis lists, ~~used~~ using (√) diagnostic tests to rule disease in/out, and ~~formed~~ creating (√) treatment plans for a variety of species.

Periods

Periods are *not* used in Headlines, Profile Summaries, Educational Sections, or Related Activities, because none of these statements form grammatically correct sentences.

Personal Pronouns

Personal pronouns ("I," "we," "our," "my," "their," "his," "her") are *not* used in résumés.

Quantitative versus Qualitative

Quantitative information is recommended for maximum impact in résumés. Use numbers, measures, and facts (quantitative information), whenever possible, to prevent assumptions and misinterpretations.

Strategic Tips

> *No one cares how you want to use your experience. . . No one cares that at this stage of your career you do or don't do such and such. . .The only thing the hiring people care about is their problem. If hiring you can help solve their problem, then you have a shot at the job.*
>
> — Jeffrey J. Fox

Describe *your strengths*, not someone else's. If you *own* your résumé, you will find it much easier to market. In other words, your job search can be more focused when you match your skills to your target employer's needs. The interviewing process will be much less stressful, if you take the time to write a SMART résumé.

Define your ***value*** at the outset (takes time and energy!)—analyze your value and ensure that your Value Proposition is obvious in **each and every statement** on your résumé.

Develop a "buddy system" with a friend or colleague, in order to provide each other with objective edits as your résumé continues to evolve. Consider your résumé to be a "work in progress." During this edit, ensure your Value Proposition is clear, your transferable skills are obvious and targeted, and your vocabulary is both varied and powerful.

Prepare at least one professional example (situation from work) for each claim you've made on your résumé, as groundwork for your job interviews. Interviewers often draw from these two sections when they frame such questions as "What do you mean by 'Enthusiastic'?" or "What do you mean by 'Interpersonal Rapport'?" or "Tell me what you mean by…".

The Bottom Line: If your potential employer sees you as the answer to his or her problem, they will call you for an interview.

References

1.   *Top Secret Executive Resumes.* Provenzano, S. Career Press; Franklin Lakes, NJ: 2000.
2.   *101 Best Resumes to Sell Yourself.* Block J. McGraw Hill; New York, NY; 2002.
3.   *Dynamic Cover Letters Revised.* Hansen K, Hansen R. Ten Speed Press; Berkeley, CA; 2001.
4.   Shergill S. Job and Career Resources for Global Job Seekers. http://www.quintcareers.com/culturally_competent_resume.html

Biography

Heather Erskine is an Educator/Résumé Consultant with teaching experience in the fields of Business Communication, English as a Second Language, and Nursing. She is *Ivey's* Professional Writing Club's Coach and she teaches Advanced Business Communication, Résumé Writing, Interviewing, and Presentation Skills to the International MBA students at the *Richard Ivey Business School* in London, Canada.

An experienced writer, Heather has written extensive business correspondence; developed and written policy and procedure manuals; generated patient information documents, position descriptions, program protocols, educational materials (including video scripts), and educational pamphlets.

Most recently, she has produced résumé-writing materials, including *Executive Résumés: The Bottom Line.* Heather has edited/written over 1500 résumés for clients from many different professions including medicine, business, social work, marketing and sales, engineering and IT.

Heather sat on the certification committees for *Career Professionals of Canada* (CPC), preparing workbooks and examination materials for the designations of CRS (Certified Résumé Strategist), CIS (Certified Interview Strategist), and CCS (Certified Career Strategist) and continues to offer pre-certification "teleclasses" for CPC. As well, she grades the required pre-certification materials (résumés and cover letters) for the CRS certification designation.

Heather is an accomplished photographer who displays her photos in art shows in Canada and the US, and sells them in the form of note cards. Her hobbies include beading and playing Bridge. She is married to Jim Erskine, a professor and consultant, who teaches the Case Method of teaching, globally, to interested faculty in the form of Case Writing and Case Teaching Workshops. Together they have two adult children, both of whom live in Los Angeles. Laura is pursuing her PhD in Business and Brian is an accomplished chef.

Interview Skills:
Putting Your Best Foot Forward

John Tait, BSc, DVM, MBA, CFP, ADR
Managing Partner, Ontario Veterinary Group,
Toronto, Ontario
Assistant Professor, Ontario Veterinary College,
Guelph, Ontario

> *Knowledge is power, but enthusiasm pulls the switch.*
>
> — Ivern Ball

One of the experiences we often regard as harrowing and nerve racking is the face-to-face interview; however, interviews don't need to be intimidating or negative—in fact, for a well-prepared interviewer and interviewee, they can be quite enjoyable, informative, and provide a forum to put your best foot forward. Regardless of the topic, preparation for an interview is key to getting the information you need and delivering the information you want to put forward. An interview should be more a dialogue rather than an inquisition.

Before the interview, I suggest you prepare by gathering background information on the business itself, its history, and Web site and advertising materials that are available. Tour the area where the practice is located, and, if possible, asking for references from the employer from past employees who have occupied the same position. If a former employee has had a good experience in the practice, the employer should not be hesitant about providing them as a reference.

The basic skills you need during the interview are an ability to establish rapport with the interviewers, an ability to convey energy and passion about the position you are applying for, and also an ability to introduce the distinctive competencies or skills that are unique to you. Your goal as an interviewee is to instill confidence in the minds of the interviewers and satisfy their expectations.

There are various types of interviews that you may experience, including behaviour-based and more generic or "résumé crawl" type interviews. Interviewers themselves will have varying levels of experience and preparation of questions. Behaviour-based interviews are valuable for both parties involved in the interview process, as they are based on the premise that past behaviours and responses to specific situations are good predictors of future behaviours. Behaviour-based interviews are more likely to be conducted by experienced interviewers who are capable of constructing more informed questions. Such questions might surround character traits and situations that involve conflict, working together, stress management, and dealing with people in a service-based environment. Expect, however, to be questioned on your own experience and training, character traits, motivation, initiative, and possibly your knowledge base on everything from clinical issues to computer literacy. Vignettes, stories, and examples can better help create a positive impression about any of these categories in the minds of an interviewer, so come prepared with some.

As interviewees, it is possible to ask questions that help satisfy your curiosity with respect to how the employer and environment respond to situations and potential stressors that are of concern to you. As an interviewee, you can prepare your own behaviour-based questions. Ask the "what do you do when" questions. The character traits of the employer who sets the culture will influence your workplace environment. Following are some questions you might consider asking, which will help identify a culture and approach:

"What are the reasons for your success?"

"How do you show an interest in your employees?"

"How do you discipline and review employees?"

"Are you competitive?"

"Do you consider this practice to be innovative?"

"What would you like the practice to be remembered for?"

Generic-based interviews that proceed through your résumé and documented background information will more or less ask for expansion on the information contained in your cover letter and résumé and past experience; suitability for the job is largely based on your résumé and how well you back it up.

Situational questions should be dealt with first, in advance of due diligence-type questions about the structure and terms of the employer-employee relationship. As those questions arise in an interview, have your priorities identified and address them first. The most influential due-diligence question tends to be the salary issue. If and when the subject of salary comes up, indicate that you are willing to be flexible and fair, but have a number in mind that provides some room for flexibility and negotiation (see next chapter on negotiation skills).

Ultimately, interviewers rate their candidates on perceived suitability, and perceived suitability is based on how well they feel you fit in with their practice or business philosophy. The first five minutes of an interview are particularly important, as you'll set the tone for a number of influencing factors. Such influencing factors include your appearance, how much eye contact you make, how long or short your answers are, whether or not you keep a positive tone to the answers (negative answers about past employers or experiences are not received as well), and how well you use humour and your communication skills.

In some cases, practices will hold multiple interviews to create a short list of candidates. When second interviews are conducted, often these will be working interviews or "realistic job previews," whereby the employer seeks to immerse the prospective employees in the workplace to better assess "fit." This can be very much influenced by the consensus opinion received from the staff. The first interview may be a screening interview, with the second interview in front of the actual decision maker(s). If the personnel interviewing are different the second time around, avoid repeating the same answers and illustrative examples provided during the first interview, if at all possible. Negotiations on terms are sometimes left until after the second interview. A working interview provides an opportunity for the interviewers to focus on a candidate's behavioural attributes and communication with other staff members.

There are a number of interview questions that employers are not supposed to ask prospective candidates. These include questions about religion, age, weight, height, national origin, sexual orientation, marital status, memberships, or family intentions. Prospective employees are well within their rights to indicate that they feel uncomfortable answering these questions.

There are some common perceived barriers or risk factors that interviewers/employers may consider contrary to your ability to perform the position for which you are being interviewed. These include frequent job changes, past experience, lifestyle limitations imposed by children and handicaps, long commutes, and gender and marital status.

Frequent job changes raise potential concerns that a candidate may have an inability to make a commitment to a job, to fit in with the practice and staff, or simply be unsettled in his/her goals. If you have frequent job changes in your background, be prepared to explain them. Even if a position was not a good fit for you, explain why without criticizing any individuals or personalities at former places of employment. If you are prepared to commit to the prospective position longer than your history shows, emphasize that in your interview.

Experience is something only the calendar can build. Some practices prefer newer graduates, because they bring current ideas to the practice and command lower salaries than their experienced counterparts; other practices that have no time to mentor and are based on a quicker production schedule, will prefer experienced individuals. Your distinctive competency or unique skills can be enough to make a relatively clinically inexperienced veterinarian look more desirable, so be sure to emphasize those.

Areas such as children, handicaps, long commutes, and marital status are off limits for interviewers to ask about directly; however, these issues can arise indirectly when interviewers describe the requirements of the job and ask if there are any circumstances that would prevent you from physically performing a task, or working late, or coming back evenings, to mention a few. If you have personal commitments and obligations elsewhere, it is best to raise them up front and set expectations accurately and not set the stage for conflict later.

Gender balance is sometimes sought in practices, in order to offer clients a choice in case they are more comfortable with one gender or the other. Employers have the right to use gender as a consideration when hiring.

Employers may also choose to do a background check on you. They have the right to check a number of things, including your personal references, academic and license verification, criminal and civil court records, drug testing, and even your driving record.

Your personal references are often the best sources for providing information that will be very relevant to employers, and those references should be prepared to speak on the same key categories and attributes that you will be trying to convey in your interview. Such attributes may include your conscientiousness, ambition, attention to detail, motivation, ability to work with others, confidence, esteem, ethics, leadership abilities, honesty, customer orientation, and flexibility. Clinical skills and abilities will have some importance, so the best choice for personal references are people who can present a comprehensive and balanced picture of your skills required to be a veterinarian and your complementary personal skills and strengths. Giving your referées advance notice of impending calls, along with a copy of your résumé will result in a more positive reference.

Additional Recommended Reading

The Complete Q and A Job Interview. Allen JG. John Wiley and Sons; 1988.

Biography

For Dr. Tait's biography, please see the Section 1 Introduction on page 3.

3-4

Negotiating Strategies and How to "Sell Yourself"

John Tait, BSc, DVM, MBA, CFP, ADR
Managing Partner, Ontario Veterinary Group,
Toronto, Ontario
Assistant Professor, Ontario Veterinary College,
Guelph, Ontario

> *Wisely and slowly. They stumble that run fast.*
>
> — William Shakespeare

While not a new concept to most, negotiating suddenly can become a necessary skill and task to master for the graduating veterinarian. All of us start crude negotiating early in life—whether to stay up late, buy something we don't need, get a car, or trade money for chores—all involve negotiation. Regardless of cause, the process and desired outcome is the same—a discussion that is an attempt to reach an agreement, whereby we try to influence, coerce, persuade, and possibly demand something of another party. And while the process remains essentially the same, over time it's the stakes and maturity and sophistication with which we go about the process that change. However, the definition of successful negotiation does not change, regardless of the circumstances; both parties get most of what they want and walk away satisfied (i.e., win-win outcome). Successful negotiation is a balance between substance, process, and relationship. There should be attention paid to all three facets to reach a successful outcome in any negotiation.

Veterinarians will find themselves in a multitude of situations during their professional careers in which negotiations are required. Examples include employment terms as associates, employment renewals, time off, partnerships, leases, disputes, practice purchases and sales, expansions, retirement, and client conflicts. Regardless of the situation, the negotiation atmosphere is key to achieving success. By simply focusing on individual demands and positions, rather than applying a collaborative approach that focuses on mutual interests and the interests of the other party, the atmosphere will be tainted and successful negotiation at risk. Regardless of the reason for the negotiation, the end result should be to create value on both sides. Building value includes creating an environment that builds trust, asking the other side a lot of questions, making sure that you give away some information so you are not viewed as being too closed, and being flexible. Starting a negotiation process by focusing on the interests rather than the positions of both parties helps facilitate collaboration on ideas and gives both parties a better understanding of what is important to the other party, rather than starting with a more rigid positional demand (e.g., "this is what we are offering;" "this is what it will take to get me here"). Certainly bargaining or haggling, even arguing over prices of items, has its place for price-focused issues, but not for some of the other major transactions and issues veterinarians will encounter. Interests can be joint or shared, differing, or competing. Depending on how interests relate, the approach to negotiation can be one based on exploring common ground, discussing trade offs, or in the case of competing objectives, using objective criteria as a template for an agreement.

It's important to have an approach or philosophy and to be prepared before starting a negotiation. Do your research or due diligence on the practice, the staff, and the area, if you are considering employment at a practice. Spend some time in the practice, if possible (the so-called "realistic job preview"), ask questions, and ask for references. Determine what you need and what you want. Also recognize that if things are not going well in the negotiation process, you (as well as the other party) can simply walk away at any time, either permanently, or temporarily to regroup.

Be prepared for some "give-and-take" and prioritize your own interests, before starting the negotiation process. Negotiation should be a balance between empathy and assertiveness, a proper balance of each will facilitate the most effective decision. Focusing on interests brings a more friendly approach to the discussions, and tends to facilitate better communication and stronger relationships. The negotiation process is an exchange of information and an exercise in constructive, not adversarial, communication. Interpersonal skills, including an ability to listen, ask good questions, and compromise "once and a while," will play a role in a successful outcome. Argumentative, humourless and hostile tones, or giving up and shutting down the conversation are not the paths to successful negotiations. Negotiators will typically take on one of a selection of approaches. "Competitors" will play to win and get everything out of you that they can. "Accommodators" will often agree with you very easily. "Avoiders" will often avoid dealing with thorny or difficult details. Your response tactics will be based on the type of personality you are dealing with. In dealing with competitors, the most effective response is to use standards and objective market statistics as the basis for discussion. In dealing with accommodators, the most effective response is to set high goals to prompt a real rather than deferral response. In dealing with avoiders, you must address the areas of conflict and not leave them to be settled later.

Negotiation itself is a process that can take time; skilled negotiators can move through the process quickly and efficiently, avoid pitfalls, and come away with a fair solution. It is important to recognize that we all will encounter situations where we are not able to come to an agreement. We should give some thought, in advance of commencing a negotiation, as to what our options are if no agreement can be reached for the given situation. These prepared alternatives or other possible courses of action may help take the pressure off having to reach a compromised settlement where nobody is entirely happy, and are avenues to ensure that negotiations continue in a positive manner.

We've helped ourselves in veterinary medicine through the creation of comparables and standards that have been arrived at objectively. These objective standards, whether for salaries, benefits, purchase prices of practices, and so on, can be great helps in the negotiation process. They provide available, balanced, and fair criteria for areas in which mutually agreed upon decisions may be difficult. These criteria provide objective standards to measure against, are usually rational and without challenge, and prevent or hold back any one party from trying to be too extreme in their offering.

Attempting to support your position based on financial or other stressors in your life does not justify a more lucrative deal; however, selling the employer based on your interests does. If you have a distinctive competency, or something that you can contribute that is unique or different to help the business (e.g., "I have done extra training in behaviour consultations, so I could develop that service here" or "I have a particular interest in equine ultrasound and have done some extra continuing education in this area"), you're adding a skill set to the practice that they might not already have and this can be advantageous to both parties.

Most veterinarians early in their careers will encounter the negotiation process when it comes to agreeing on the terms of their employer-employee relationship. Both sides have power in this relationship, but the key to both sides walking away happy is a set of terms that is win-win, ultimately resulting in the business becoming more profitable. The potential for increased profitability is attractive to employers and a powerful sales tool for a prospective employee with a valuable skill set.

The negotiation process to arrive at an employment agreement is itself about reaching agreement on a set of items, prioritized based on the interests of each party. A number of content items can be discussed when entering into an employment arrangement as an associate. These include such things as length of commitment; base salary; employment status (employee versus self-employed); production-based component to compensation, if any; benefits; time off; continuing education (CE); and non-competition clauses. Other content items are sick time; uniforms; notice periods; bereavement; work schedules; renewal and review dates; responsibilities; statutory holiday coverage; and future buy-in options.

While it would nice to anticipate that each item will be discussed in a fair and rational manner, each party should be prepared for a number of different responses or approaches that may arise. Effective negotiators set the stage for the process and how they would like it to work; this is where interests will be presented to justify a position, rather than just a statement of position. If you want a particular salary range or benefit, then state the reason. For instance, state "I would like three weeks' vacation and another week off for CE, because I am aware that this amount is the entry-level standard for new graduates" and not "I need three weeks off each year." Similarly, an employer may state, "We offer two weeks' vacation a year here," a comment that does not justify the position in the mind of a potential new employee. If, however, the employer stated, "We have a progressive benefits policy here, to be fair to all the veterinarians and a policy that states all doctors must work for us for a year before they receive three-weeks' paid vacation," the potential employee, while they may not agree, will at least understand the rationale behind the employer's decision. This understanding should temper their frustration.

If one party appears more rigid, refuses to budge on his or her position(s) and tries to get you to concede, without giving anything back, s/he is conveying a "take it or leave it" position. Should this occur, it might be time to refer back to the standards in the profession for the item under discussion, and to consider the agreement as a whole rather than a piece-by-piece document. Additionally, refer back to your interests and agreed-upon process for the negotiation, and consider what the culture will be like in the practice once you are employed.

The most common area for discontent is if the wage is not on par with the marketplace; however, remember that the benefit package also costs the employer and should be considered as part of the entire compensation package. Further, the cost of living in a particular area may leave you with more discretionary income than someone making a higher salary in an area with a higher cost of living. If you feel strongly that the compensation package is below what you are willing to accept, you should delay accepting the offer and continue to focus on your interests—"I don't feel I can accept this offer because of the pay, I've been thinking all along that I'd be comfortable making "X" as apposed to "You're paying too little" or "This is less than my offer at another practice."

One way to quickly head down the path of ineffective negotiation is if the principal decision maker is not present. It is important to talk directly with the person who is calling the shots. A representative simply does not have the authority or the interests of the principal decision maker at heart, and the process gets diluted and slowed down.

In respect to timing, negotiations generally take place after an interview process of some sort. The start of the negotiation will set the tone for the rest of the conversation, so it is a good idea to try and agree on some non-disputed or non-priority areas first. It does not matter who actually starts the conversation or list of agenda items; however, it can be an icebreaker for you, as the potential employee, to start with some sort of prelude about whom you are, what you are offering the practice, and what you like about the possibilities. As the conversation progresses, never be afraid to ask questions and or for clarification, rather than make assumptions about what the other person is saying. If you have to give in a point, hopefully it will be something that is not that significant for you. If you are really stuck on something, come back to it, take time to think about possible creative solutions to an impasse, use your own resources to help with a possible solution, and/or ask for time to regroup and re-think.

As negotiations near completion and you are feeling a successful agreement is imminent, and your due diligence on the practice, area, and opportunities is complete, it is a good idea to capture all the terms and conditions in writing. Most associate-veterinarian agreements and, of course, all transitions into ownership or partnership will be addressed in writing. Do not accept a position verbally, until you see the terms in writing. If it makes you more comfortable, have an advisor of some sort proof read the contract or documents in question for you. Terms you thought you understood one way during the negotiation process may change when they are reflected in writing, and it is best to clarify and solidify terms before starting a position, not once you are in the position. The biggest barriers to successful negotiation are often ego and emotion. You want a negotiation to end will a feeling of success. "Success" can be defined in a number of ways and by a number of feelings or perceptions including a feeling that "we got a deal", or "that was easy" or "I feel I got a fair deal" or "the other party had to give up more than I did". End a negotiation with one of those perceptions, and you're on the path to a positive outcome, deal and relationship!

Biography

For Dr. Tait's biography, please see the Section 1 Introduction on page 3.

CHAPTER 3-5

The Right Fit: Recruiting for Performance and Mutual Gain

Mark Woolnough, BSc, MBA
Veterinary Business Management Services,
Guelph, Ontario

> *Getting focused on outcomes is one thing. Figuring out which outcomes are right is something else entirely.*
>
> — Marcus Buckingham and Curt Koffman

Introduction

Personal assessments of aptitudes, behavioural styles, and personal preferences offer useful insights on career choices, preferable operating environments, and communication styles. While no single assessment tool will provide all the answers, most will contribute significantly in decision-making for new veterinary graduates faced with the multitude of opportunities that require various strengths, risk tolerances, and suitability factors.

Your Unique Ability™, a concept by Dan Sullivan of The Strategic Coach®, describes four characteristics: 1) a superior ability that other people notice and value; 2) you are passionate about using it and want to use it as much as possible; 3) it's energizing for both you and others around you; and

4) there's a sense of never-ending improvement—you keep getting better and better and never run out of possibilities for growth. Since your unique ability is fueled by incredible passion, it can create enormous value for others. As described by The Strategic Coach,[1] "when you combine talent and passion you have the recipe for never-ending improvement, energy and excitement, and higher and higher levels of achievement." Identifying and describing your particular unique ability will provide direction regarding the environment you require to be at your most productive and satisfying level. Examples of your unique ability within veterinary medicine could range from aptitudes and passion for a specialized area, such as surgery or research, to a passion for herd health delivery to dairy clients in private practice. Using various assessment tools to identify and confirm your unique ability can help you as a new graduate to make confident career choices and identify preferred operating environments and working styles.

For practice owners, the largest budgetary expense is the compensation expense of their human resources, both veterinarians and staff. Viewed as an investment, veterinarians and staff offer the greatest opportunity to expand both revenues and profitability for employers. Indeed, long-term employment can generate immense satisfaction, revenue, and stability for both employees and employers. With recruitment as the start of the employer-employee relationship, the establishment of candid communication and understanding is beneficial to both parties in determining the fit of new employees within a practice setting. Hiring and retaining high-quality associates and technicians were identified in the "Best Methodologies" veterinarian interviews as key success factors;[2] however, most practices find this increasingly difficult. This chapter will attempt to describe the method of ensuring the right fit for employers and employees, including: why an investment in recruiting is warranted; what tools and services can make the process more objective and accurate; how they work; who exists as resources; and where to find them.

Superior Performer Versus Warm Body: An Employer Perspective

Variable performance in a job has an impact on both the top and bottom line of private veterinary practice. For the employer, recruiting superior performers produces top-line impact with increased client satisfaction, supporting higher fees and client loyalty. Recruiting for the right fit within a practice culture will result in reduced cost to hire, shorter time to full productivity, and increased longevity of new hires. The opportunity cost of employee turnover for a poor hire will run in the range of $12,000 to $15,000.

As the quality of potential candidates varies with a number of factors (e.g., the economy, location, workload, etc.) and as the time and cost of recruitment for both employer and employee can be significant, it is logical to make every effort in finding the right person for the job. The impact on the return-on-investment (ROI) for a superior performer versus just a "warm body" is substantial. Likewise, employees typically find increased satisfaction and motivation from positions in which they are well suited. Superior performance in veterinary practice typically increases customer satisfaction by increasing value perception.

Value, by definition, is "how much a product or service is worth to someone relative to other things, often measured in money." From a consumer perspective, the purchase of a good or service is interpreted as "good value" when the satisfaction with the purchase exceeds their expectations when compared to prepurchase expectations.[3] In veterinary practice, clients experience a number of determinant "moments of truth"—from face-to-face interaction, to telephone calls, to receiving an invoice. These "moments of truth" are episodes in which the client comes into contact with any aspect of the practice, however remote, and gets an impression of the quality of its service. The most obvious "moments of truth" in practice are the personal interactions between veterinarian-client and technician-client. Therefore, the right veterinarian plays a pivotal role in determining the client interpretation of value received. Happy, satisfied clients have the greatest receptivity to increased visits, new services, fee increases, and new products.

The professional element of veterinary medicine ensures basic skills and competency in the required areas of technical practice. This in itself is the commodity aspect of veterinary medicine. A clinic providing veterinary services is typically delivering a commodity "technical" service. Differentiation is determined by the quality of service delivery to the client. The single largest determinant of service delivery is the provider: veterinarians and staff.

What Makes for Effective Recruitment?

Private practices require an effective recruitment process to ensure the best-fit candidates are selected. While business metrics typically utilize various measures to evaluate the efficiency of hiring practices, veterinary clinics are increasingly focused on the time to hire and time to productivity. From a new graduate's perspective, then, attention to gaining experience and exhibiting independence and proficiency is increasingly valued.

The E-Myth of Veterinary Practice and Leveraging Outside Resources

Veterinarians fit the classic "E-Myth"[4]—the myth of the entrepreneur "suddenly stricken with an Entrepreneurial Seizure" in the assumption that "if you understand the technical work of a business, you understand a business that does technical work." As small business owners, most veterinarians have little or no training and/or experience in business management and strategic planning; this results in increased potential for missed opportunities, anxiety, and frustration.

In applying The Veterinary Lifestyle Experience[TM] process,[5] a key element of The SERVO Fitness Model[TM], the importance of personal preferences and managerial style of the owners is identified. Determination of personal and managerial styles provides important insight for operational system designs, work allocation, technology adaptation, and human resource management.

It is rare that a practice owner delegates the recruitment process to an outside talent recruitment firm, due to the typical 30% fee (of the first year's salary) and the lack of specialized recruiters familiar with veterinary medicine. As a result, most owners give up billable time to handle the details themselves. In either situation, the process traditionally involves advertising, developing a short list for interviews, interviewing, and a week in the practice for hands-on exposure. Shortfalls of this approach include poor interviewing skills and subjectivity on the part of the interviewer and the unintentional style adaptation of the candidate (i.e., interview candidates are on their best behaviour and unintentionally modify their responses and actions to put themselves in the best possible light). This increases the probability of a poor hire and the recruitment of a candidate that is a poor fit for the culture and expectations of the practice. Clear communication of expectations and requirements is the starting point for the practice owner and the applicant.

Value-Statement—the Position Description

A Position Description focuses a practice owner to ensure that they have a general Statement of Purpose for the position, detailed qualifications including any specific species or systems knowledge, prioritized Key Responsibility Areas (KRAs), and prioritized, specific activities required. The prioritized specific activities should provide an approximate percentage breakdown of time spent per week, including elements of appointments, surgery, emergency work, billing, medical records, and continuing education. The KRAs should clearly describe the three areas that set out the key functions of this position in the organization (using verbs, end result, and means). For example, an associate veterinarian KRA might include "maximize billing revenues through practice of veterinary medicine, both in daily billings and the long-term client relationship-building and new-client recruitment." The KRA purpose is to communicate functional responsibility while still providing the freedom for an associate veterinarian to use his or her initiative and creativity to achieve superior performance in this area.

Tools and Services for Effective Recruitment

As described earlier, benefits exist both for graduating veterinarians and practice owners to have a clear idea of the operational requirements of a job, from satisfaction and personal growth and from revenue growth/productivity to reduced employee turnover. With the advent of the industrial age, psychologists have developed profiling tools to segment people in order to increase the probabilities of success in job performance.

The Kolbe® Indices

Dr. Kathy Kolbe has developed a particularly powerful personality profile known as the Kolbe Index, which provides an interpretation of an individual's cognitive or striving instincts.[6] Kolbe spent 10 years researching the critical thinking and creative processes of gifted children. This work enabled her to identify the cognitive part of the mind, which is essential to decision-making and problem-solving and is our typical action pattern. She discovered that when people are free to act according to their own natural talents—and respect those of others—positive events begin to happen. Individuals become more effective and less stressed, teams perform better, relationships improve, and people stop forcing others to do things "their way." Unlike IQ tests, which tell you what you can do, and personality tests, which tell you what you want to do, Kolbe tells you what you will or won't do by measuring natural instincts.

The Kolbe® system can be very useful for identifying the strengths of individuals and aiding in the screening of applicants for new positions. We have used it in our office, and a number of our clients have found it very helpful. Kolbe's research has shown that people's natural creative instincts shape how they accomplish tasks and solve problems. Four basic action modes are seen: "Quick Starts" are innovators, who think on their feet; "Fact Finders" enjoy gathering information and becoming experts; "Follow Thrus" are natural organizers who complete tasks in a methodical way; "Implementers" figure things out by building models.

As with most personal assessment tools, there is no right or wrong answer, but rather an insight into differences between people's "modus operandi." Picture, for example, two partners who are constantly clashing with their associate veterinarian and can't figure out why. When their Kolbe results come back, it is discovered that the partners are primarily "Quick Starts"—big-picture people—while the associate veterinarian is primarily a detail-oriented "Fact Finder." To reduce conflict, the partners agree to start providing their associate with more detailed information.

The Kolbe indexes are the tools used to determine a person's unique combination of creative instincts and to put together groups of people who will perform successfully. Understanding one's natural instincts allows the job-seeker to look for the appropriate environment and culture. The Kolbe A Index measures a person's instinctive method of operation that allows him or her to be most productive. These same natural instincts will assist the employer in objectively assessing the likely fit of a recruitment candidate.

Myers-Briggs Personality Type Indicator®

The most widely known personality assessment, the Myers-Briggs Type Indicator (MBTI), is a self-assessment questionnaire designed to make Jung's theory of psychological types understandable and practical.[7,8] Results of the MBTI describe valuable differences between people—differences that can be the source of much misunderstanding and miscommunication. The MBTI tool assists in identifying an individual's strengths and unique gifts, in understanding individual differences, and uncovering new ways to work and interact with others. The MBTI "indicates the differences in people that result from:

1. Where they prefer to focus their attention (extraversion or introversion)
2. The way they prefer to take in information (sensing or intuition)
3. The way they prefer to make decisions (thinking or feeling)
4. How they orient themselves to the external world—whether they primarily use a Judging process or Perceiving process in relating to the outer world (Judging or Perceiving)"

As one uses his or her preferences in each of these areas, one tends to develop behaviours and attitudes characteristic of other people with those preferences. Again, there is no right or wrong to this assessment; rather, these preferences produce different kinds of people who are interested in different things and drawn to different fields. People with preferences different from yours tend to be opposite from you in many ways. Each type has its own strengths and blind spots.

The Myers-Briggs personality profile can be a powerful tool in determining your leadership impact, your cultural fit, and your operational style. When faced with working in the typical team environment of today's modern veterinary practice, the identification of MBTI types can provide direction in reducing friction and maximizing productivity.

The TriMetrix™ System

Industry is constantly looking for better ways to recruit the talent necessary to its success. Jobs and the specific talents of the people who fill them are the key building blocks of practice success. But what talents does a "job" require for excellent performance? Only the JOB has the answer, so let the job "talk," and listen carefully.

The TriMetrix™ System enables businesses to benchmark jobs and assess the talents they require for superior performance.[9] Job benchmarking, a process that hiring professionals use to identify potential top performers, is a new development made possible by the innovative TriMetrix™ System. Key people who are intimately familiar with a job answer a series of three scientifically developed surveys (Dr. Robert S. Hartman, with doctorates in philosophy and mathematics, developed the Attributes Index component of the TriMetrix™ and was nominated for a Nobel Prize for his work). The results are a crystal-clear, 22-page report of what the job requires in regard to talents, motivations, and behaviour. You will see your job from the inside out, including identification of the top 23 attributes (these are the same as talents, and this is out of a possible field of 80 attributes), six motivators, and eight behavioral traits.

Veterinary Business Management Services (VBMS), working in partnership with Steve Maloney, Newport Group Inc.,[10] has applied the TriMetrix System to two key revenue-generating positions within veterinary practices: Associate Veterinarian and Registered Veterinary Technician. Working with top veterinary practices in Canada, our research has produced the following list of "key accountabilities," which the practice owners describe as being the critical goals and key business successes the Associate Veterinarian position is accountable for producing (% of week):

1.   Quality veterinary medicine/surgery (60%)
2.   Communication with clients (20%)
3.   Staff coaching and supervision (10%)

4. Revenue generation, invoicing, records (5%)
5. Support and administration (5%)

When defined, they serve as a reference point in producing the TriMetrix Job Report, the benchmarks for associate veterinarians. This report provides a template for specific talent selection for the successful performance of that job. Based on a unique, 37-factor analysis, the TriMetrix Job Report lists the requirements of the job as three separate talent categories: 1) rewards/culture hierarchy (six areas clarifying "why" and "in what kind of environment" this job will produce success); 2) behavioural hierarchy (eight areas exploring the behavioural traits demanded of the job); and 3) job attributes (23 key job attributes and a quantification of their importance to the job). Each job has a unique ranking of attributes, reflecting different levels of capacities required by different positions for superior performance.

Research has proven that job-related talents are directly related to job satisfaction and personal performance. People are well positioned to achieve success when they are engaged in work suited to their inherent skills, behavioural style, and unique values. When the talent required by the job is clearly defined and, in turn, matched to the individual, everyone wins.

The VBMS-TriMetrix research composite of employers identified the job attributes (Table 1), the rewards/culture system (Table 2), and the behavioural traits (Table 3), which are most important to them in the position of Associate Veterinarian.

The VBMS-TriMetrix Associate Veterinarian Job Report provides a more detailed understanding of the job attributes required for superior performance. This is designed to coach employers and provide developmental activities for anyone recruited as an associate.

Job Interviews: Not Typically a Veterinary Skill

Most practice owners have little training or experience in interviewing, and they describe the process as a necessary evil that incurs an investment of billable hours and time. In an effort to increase the probability of recruiting superior performers, the VBMS-TriMetrix Associate Veterinarian Job Report provides employers with 60 suggested interview questions designed specifically to focus interviews on the key job performance attributes.

However, interviewers agree that the interview process is minimally effective at best. What is needed is an unbiased assessment that reveals people's VALUES that motivate them to do a job, the BEHAVIOURS they will bring to the job, and whether they have the specific talents—or ATTRIBUTES—

Table 1
Associate Veterinarian—Desirable Attributes

1. Self management
2. Customer focus
3. Personal accountability
4. Teamwork
5. Results orientation
6. Problem solving
7. Planning and organization
8. Diplomacy and tact
9. Flexibility
10. Interpersonal skills

Table 2
Desirable Bevioural Traits of Associate Veterinarian

1. Customer-oriented
2. Frequent interaction with others
3. Versatility

Table 3
Rewards/Culture Required by the Job

1. Theoretical (a passion to discover, systematize, and analyze; a search for knowledge)
2. Utilitarian/economic (a passion to gain return on investment of time, resources, and money)
3. Aesthetic (a passion to achieve self-actualization, balance, and harmony in one's own life)

needed for the job. The VBMS-TriMetrix™ Personal Talent Report for Associate Veterinarians provides a summary of a candidate's talent to match the identical areas outlined in the VBMS-TriMetrix Associate Veterinarian Job Report.

Within the framework of a clinic's overall selection and development processes, this report reveals the WHY (values, motivators), HOW (behaviours), and WHAT (attributes, personal skills) an individual can contribute to the job. This convenient, online approach developed by VBMS and the Newport Group, enables North American veterinary clinics to replace common biases often involved in the selection process with factual data based on JOB REQUIREMENTS. Utilizing the job benchmarking capabilities of the VBMS-TriMetrix Associate Veterinarian Job Report and the results of the VBMS-TriMetrix Personal Talent Report of the candidate(s), VBMS provides hiring recommendations to clients prior to hiring decisions being made.

Case Study: TriMetrix Reveals a Bad Hire

The Newport Group has experience utilizing the TriMetrix System in numerous industries. The following example illustrates the value of the job benchmarking approach in the recruiting process, indicating the importance of using the three dimensions of motivators, behaviours, and personal skills (commonly known as the why, how, and what of people's actions) when considering a candidate for hire. The Kolbe Indices and Myers Briggs assessments lack this capability.

In February 2005, a major Newport client was looking for a Sales Director. Key accountabilities included management of sales force, servicing existing national corporate accounts, and targeting new multi-national accounts. After interviewing several candidates and spending much time, money, and energy, the company thought they had found the perfect candidate and offered the applicant the job. The position paid roughly $85,000 in salary, and the package also included commissions and bonuses, a car allowance, and a benefit program. After the offer and acceptance process, the company had the applicant complete Newport's Personal Talent Report, which measures applicants in 37 key areas that are broken down into 23 personal attributes, six personal interests and workplace motivators, and eight behavioural traits. A review of the "Bad Fit Sample" below illustrates these findings.

The Good:

- The candidate matched up very well with the usual top three Personal Interests, Attitudes, and Values (Workplace Motivators). Utilitarian/ Economic, Theoretical, and Individualistic/Political are the top three motivators of most sales executives. These answered the "why" question for the hiring committee.

- The applicant scored very high on the behavioural characteristics of Competitiveness, Urgency, and Frequent Change. Most people and hiring committees would be attracted to these traits when interviewing a candidate for a senior sales position, and they would erroneously assume that these would be the appropriate behaviours for "how" the job should be done.
The applicant had all the hard skills and work experience, interviewed well, and projected an air of self-confidence.

The Bad:

- The applicant's personal scores fell well below and to the left of the bar graphs that are shaded (representing 68% of the general population). What this means is that this applicant falls in the bottom 16% of the general population in 17 of 23 key attribute and personal skill areas.
- Key accountabilities of the job included managing sales force, servicing existing customers, and retaining new major accounts. However, the applicant was in the bottom 16% in such attributes as developing and leading others, interpersonal skills, customer focus, self-starting, influencing others, goal achievement, and self-management.
- The applicant's internal factors, such as role awareness and self-direction, were well below the national mean. This person did not have a realistic evaluation of him/herself.
- Low scores on almost half of the attributes on the Core Attribute List revealed that the candidate had a poor understanding of these skills.

Conclusions and Consequences

- Employee was dismissed in July 2005.
- Company was spared the usual 30% recruitment charge in this case, but was out $4,000 in job advertising costs.
- The company was out $28,000 in direct salary costs.
- Company lost goodwill when clients called in to complain.
- Company lost some sales representatives, as they found working with the new Sales Director difficult.
- Even though the Talent Report was filled out too late, had the company not filled it out, this bad hire would have been filed under the win some/lose some category.
- Company wasted time, money, and energy and lost five of its best cyclical sales months because of a preventable bad hire.

Know Your Strengths and Weaknesses

The average graduate hopes his/her strengths and talents are obvious to potential employers reading a resume; but increasingly, most employment decisions are based on face-to-face communications supported by cultural fit and assessment comparisons. Being able to communicate your talents in an interview can be the difference between obtaining and not obtaining a position. The VBMS-TriMetrix™ assessments give insight to personal strengths and talents and therefore help candidates express them more clearly and convincingly in interview situations.

Available Resources

For a graduating veterinarian, the investment in a number of these personal assessment tools will pay dividends in job satisfaction and career development. Communication skills, leadership development, and self-understanding play a major role in achieving superior job performance.

The Myers-Briggs Type Indicator (the cognitive assessment that identifies how you take in information and organize and process that information to make decisions) and the Kolbe Indices (the cognitive assessment of your striving instincts) can be accessed online at less than $100 each.

The VBMS-TriMetrix Associate Veterinarian Job Report/Benchmarks, including the full description of desired attributes, rewards/culture system, and behavioural traits—as well as 60 interview questions and the VBMS-TriMetrix Personal Talent Reports, can be purchased online.

While the Internet has made many of the personal assessment tools available, one needs to keep in mind that the true value of these assessments is in the interpretation and integration of the results.

Summary: A Positive Return-on-Investment

In this chapter, we have illustrated that superior performance of associate veterinarians impacts the revenue growth of private veterinary practice. High performers generate up to 67% more in revenues than average performers. Superior performers have been benchmarked by VBMS to include those motivated by specific values and those having specific behavioural attributes and talents; they can be objectively selected with the VBMS-TriMetrix Associate Veterinarian Job Report.

Due to the opportunity costs of employee turnover (more than $15,000), the financial impact of making a "good hire" (40% to 67% greater productivity), and the inherent lack of recruiting expertise by veterinarians, the use of job benchmarking ($1,500 to $6,000) and recruiting assessment is a wise investment when recruiting associates.

References

1. *Unique Ability: Creating the Life You Want.* Nomura C, Waller J The Strategic Coach, Toronto, ON; 2003.
2. Arthur Anderson Consulting. The Best Business Methodologies Report – OVMA/AVMA. January, 1999:24-27.
3. Bolton RN, Drew JH. A multistage model of customers' assessments of service quality and value. J Cons Res 1991;17:375-384.
4. *The E-Myth Revisited.* 1st Edition. Gerber ME. HarperCollins Publisher, New York, NY; 1995.
5. Woolnough M. The Veterinary Lifestyle Experience.™ Veterinary Business Management Services 1998. www.veterinarybusinessmanagementservices.com
6. *Pure Instinct.* Kolbe K. Random House Inc, New York, NY; 1993.
7. *Introduction to Type.*® 5th Edition. Briggs Myers I. Consulting Psychologists' Press Inc., Palo Alto, CA; 1993.
8. *Memories, Dreams and Reflections.* Jungs C. Pantheon Books, New York, NY; 1989.
9. *If I Knew Then What I Know Now.* Bonnstetter BJ. Forbes Publishing, New York, NY; 1999.
10. Maloney S. Newport Group Inc, Burlington, ON; 2005. www.newportgroup.ca

Biography

With a degree in Wildlife Biology (University of Guelph, 1982), Mark Woolnough was exposed to the entrepreneurial style and speed of small environmental consultants in the Yukon and Northwest Territories, and the lengthy bureaucratic processes of Alberta Fish and Wildlife. In 1983, Mark joined the multinational pharmaceutical firm Boehringer Ingelheim Inc., playing a major leadership role in the marketing and operational success of management teams in Canada, the United Kingdom, and the United States.

In 1995, Mark worked closely with the forensic accounting and services marketing faculty in the completion of his MBA (Wilfred Laurier University, 1995). Focusing on the organizational and revenue challenges of large animal and mixed veterinary practices of southwestern Ontario, Mark developed "The Veterinary Lifestyle Experience™"—a unique, evolutionary business coaching and leadership process for veterinarians. Mark confirmed the need and interest for veterinary business services in 1996 through a series of veterinary seminars with more than 50 practices. Entitled "Expanding Your Competitive Strategy: Differentiation-vs-Low Cost – Marketing Development Through Leadership & Service/Product Differentiation", these seminars attracted the attention of the Ontario Veterinary Medical Association (OVMA) Large Animal Issues Committee.

In 1997, Mark was recognized by Dr. Paul Dick, OVMA President, on behalf of the OVMA Board, Executive Committee, and Large Animal Issues Committee for his work in creating the "Reducing Price Sensitivity Through Improved Perceptions of Value: A Benefits-Oriented Public Relations Project and Veterinary Service Development Program," stimulating the OVMA to take action toward helping the large animal veterinarians of Ontario.

Focused on providing clarity and definition, removing complexities, and simplifying challenges, Mark is a certified Kolbe® Coach and an eight-year veteran of The Strategic Coach® program. Productivity services include recruitment of superior associates and staff through The VBMS-Recruitment System and the benefits of proven organizational alignment with Franklin Covey training.

Section 4

ACQUIRING WEALTH:

Financial Planning for Tomorrow and the Future

Introduction

Leaving school and entering the workplace is a milestone for anyone. It's a time that's filled with possibilities – and decisions. As a veterinarian, where do you want to live and work? What kind of practice do you want? How do you see your career shaping up?

Relax, you don't have to have all the answers right now. Few people have a set roadmap for their life. Almost certainly, there will be detours. The hopes and dreams you have for yourself professionally as well as personally – things like home, family and lifestyle – can evolve over time. But one thing is for sure – your ambitions come with financial considerations.

The more you know about yourself and what you want from life, the better able you are to make the financial decisions that support your goals.

Here's the good news. After investing significantly in your education, including four years studying veterinary medicine, you don't need a financial degree to make sense of your financial future. What is important is an understanding of how to manage your finances so that you can set yourself up to achieve your professional and personal goals.

The chapters in this section give you a sense of some key points for consideration that you will need to plan for over the next couple of years – financial planning, tax management, your income and investments, employment compensation and contracts, insurance, owning a practice and managing debt, and developing your banking relationship. The information here offers solid guidelines and a context for decision making. It also provides the grounding you need to ask the right questions of the financial experts.

Part of learning more about financial matters, and making the most beneficial financial moves, is having the right advisors to lean on.

At any phase of your career, perhaps especially at this early stage, it's wise to seek out and nurture relationships with bankers, accountants, insurance advisors and lawyers – experienced and knowledgeable people who can help you navigate through your financial options.

You have studied hard to reach this point in your life. You want to put yourself in a position where you can devote your time and energy to your passion, caring for animals, and to tending to your professional development and personal goals. By starting to think about how finances fit into your plans, you can help ensure that you'll make those plans a reality. I wish you all the best during this exciting period of your career.

Mike Feaver BA (Economics), MBA
National Manager, Health Care Professionals
RBC Royal Bank®, Toronto, Ontario

Mike Feaver's banking career spans 15 years as a Commercial Account Manager and VP Commercial Banking. As National Manager, Health Care Professionals for RBC Royal Bank, he is responsible for supporting the bank's service to doctors, dentists and veterinarians.

Mr. Feaver supports a team of account managers across Canada who are experts in serving the needs of veterinarians:

Ryan Quick, Atlantic Canada, ryan.quick@rbc.com
Diem Nguyen, Quebec, diem.n.nguyen@rbc.com
Michael Nimeh, Ontario North East, michael.nimeh@rbc.com
Marianne Dilello, Ontario South West, marianne.dilello@rbc.com
Shannon Mahon, Greater Toronto Region,
    shannon.mahon@rbc.com (905)-858-8692
Dean Prosky, Manitoba/Saskatchewan, dean.prosky@rbc.com
Todd Van der Loos, Alberta, todd.vanderloos@rbc.com
Emily Kerr, British Columbia, emily.kerr@rbc.com

To locate an RBC® Health Care Professionals specialist, please visit www.rbcroyalbank.com/health-care-prof

Planning for Financial Life Stages

John Tait, BSc, DVM, MBA, CFP, ADR
Managing Partner, Ontario Veterinary Group,
Toronto, Ontario
Assistant Professor, Ontario Veterinary College,
Guelph, Ontario

> *To expect life to be tailored to our expectations*
> *is to invite frustration.*
>
> *—Anon*

As professionals, we move through a series of "life cycle" stages from the time we graduate to the time of our retirement. This time period commonly consists of five stages, as outlined in Figure 1 below, with differing financial needs and priorities relevant to each stage.

Veterinarians in practice progress through a pathway that often includes early career debt from their education, additional debt as they enter into practice ownership, a parallel escalation in their earnings and equity-based wealth, followed by later career diversification as they transition out of practice ownership into their retirement years. The financial stressors encountered may never totally go away; however, they usually change and evolve. tice ownership, a parallel escalation in their earnings and equity-based wealth, followed by later career diversification as they transition out of practice ownership into their retirement years. The financial stressors encountered may never totally go away; however, they usually change and evolve.

Early in a career, the veterinarian commonly has questions surrounding such financial concerns. How do I manage my student debt and other debts I plan to take on? How will my income change and grow? How can I find money and time to do the things I enjoy in life? Can I afford to buy a practice? Can I afford not to buy one? How do I go about the financial assessment to buy a practice at a reasonable price, and how do I transition into ownership? How do I build my wealth portfolio?

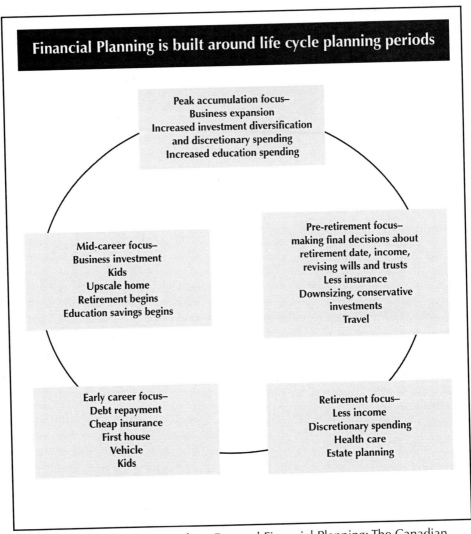

Financial Planning is built around life cycle planning periods

Peak accumulation focus–
Business expansion
Increased investment diversification
and discretionary spending
Increased education spending

Pre-retirement focus–
making final decisions about
retirement date, income,
revising wills and trusts
Less insurance
Downsizing, conservative
investments
Travel

Mid-career focus–
Business investment
Kids
Upscale home
Retirement begins
Education savings begins

Early career focus–
Debt repayment
Cheap insurance
First house
Vehicle
Kids

Retirement focus–
Less income
Discretionary spending
Health care
Estate planning

Figure 1—Financial life stages (from Personal Financial Planning: The Canadian Institute of Financial Planning; 1998)

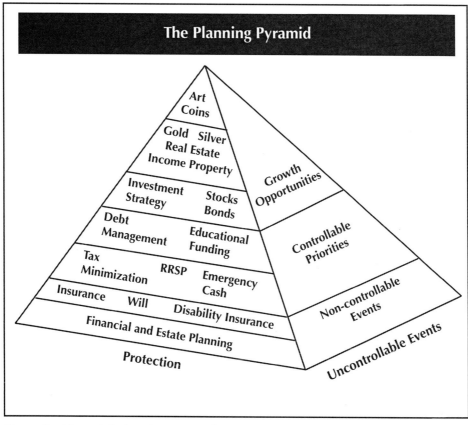

Figure 2—Financial planning pyramid.

As soon as possible, you as a new graduate or associate veterinarian should seek to establish or create a balanced financial plan that not only considers the life-cycle stage you are currently in but addresses the stages to come. Not having a balanced financial plan can have numerous negative implications, including an inefficient use of your resources, paying too much tax, failing to meet your financial objectives, not being prepared for retirement, and not anticipating a sudden downturn in the economy. Therefore, a financial plan, by definition, is the tool that will facilitate management of your career life stages and be an instrument that assesses your financial situation and identifies resources, vehicles, products, and tools to further facilitate efficiency and effectiveness in financial planning. In summary, you need a financial plan because:

1. It helps identify short- and long-term personal financial goals, business investment goals, and personal investment goals, and it provides recommendations for the most effective ways to reach those goals.

2. It assesses your risk tolerance with respect to investments.
3. It provides you with protection in case you are injured or disabled.
4. It can assist you in creating optimum employment conditions.

A balanced financial plan includes three broad categories: protecting your income, living off your income, and growing your income. Building a financial plan is analogous to building the pyramid on the previous page, starting at the foundation and moving toward the top.

Protecting Your Income

Protecting your income involves planning for unforeseen events, and these are best protected against by insurance. There are many different types of insurance, including:

- Life
- Disability
- Liability
- Critical Illness
- Travel
- Health
- Partners
- Business Overhead
- Mortgage

The mix of insurance an individual chooses depends on individual needs. Most critical for newer graduates (especially with dependents) is life insurance, and for associates in any situation, disability insurance represents the most important type of insurance to have in place. Veterinarians thinking of buying practices will have great difficulty being able to obtain debt financing without disability insurance. The odds of at least one in 100 veterinarians being disabled for a period longer than six months is nearly 100%, and unless the resources are immediately available to replace your income, personal disability insurance will act as a source of tax-free monies coming in that will replace your income. The odds of becoming disabled are higher the younger you are; however, the premiums are lower the younger you are when you start disability insurance.

Numerous features or options are available with disability insurance policies. As salaries of veterinarians escalate, it is possible to secure additional coverage with a "future insurance option" that does not necessitate repeating medical screening.

Talk to your insurance or financial advisor to determine what insurance coverage is most appropriate for your needs.

Living Off Your Income

Living off your income means balancing your current lifestyle needs with managing debt and setting aside something for future spending, including children's education, investment in a practice, or your own retirement.

Planning or budgeting to live off your income is based first on an understanding of your current financial situation, then a determination of what risk tolerance you have, and, finally, what your objectives are prior to setting a strategy and developing a budget to fit that strategy. Objectives may include paying off debt quickly, short-term cash for investments, long-term investment security, or maximizing retirement funds.

Determining where you are financially and setting a budget can be done with the aid of simple tables (examples on the pages that follow) that can be updated periodically. These tables aid in assessing your individual net worth, how much you own above and beyond what you owe, or vice versa. The ratio of debts to liabilities will affect your ability to borrow money and have implications for your cash flow, budgeting, lifestyle, future needs, and even retirement planning.

Funds from current income sources can be allocated to various priorities and sources of debt, especially when indebtedness is high. Most financial planners will recommend an allocation of current income to maximize the creation of wealth and simultaneous reduction in debt, while maintaining a reasonable lifestyle (such that approximately 65% of after-tax income is used for current living expenses, 25% for debt repayment, and 10% for investment purposes). Risk and psychology always play a role in an individual's ability to deal with debt and the choice of an investment portfolio. The table below illustrates a working budget template to assess whether period cash flows are positive or negative. However, it is somewhat of a moving target with time. For example, if debt obligations chew up more than 25% of after-tax income and there is no opportunity to defer or reorganize this debt, then lifestyle expenditures and/or investment opportunities must be delayed in order to accommodate mandatory debt repayments.

Incomes among associates typically rise to a point where practice owners cannot justify further increases in compensation, as the owner's own return on investment becomes progressively reduced. Industry benchmarks, established over a decade ago and based on the ideal allocation of each dollar coming into the practice, indicate that today's associates in companion animal practice generally should receive total compensation (salary and benefits) of up to 25% of the gross income they generate for professional services. As associate incomes evolve to more production-based and less time- and effort-based "guaranteed" compensation plans, personal financial budgets and allocations of current income can carry with them more risk. Portfolios and financial plans should, therefore, incorporate a periodic review to reduce uncertainly, and reassess and review "ideal" portfolios for investment, debt management plans, and general risk. While production-based compensation may carry with it more risk, industry data supports the conclusion that associate compensation is higher.[1]

Growing Your Income

Part of a balanced financial plan is investing and preparing for the future. Investing involves both short- and long-term investments and also assesses risk, age, and objectives. A number of financial instruments exist, depending on your tolerance for risk and your investment time frame. The various financial instruments combine to make up the financial portfolio, and preferred financial portfolios exist to maximize return and align with the stage of your career life cycle. Regardless of the financial portfolio chosen, uncertainty is a fact of any investment strategy. Specific investment tools also exist for well-defined goals and individual time frames, including retirement savings instruments and educational funding.

One of the largest purchases or investments you will make as a veterinarian is a practice. The effects of supply and demand have reduced practice sale prices in the last decade for all types of practices. Practices can be assigned a fair market value through one or a combination of evaluation techniques. Practices can be evaluated in both the relative and absolute marketplace. Buyers can afford to be more selective, and, as a result of lower prices, can and should eliminate their debt load for the practice within five years. Depending on the transition model, objective information (particularly regarding the suggested fair market value) is very important to arrive at a price and justify financing. The purchase of a practice involves a series of transition stages, including the negotiation phase, inheritance phase, succession phase, and retirement phase. Agreed-upon purchase prices, or values of practices arrived at objectively, should be reconciled through the use of financial projections that reflect various performance scenarios for the practice and also take into consideration the debt load and new salary of the purchaser.

Table 1
An Example of a Personal Assets and Liabilities Balance Sheet

ASSETS $			
Cash equivalents		**Retirement Funds**	
Checking accounts	_____	Pension (present	
Savings accounts	_____	lump sum)	_____
Money market		Employee savings	
accounts	_____	plans	_____
Money market			
fund accounts	_____	**Total**	_____
Certificates of			
deposit	_____	**Personal Assets**	
Cash value of		Principal residence	_____
life insurance	_____	Second residence	_____
		Collectibles/art	
Total _____		antiques	_____
		Automobiles	_____
Investments		Home furnishings	_____
Stocks	_____	Furs and jewelry	_____
Bonds	_____	Other assets	_____
Mutual fund			
investments	_____	**Total**	_____
Partnership interests	_____		
Other investments	_____		
Total	_____	**TOTAL ASSETS**	_____

Table 1 (continued)
An Example of a Personal Assets and Liabilities Balance Sheet

LIABILITIES $

Charge account balances	_____	Home mortgages	_____
Personal loans	_____	Home equity loans	_____
Student loans	_____	Alimony	_____
Auto loans	_____	Child support	_____
RRSP loans	_____	Life insurance policy loans	_____
Investment loans (margin, real estate, etc.)	_____	Projected income tax liability	_____
		Other liabilities	_____
		TOTAL LIABILITIES	_____

TOTAL ASSETS - TOTAL LIABILITIES = NET WORTH

Table 2
An Example of a Personal Cash Flow Work Sheet

INCOME	MONTHLY	ANNUAL
Salary	_____	_____
Bonuses	_____	_____
Self-employment income	_____	_____
Dividends	_____	_____
Capital gains	_____	_____
Interest	_____	_____
Net rents and royalties	_____	_____
Pension distributions from trusts or partnerships	_____	_____
Other income	_____	_____
TOTAL INCOME	_____	_____
EXPENSES		
Home mortgage (or apartment rent)	_____	_____
Utility payments:		
Gas/oil	_____	_____
Electricity	_____	_____
Water	_____	_____
Sewer	_____	_____
Home maintenance	_____	_____
Property taxes	_____	_____
Car payments	_____	_____
Car/commuting expenses		
Maintenance & repairs	_____	_____
Gas	_____	_____
Commuting fees/tolls	_____	_____
Credit card/loan payments	_____	_____

Table 2 (continued)
An Example of a Personal Cash Flow Work Sheet

EXPENSES (continued)	MONTHLY	ANNUAL
Income taxes	_____	_____
Employment taxes	_____	_____
Insurance premiums		
Life	_____	_____
Health	_____	_____
Disability	_____	_____
Car	_____	_____
Home	_____	_____
Liabilities	_____	_____
Other	_____	_____
Clothing	_____	_____
Child care	_____	_____
Food	_____	_____
Medical expenses	_____	_____
Education	_____	_____
Vacations	_____	_____
Entertainment	_____	_____
Alimony	_____	_____
Charitable contributions	_____	_____
Gifts	_____	_____
Personal items	_____	_____
Savings/investment		
Vacation fund	_____	_____
Emergency fund	_____	_____
Investment fund	_____	_____
Other	_____	_____
Other payments	_____	_____
TOTAL EXPENSES	_____	_____
TOTAL INCOME	_____	_____
NET CASH FLOW (OUTFLOW)	_____	_____

The maximization of wealth through an equity position in a practice has several advantages, including no short-term or immediate tax consequences upon purchase and, as the practice grows, a typically higher annual income than can be realized as an associate. Purchasing a practice is a prudent investment, given a reasonable purchase price. A debt figure that appears high shouldn't be a scary sight, as long as there is a corresponding high figure coming back the other way in net or owner's income. After purchase, growth in your practice's equity position occurs mainly through your own "sweat equity" or work, and progression out of the early career life stages and a reduction in debt also results in an increase in discretionary income available.

Efficient monitoring of your business's productivity and value helps position even a new practice owner for further capital reinvestment, diversification of part or all of the business, shifts in risk or allocation in your current portfolio, and tracking progress toward future goals. Industry benchmarks help provide realistic growth and efficiency goals, and practice management assistance will help in achieving those goals.

Summary

A financial plan is a dynamic, changing plan meant to make possible maximum outcomes in your career decision-making. Astute allocation of your funds and regular monitoring of your financial health at the inception of your career will facilitate wealth building.

References

1. OVMA Report, Compensation and Benefits for Associate Veterinarians; 2006.

Additional Recommended Reading

Building the Successful Veterinary Practice, Volume 1,2,3. Catanzaro T. Iowa State University Press; 1998.
Total Business Planning: A Step-by-Step Guide. Burton E, McBride W. John Wiley & Sons, New York, NY; 1999.

Biography

For Dr. Tait's biography, please see the Section 1 Introduction on page 3.

Debt and Debt Management

John Tait, BSc, DVM, MBA, CFP, ADR
Managing Partner, Ontario Veterinary Group,
Toronto, Ontario
Assistant Professor, Ontario Veterinary College,
Guelph, Ontario

> *Worry is interest paid on trouble before it comes due.*
>
> *—William Randolph Inge*

If you have debt and a negative personal net worth, join the crowd. The average Canadian does not have a positive net worth until he or she reaches age 50, according to the Canadian Institute of Financial Planning. A balanced financial plan, therefore, will include an allocation of income toward debt management. The rule of thumb for financial planners is to allocate 25% of after-tax income toward debt, 65% toward lifestyle and living expenses, and 10% toward investments and future growth.

While these allocations look balanced on paper, in real life, veterinarians (like other professionals) can be over-burdened by debt. Debt obligations may chew up more than 25% of their disposable income. How you manage your debt is largely influenced by risk tolerance and psychology. If you are an individual who simply cannot deal with the burden of debt of any sort, your risk profile developed by your financial planner when creating a plan will illustrate this, and your financial plan and allocation of income will be prioritized toward paying off debt first. However, if you are only marginally concerned about debt, then your income may be allocated toward making only minimal payments on your debt obligations, while more income is allocated to investments and lifestyle expenditures.

Although everyone would like to be debt free, some debts are considered "good debts" while others are "bad debts." Real estate and business investments (e.g., practice ownership that provides an equity position that grows tax free, with potential tax liabilities only materializing once the practice is sold) are considered good debts. Any item that is guaranteed to appreciate in value is also a good debt. Bad debts include quickly depreciating items such as expensive cars, consumer loans, automobile leases where no tax advantage exists, and borrowing for high-risk investments.

While there is no simple way to just "eliminate" debt other than paying it off as soon as possible, there are some basic rules of debt management that facilitate both a quick repayment of debt and a rationale for assuming additional debt. Debt should be assumed for only what you need—not in excess of what you need to create a "buffer"—as that buffer (i.e., over borrowing without a specific need for all of the money received) will have the burden of interest and provide no return. Borrowing or using credit for day-to-day purchases is a symptom of an individual who cannot meet lifestyle expenditures through income. You should constantly track your debt to be assured that debt payments are serviced by your cash flow. Paying off debt as quickly as is feasible lowers the associated interest and administrative fees. Many easy-to-use commercial packages provide accurate and timely tracking of debt and are worthwhile monitoring tools.

Debt financiers (e.g., banks) are also aware of the reasonable amount of debt that an individual can hold. These financiers often employ a ratio referred to as the "TDSR," or total debt servicing ratio, which reflects the percentage of annual income allocated to total debt repayments over any given time period. If this ratio nears or exceeds 30% of income, a financier may view a potential borrower as "over-debted" and consider them a risky venture. Self-diagnosis of debt is possible as well. If you use credit cards for smaller or day-to-day purchases, live from paycheck to paycheck, have no access to credit or any reserve funds, have no savings, and make only minimum payments on items you've purchased with credit, you are likely overdebted.

Tactics to manage debt include prioritizing debt repayments. The key to ranking debts is to compare the carrying costs of a loan, or to determine what it costs to pay a loan off when you include the costs of "carrying" a debt. Those costs may include interest, administrative and account fees, management fees on investments, and commissions, among others. Note, some interest may represent an expense that is tax-deductible. The interest rate to use when comparing debts is the "effective" interest rate, which is the interest rate adjusted to reflect the impact of any tax savings. As an example, if you borrow $10,000 at an interest rate of 7% per year that is non-tax deductible you are paying $700 in interest per year. If the interest was tax deductible and you are in a 40% tax bracket, your taxable income (the figure your tax calculations are based on), or what is leftover after you deduct all your expenses of which interest in this case would be an expense, is reduced by the $700. In this case, you would save the tax, which equates to 40% of $700, or $280. The "effective" interest rate then is (700-280)/10,000 x100= 4.2% as apposed to 7% where interest is not tax deductible.

When prioritizing debts, credit cards should be the first to be paid. The interest wheel spins away constantly on these, and, if possible, credit card balances should not be carried over from one billing cycle to another. Next in line for debt repayment should be any debts that are not tax advantaged (i.e., where there is no tax-deductible component for the interest); examples include demand loans for cars and consumer items, and lines of credit for personal use. Next in the priority sequence should be debts that are tax advantaged. Business loans where interest is tax deductible and a capital cost allowance or depreciation expense on the assets purchased would fall into this category. Finally, debts that have a tax credit would be ranked as last to pay off.

Strategies for an over-debted individual or business can be designed to relieve negative impacts if the outflow of cash is greater than the inflow of cash over a specified time period. Variables to address include the effective interest rate or rates, the time period of the loan, bank or monitoring/reporting fees involved, and the use of tax or employment arrangements (e.g., employee versus self-employed/contractor) to increase after-tax income.

Consolidating loans (i.e., rolling multiple debts or loans into one combined loan) can often simplify the repayment options, terms, and interest rate, and make management of debt more streamlined. This may mean taking out a new loan and using the proceeds of the loan to pay off existing balances on the older loans. Lower interest rates may be attainable, as lenders often use other personal assets as security against a consolidation loan. Using these personal assets (e.g., real estate, other appreciating personal assets) makes the consolidation loan appear less risky in the eyes of the debt financier. Cosigners can also make a consolidation loan appear less risky; however, the cosigner is now partially liable if your loan is in default. Private companies that act in a bridging function to banks may be able to assist with loans; however, proper due diligence should be conducted in reviewing the total carrying cost of using such a facility.

Like you, banks are not eager to see their loans become defaulted. Besides the time and cost of dealing with bankruptcy or receivership proceedings, the banks never receive the total amount of any defaulted loan. They are willing to collaborate (to a point) with an individual's efforts in solving cash-flow problems. Declaring bankruptcy and its subsequent consequence of eliminating outstanding debts is not recommended because of the negative impact of having your income managed for you and being unable to access any credit for years to come.

A good budget that monitors income and expenses on a "cash in/cash out" basis is an excellent tool for factoring in debt, assessing and adjusting debt payments and allocation of debt payments, and determining potential for further debt. While business plans and analysis of your cash flow are important determinants of acquiring funds and taking on further debt, other factors considered by debt financiers are your credit rating, available collateral, and amount of personal capital contributed.

While debt is often needed for advancement of wealth accumulation, if mismanaged, it can have serious and deleterious consequences on your overall health and financial well being. Be sure to carefully use your financial planner and other resources to create an effective debt-management strategy.

Additional Recommended Reading

The A, B, Cs of Getting Out of Debt. Sutton G. Warner Books; 2004.

Biography

For Dr. Tait's biography, please see the Section 1 Introduction on page 3.

Tax Management and Employment Compensation Strategies

Andrew Shalit, CA
Principal, Tax Department, Segal LLP Chartered
Accountants,
Guelph, Ontario

John Tait, BSc, DVM, MBA, CFP, ADR
Managing Partner, Ontario Veterinary Group,
Toronto, Ontario
Assistant Professor, Ontario Veterinary College,
Guelph, Ontario

> *Satisfaction comes in three ways. One kind is creating something,*
> *one is being paid for it, and the other is the feeling that I*
> *just haven't been sitting on my ass all afternoon.*
>
> —William F. Buckley

Introduction

Throughout your professional career you will encounter many challenges. This chapter will assist you in dealing with some of the taxation challenges that lie ahead. It will provide you with an understanding of the differences between choosing to be an employee and being self-employed, such as the ability of employees versus self-employed professionals to deduct expenses incurred for business purposes. A detailed analysis of the way in which self-employed professionals can carry on their business is explained. Various tax issues relating to the veterinary professional are addressed, including the tax treatment of unused tax credits and fringe benefits. Suggestions for the selection of an appropriate professional accountant are provided, as well as supplementary reference material and useful resources.

Employee Versus Independent Contractor

As you progress through your career, you will be faced with the decision of whether you wish to work for someone or whether you will work for yourself. If you work for someone else, you must decide if it will be as an employee or as an independent contractor. If you decide to be an independent contractor, you will have to decide on the form of business that you wish to undertake.

Due to tax-related restrictions imposed upon an employee's ability to deduct expenses, many members of the labour force prefer to carry out their duties as independent contractors. Independent contractors can deduct a wide range of expenses, so long as they are incurred for the purpose of earning income. Employees, on the other hand, can claim only certain deductions for employment-related expenses. In order for expenses to be claimed as a deduction from employment, the employer must certify on a prescribed tax form (T2200) that the expenses were a necessary condition of employment. Typically, employees only may deduct travelling expenses (including parking, taxis, and transit fares), automobile costs (subject to certain restrictions), supplies, salaries paid to assistants, and home-office expenses (in limited circumstances). In order to deduct home-office expenses, you must be required under your employment contract to maintain an office in your home. In addition, the home office must be the place where you principally perform the duties of employment, or you must use it on a regular and continuous basis for meeting people in the ordinary course of your employment. Dues paid to maintain your professional status also are deductible by employees, as are union dues. Therefore, fees and dues for most veterinary organizations are tax deductible; however, if the dues are paid to a voluntary organization they are not deductible by the employee. Moving costs to start working at a different location or to start a business may be deducted by an employee if the new home is at least 40 km closer to that location. If your employer reimburses specific moving costs, you cannot claim them as a deduction.

Employers may have a bias to engage your services as an independent contractor. In so doing, the employer may not be obligated to pay wage levies associated with Employment Insurance, Canada Pension Plan, and provincial employment standards legislation and may avoid certain legal obligations, such as severance payments. Independent contractors may not be eligible for maternity leave benefits and they should consider their status carefully.

No single determining factor indicates whether a worker is an employee or an independent contractor; however, certain key elements or criteria in an engagement arrangement with the practice must be included in a written contract. A written contract outlining the terms agreed upon by the practice and independent contractor is the document of reference, in case of audit, and should be considered a critical supporting piece to hold up self-employed status. Some of the determining factors include references to who controls key terms of engagement. If the contract or arrangement shows the employer controls such factors as hours and payment of benefits, the relationship is deemed more an employee-employer relationship. Such criteria as determination of hours of work, relationship of practice income to hours, payment of salary or hourly wages without reference to the worker's performance, amount of control and supervision by the employer, source of payment of benefits, duration of the contract, ownership of tools, and ability to hire own staff will influence interpretation of the engagement arrangement. While not all of these criteria must be met to support a determination of self-employed status, the underlying theme is that the independent contractor must have some control and influence over the terms of his or her relationship with the practice.

Deductible Expenses for Independent Contractors

Should you decide to be self-employed, the same rules apply regarding deductible expenses, whether you join a partnership or form a corporation. In all cases, proper records, receipts, and documentation must be retained to justify the amounts claimed. The following types of expenses may be deducted for income-tax purposes:

- Annual dues paid to professional associations are deductible.
- Rent paid for business premises is deductible.

- Office maintenance costs and carrying charges on business premises are deductible (e.g., property taxes, electricity, insurance, repairs, and mortgage interest). If you use a portion of your house for business purposes, you can claim the applicable portion of the maintenance and carrying charges.
- Salaries paid to assistants are deductible.
- Contributions to pension plans and various group-benefit plans are deductible.
- Fees paid to professional advisers or consultants are deductible.
- Telecommunication, postage, stationery, and office expenses are deductible.
- Property insurance and insurance against lost revenue (e.g., malpractice insurance) is deductible.
- The cost of a professional library is not deductible; however, depreciation on the cost of the library is permitted as a deduction. Professional periodicals and library books purchased individually are deductible, as are professional library fees.
- Travel costs are deductible and automobile-operating costs may be deducted, if used for business purposes; however, restrictions exist on deducting depreciation, interest, and lease costs.
- Expenses relating to attending professional conventions per year are deductible, up to a maximum of two conventions per year. The location of the convention is important when determining if it is deductible; the convention must be held in a location that reasonably can be considered to be within the scope of host organization.
- Promotion, gifts, and entertainment costs are deductible if they were incurred for the purpose of earning income, subject to certain limitations (e.g., meals and entertainment expenses are 50% deductible; however, club dues generally are not deductible).
- Medical, surgical, and similar supplies (other than capital expenditures) are deductible.
- Depreciation on equipment is deductible for tax purposes, subject to certain limitations.
- Provisions for doubtful debts (i.e., likely to become a bad debt) and bad debts are deductible.

Notwithstanding the previous types of expenses that may be deductible, various other types of expenses may be deducted if they were incurred for the purpose of earning income. You should consult with your tax adviser to determine the eligibility and the amount you are permitted to claim as a deduction.

Types of Business

In general terms, a business can be carried on in one of three ways. These include the following:

1. Sole proprietorship
2. Partnership
3. Corporation

Why an individual would choose to use one of the three business entities is based on various business, legal, and tax reasons; however, the same rules generally apply to the deduction of business costs for tax purposes for each.

Before discussing the three business entities in detail, it is important to have an understanding of the way in which income is computed. Two methods of computing income are used for tax purposes, the "cash" basis and the "accrual" basis. Under the cash basis of accounting, revenues and expenses are included in the computation of income when they are received or expended. Under the accrual basis of accounting, income is computed as it is earned, even if it has not yet been billed or collected. Expenses under the accrual basis of accounting must be computed as they are incurred, even if they have not been paid. For tax purposes, income from a business must be calculated under the accrual method. Under this method, you must include any "work in process" (i.e., work that has been done, but has not yet been billed) in your revenue. However, you may file an election with your tax return to use a modified accrual method of accounting for income, permitting you to exclude work in process from your income. While most practicing professionals choose to make this election in order to defer tax, you may not wish to make this election in the first year or two of your professional practice if your income is relatively low and you are in a low tax bracket. Once the election is made, you are generally bound by this accounting treatment for all future years.

Sole Proprietorship

A sole proprietorship is a method of carrying on business directly by an individual where the business revenues and expenses are kept separate from the individual's personal affairs. At the end of the fiscal year, the revenues and expenses of the sole proprietorship must be reported on the individual's tax return and included as taxable income. For tax purposes, the net income from the sole proprietorship is added to the individual's income from other sources. The total income of the individual, including the income of the sole proprietorship, ultimately will determine the individual's tax bracket and taxes payable.

The main advantage of a sole proprietorship over a partnership or corporation is in its simplicity. A sole proprietorship does not need to file separate income-tax returns; the individual merely reports the income or loss from the business on his or her personal tax return. The after-tax profits of the sole proprietorship may be reinvested in the business or used for any other purpose at the discretion of the proprietor. Another advantage of a sole proprietorship is that this form of business permits you to convert your business into a partnership or corporation at a later date, without triggering any immediate income-tax consequences. As a result, you may wish to commence business activities as a sole proprietorship and later transfer the business into a partnership or corporation.

Partnership

Each province has its own set of laws governing partnerships; however, the laws of each province are quite similar. Essentially they describe a partnership as a relationship that exists between two or more persons carrying on business in common, with a view to generate profit. In most cases, a partnership agreement stipulates the terms governing the operations of the partnership, including the sharing of profits or losses. Profits or losses do not have to be shared equally amongst the partners.

For income-tax purposes, a partnership is not a person. In fact, "partnership" is not defined in the *Income Tax Act*; the *Income Tax Act* merely describes the tax treatment applicable to partnerships. Even though a partnership is not a person, a partnership must compute its income as if it were a separate person and the partnership then allocates its income to the partners. Any profits that are not distributed to the partners may remain in the partnership and form part of the partnership's capital. This capital could be distributed to the partners at any time without triggering income tax to the partners. The partnership's capital can be calculated at any point in time by adding up the following items: initial money invested by the partners, cumulative profits or losses, and subsequent cash contributed by the partners. Any cash withdrawn from the partnership must then be deducted from this total.

How Are Partnerships Taxed?

Partnerships do not pay tax. Profits or losses are computed at the partnership level; then the net profit or loss is allocated to the partners. The partners, in turn, report this income or loss on their respective income-tax returns. It is important to note that partners are liable for tax on partnership profits, even if they have not taken any money out of the partnership. Conversely, money withdrawn from a partnership is not taxable. Profits withdrawn from a partnership are not treated as salary or dividends; the funds removed from the partnership are considered to be drawn out of the capital of the partnership. Since each partner's personal tax situation is unique, in the event of a loss, each partner may decide to carry the loss back or forward, if it cannot be deducted currently.

A partnership does not file an income-tax return. Instead, partnerships with more than five partners must file an information return with the taxation authorities. The information return summarizes the tax information of the partnership and the applicable amounts allocated to each partner. A supplementary information slip is given to each partner that contains particular information needed to prepare his or her personal income-tax return.

The taxation authorities possess the power to determine whether the net income or loss reported by the partnership is correct. This "determination" is similar to an assessment of tax, in that it is binding upon the partners. If the partners disagree with the "determination," a formal Notice of Objection should be filed. Rather than all of the partners filing separate objections, the partnership designates one partner to file the Notice of Objection on behalf of the entire partnership.

What Happens If You Sell Your Share of the Partnership?

Your share of the partnership is referred to as a "partnership interest." In the event that you wish to sell your partnership interest, a capital gain or loss may be realized. When you sell your partnership interest, you are deemed to sell it at the fair market value and the capital gain or capital loss that results from the sale is calculated as the difference between the fair market value of your partnership interest and your "adjusted cost base." In simplified terms, the adjusted cost base is calculated by adding the initial cost of your partnership interest to the subsequent cash invested in the partnership and your share of partnership profits; from this total, your share of partnership losses and cash withdrawn from the partnership are deducted.

If you sell your partnership interest, any capital gain or capital loss that results from the sale must be reported on your personal income-tax return. Under current tax rules, capital gains are only 50% taxable and capital losses are only 50% deductible. You should be aware that capital losses may be deducted only against capital gains; they may not be deducted against other sources of income. If you do not have any other capital gains in the year of the sale to offset the capital loss, then the capital loss may be carried back or carried forward to offset capital gains.

Corporation

A corporation is a separate legal entity, distinct from its shareholders, directors, officers, and employees. A corporation has the same rights and obligations as a natural person; it has the right to own property, go into debt, enter into contracts, to sue or be sued, and can even be found guilty of committing a crime. Like a natural person, a corporation must file an income-tax return and pay income tax. Unlike a sole proprietorship or partnership, corporations continue to exist even after the owner dies.

Corporations effectively limit the liability of the owners or shareholders; as a general rule, shareholders of a corporation are not liable for the corporation's debts. If the corporation is unable to repay its debts and goes bankrupt as a result, then the shareholders of the corporation will not lose more than their investment. Creditors cannot sue shareholders for the liabilities incurred by the corporation, even though the shareholders are the owners of the corporation. It is important to note that if the shareholder is also a director of the corporation, s/he may be liable for the liabilities of the corporation under certain circumstances.

One of the main advantages of incorporating your business is to take advantage of tax deferral. If you can afford to leave some of your profits in the corporation to be reinvested, incorporation could result in significant tax savings, since corporate tax rates are lower than the rates applicable to top-bracket individuals. If you need all of the cash generated from your business for your personal needs, the costs of setting up a corporation as well as annual maintenance costs may exceed anticipated benefits.

As discussed, corporations must pay tax on income earned. The after-tax profits that are not reinvested then may be distributed to the shareholders as taxable dividends. Theoretically, the combined rate of corporate tax and personal tax on the dividends is designed to result in the same rate of tax as if the income been earned through a sole proprietorship; however, for various reasons, this is not always the case. Before you decide to incorporate your business, you should consult with your tax adviser to determine if the tax savings outweigh the costs.

Another significant advantage of incorporating your business is the ability to shelter from tax up to $500,000 of capital gains. Under certain circumstances, the shareholder may claim the capital gains exemption when s/he sells the shares of a corporation. The rules pertaining to the capital gains exemption are extremely complex; therefore, shareholders should consult with their tax advisers in order to ensure that they may qualify for this deduction.

Incorporating your business will involve significant start-up costs that do not apply to sole proprietorships or partnerships. In addition to the professional fees for legal and accounting services, you will be required to devote significant time and effort to ensure that your corporation is in full compliance with its commercial, legal, and tax obligations. Upon formation of the corporation, the articles of incorporation generally indicate the number of directors to be appointed; the shareholders who own the corporation then are required to appoint the directors. The directors have the responsibility for supervising the management of the corporation's business. The directors typically appoint the officers of the corporation, who are given the responsibility to manage the day-to-day business of the corporation. Typical officer positions are President, Chief Executive Officer, Secretary, and Chief Financial Officer. The duties of the corporation's officers typically are found in the bylaws. It is possible, and quite common, for the sole shareholder to be the sole director and sole officer of a corporation.

Deemed Dispositions

If you decide to emigrate from Canada, a disposition of all your assets is deemed to occur at fair market value; this deemed disposition may result in a capital gain or capital loss. The same deemed disposition rules apply in the event of death.

Other Tax Issues

Tuition and Education Tax Credits
As you embark on your professional career, you may discover that you not only have accumulated a sizable student loan, but you have accumulated unused tuition and education tax credits. Students typically have low levels of income during their student years and, as a result, are unable to fully utilize their tax credits. Unused tuition and education tax credits can be applied

against your income tax in any future year. After joining the labour force, you should ensure that you take advantage of claiming any of your unused tax credits. Similarly, interest incurred on student loans can be claimed as a tax credit in the year it is incurred or it can be carried forward to be claimed in any of the next 5 years. You may wish to consult your tax adviser to ensure that you are claiming all of the credits to which you are entitled.

Employees' Fringe Benefits

As a general rule, employees must pay tax on the value of fringe benefits they receive by virtue of their employment. To the extent that the fringe benefits are taxable, the employer must report the value of the benefit on the employee's T4 slip. The most common forms of taxable fringe benefits include the following:

- Board and lodging
- Rent-free and low-rent housing
- Travel allowances that are considered unreasonable (travel costs for spouses who accompany you on a trip also are considered taxable benefits)
- Personal use of the employer's automobile
- Gifts to employees are taxable; however, an exception applies for special occasions (e.g., celebration marking 5th year employment anniversary), subject to certain limitations
- Prizes, incentive awards, and holiday trips
- Employer-paid educational costs are taxable to the employee only if the training is primarily for the benefit of the employee
- Interest-free or low-interest loans

Certain exceptions exist to the general rule that employees must pay tax on the value of fringe benefits. Common non-taxable fringe benefits include the following:

- Professional membership fees, if the employer is the primary beneficiary of the payment
- Employee-counselling services
- Discounts on merchandise and subsidized meals
- Transportation to the job
- Usage of the employer's recreational facilities
- Moving expenses for specific costs incurred

How to Select an Accountant

Virtually every business needs an accountant at some point in time. You should not hesitate to seek professional advice early in your career, to ensure that you start off on the right track. Most accountants charge an hourly fee for their services so it helps to be prepared before you engage the services of an accountant.

Before you begin the process of selecting an accountant you must first identify your needs. If your own accounting knowledge is limited, you should seek an accountant who is capable of explaining issues in simple terms. You should compile a list of services you require, such as bookkeeping, preparation of financial statements and tax returns, tax planning, and assistance in obtaining financing. Consider the amount of assistance you currently require, as well as what you anticipate needing in the future, as this will help determine whether you need to hire an independent accountant or to use the services of a larger firm.

Ask your colleagues for referrals as this could lead to finding an accountant who has experience in your industry and who understands your business. Do not hesitate to ask questions during your search. Not only do you want to get a clear understanding of the accountant's capabilities, you want to ensure that you can execute the recommendations accurately. Furthermore, you want to know that the accountant listens to and understands your concerns. You should feel comfortable talking with your accountant since you will be building a relationship with him/her and will inevitably be discussing your intimate personal financial affairs.

Not only is it important to select a qualified accountant, you should seek a professionally designated accountant. Designated accountants, such as chartered accountants (CAs), certified general accountants (CGAs), and certified management accountants (CMAs), all have formal training and are governed by their respective professional bodies. All accountants must follow a single set of accounting standards known as Generally Accepted Accounting Principles (GAAP) and all must work with the same tax law (i.e., *The Income Tax Act*). To best understand the difference between these professional accounting designations, you should visit their respective websites at www.cica.ca, www.cga-canada.org, and www.cma-canada.org.

Useful Resources

In addition to the previously listed websites, the Canada Revenue Agency's web-site (www.cra-arc.gc.ca) contains a plethora of useful tax information.

Toll-free telephone numbers and locations are listed on the website, should you wish to communicate with them directly. Another useful tool is Industry Canada's website (www.strategis.gc.ca). This website contains information relevant to Canadian business and many useful links, such as "starting a business." The department of finance website (www.fin.gc.ca) contains links to fiscal information such as federal budgets, taxes and tariffs, as well as Canadian economic information.

Biographies

Andrew Shalit is Principal in the Tax Department at Segal LLP, Chartered Accountants. He obtained his bachelor's degree from McGill University and went on to obtain his CA designation. He is currently a member of the Canadian Institute of Chartered Accountants, the Institute of Chartered Accountants of Ontario, and the Canadian Tax Foundation. Andrew specializes in providing tax advice to professionals and corporations. He has extensive experience dealing with domestic and international tax issues and has assisted many clients with inbound/outbound tax planning, United States and international expansion, cross-border planning, mergers and acquisitions, and corporate reorganizations. Andrew also has significant experience in negotiating with the tax authorities.

For Dr. Tait's biography, please see the Section 1 Introduction on page 3.

Compensation and Employment Contracts

John Tait, BSc, DVM, MBA, CFP, ADR
Managing Partner, Ontario Veterinary Group,
Toronto, Ontario
Assistant Professor, Ontario Veterinary College,
Guelph, Ontario

> *Ya gotta do what ya gotta do.*
>
> *—Sylvester Stallone*

One of the realities of today's business environment is the employment contract. The majority of employed veterinarians or associate veterinarians have an employment contract or written agreement that outlines the terms of employment. An employment contract is not a document that either party should be afraid of – in fact it should be quite the opposite. These documents verify the terms of employment and subsequently set expectations on the parts of both employer and employee.

The terminology and terms will vary somewhat depending on whether an individual is an employee or acts as an independent contractor and/or operates under the auspice of being self-employed; however, the independent contractor should take special care to include wording that captures the criteria Canada Customs and Revenue Agency expects to validate self-employed status.

Veterinarians have traditionally avoided employment contracts because our historic behaviour has been to agree on everything verbally and deal with problems as they arise. While that may seem a collegial and non-confrontational method to enter into a professional or business relationship, the expectation is that both sides understand the terms of employment and these are both fair and mutually beneficial. However, should something goes wrong, there is no reference document to refer back to, meaning no reference document to afford both parties legal protection. Requesting an employment contract does not imply an atmosphere of mistrust, but conveys desired security for both parties involved.

The content items to discuss and agree upon in a contract are generally items of negotiation and should be prioritized by both parties. Many items will have marketplace or industry comparables or norms for both parties to refer to when deciding on the specifics.

The content items should include:

- *Length of contract.* Most will be for one year, but it is possible to have a contract that either extends beyond or is shorter than one year. Although the term on a contract may be fixed, they often automatically renew on the contract anniversary with only certain terms to be re-negotiated after the contract term expires. Some terms (e.g., non-competition clauses) will endure after the contract expires and an associate has left the practice.
- *Scheduling and responsibilities.* A template schedule and outline of job responsibilities is often a valuable addition to visualize how time will be spent and how balanced the schedule is between front office, surgery, back office, etc.
- *After hours.* This area should verify how much after hours work is expected and attendant remuneration.
- *Insurance.* The practice may have extended benefits for their staff that includes insurance such as medical, dental, life insurance, disability, etc. and pay a portion of the premium costs. The coverage and percentage paid by the owner of the practice should be noted, as should eligibility requirements, probation periods, and cancellation rules.
- *Vacations.* The amount of vacation, amount paid, probationary period, limitations, and ability to take consecutive weeks (i.e., more than one week at a time and how many) should be noted.
- *Statutory holiday.* These may be handled based on the way they fall in the schedule, by seniority, evenly among vets, or exclusively to one or

a limited number of individuals. Regardless of the methodology holiday coverage should be noted.

- *Continuing education (CE).* There are a number of factors that should be taken into account when defining CE including, amount of paid time off, probationary period, limitations, employer's financial contributory, etc.

- *Non-competition clauses.* Different geo-demographic areas will have different precedents for non-competition clauses. Legal advice should be sought if one is not comfortable with the wording in a non-competition clause. Non-solicitation clauses often accompany non-competition clauses. (see chapter in Section 5 for more information).

- *Auto expenses.* Compensation for automobile expenses may come in the form of cash reimbursement or the owner's validation of driving expenses incurred when filing taxes. In some cases a practice owned auto is provided with terms of use included.

- *Profit sharing plans.* Employees participating in profit sharing plans should have a sound understanding of how the plan works and its financial implications prior to agreeing to such a plan.

- *Maternity policy.* Contracts cannot over-ride federal or provincial laws on issues such as maternity leave here in Canada, even if they are present in the employment contract.

- *Notice period.* Most contracts are not binding (i.e., they include the ability of an associate to leave or be terminated with specific notice). Employers must follow provincial severance rules for termination and employees should follow an agreed upon number of weeks of notice in case they decide to leave the practice.

- *Bereavement.* The contract should note whether or not bereavement is included separate from or part of vacation time, and how much is permitted.

- *Performance review.* This clause triggers a performance review that often leads to a salary renegotiation and should be set at a point in time prior to termination of the contract period.

- *Special circumstances.* There may be mitigating or unique circumstances in a given employment arrangement (e.g., unpaid leave for a planned extended trip, additional time for an upcoming wedding, etc.). These should always be included so that expectation cannot be violated.

- *Boilerplate.* While a signed "paper napkin" agreement can be deemed an effective contract, better and more detailed written ones will include some legal jargon that also protects both parties. Legal guidance to interpret boilerplate or additional clauses is recommended in cases where either party is uncertain of the nature of what they are signing.

- *Compensation and benefits.* The critical monetary clause of the contract, it outlines how much, when, and what deductions an individual will encounter when being paid. There are a number of salary options detailed below. As more associates are paid on production-based compensation rather than strictly time-and-effort based compensation, the formulaic nature of the production based component should be outlined.

Compensation Formula Alternatives for Associates

Goal: Keep the associate(s) motivated and making a wage they feel is worth their effort and maintain a steady profit margin for the employer.

While the advantages and disadvantages listed for each salary option below are directed to the practice owner, the points made for each can also provide the employee with an idea as the pros/cons of each remuneration option specific to their individual situation.

Salary Options

1. *Flat base salary.* Also called time and effort compensation. This formula pays a continuous flat wage despite the effort of the employee.

Employer advantage: Predictable for budgeting; conservative; potential way to encourage a poor team player or producer to leave by freezing their wage.

Disadvantage: Can get caught by increases in the prevailing market rate if don't keep up resulting in the loss of a good associate; not very motivational for associate and they don't often feel included; it can subsequently cost the practice owner profit dollars if they have an associate not diligent about their charging habits.

2 (a). *Base + percentage of overall gross revenue.* Under this option a base salary is still paid and the practice owner starts paying production when their annual gross hits a certain amount.

> Example: Associate A is employed at a salary of $40,000 per year + 20% of his/her earnings over $200,000 (i.e., 5x their earnings), paid monthly once s/he hits $200,000 in gross revenue produced. In 2000 Associate A produces $425,000 in overall revenue. S/he earns $40,000 base + (425,000-200,000) X 20% or $40,000 base

+ $45,000 production = $85,000 total. That is exactly 20% of what s/he produces so the hospital maintains an 80% margin all the time.

Employer advantage: the associate has to produce a minimum amount of gross revenue before the production percent kicks in so they are anxious to get there as soon as possible to start earning their bonus. Generally, this is a good motivator for associates.

Disadvantage: since the associate has to produce the $200,000 first, it usually does not kick in until later in the year, leading to some lack of motivation early in the year and a cash flow for the practice that is skewed to the later months.

2 (b). *Straight percentage.* In this case there is no base, just a commission percentage.

Example: Associate B earns $425,000 in income for the practice in 2000. S/he gets a straight 20% of what s/he produces, paid monthly. They earn a total of $425,000 in 2000 and therefore gets 20% of earnings of 425,000 X .20 = $85,000.

Employer advantage: easy to calculate; provides higher cash flow to associate earlier in year.

Disadvantage: this time production can lag a bit after peak spring season when things slow down (i.e., during the slower seasons gross revenue generated by each veterinarian is not as high as in peak season and the associates may have more difficulty hitting their production targets strictly due to caseload).

3. *Split rate formula.* Under this formula the practice maintains a better margin by applying two different commission percentages, one for professional services and one for items with a hard cost (e.g., medicines and food sales). Since the practice has a higher cost for medicines and food sales and generates less profit than it does for professional services, it makes sense to give the associates a larger percentage of the professional services they generate and a lower percentage of medicines and foods.

Under a split formula the idea is to encourage the generation of high profit medical services and not the sale of lower margin drugs and food.

Example: Total professional fees generated by associate $330,000
Total medicine/food sales generated by associate $70,000 Total

revenue generated by associate $400,000
Associate gets 26% of professional fees $85,800
Associate gets 7% of food/medicines $4,900
Total associate compensation $90,700

Employer advantages: Associates are not as tempted to push higher end medicines yet they still have a margin provided to encourage them to recommend/sell medicine and food.

Disadvantages: the practice IT system must be able to track and segregate the numbers.

A note to employees about production-based compensation: either full or partial production-based compensation facilitates open-ended remuneration; simply put, an associate will earn more the more revenue they generate. Motivation and creativity are often enhanced as associates take more ownership over the financial success of the practice and being paid on production better prepares associates who are planning to become owners on the realities of owner compensation. Business acumen is often better developed through closer attention to financial case management and the perception of value for services rendered can be enhanced. The scenario of negotiating a new salary every year can also be avoided if salary paid is ultimately tied more to production than a subjective judgment of performance. Disadvantages include lack of revenue potential for an associate to hit their target. For example, if Associate A enters a two doctor practice as the third full-time veterinarian with a production target of $300,000 gross revenue per year and the gross revenue of the practice is $750,000 when Associate A joins, there is currently not enough revenue potential ($750,000÷3) for Associate A to hit their target right away. Another potential disadvantage is competition for cases in multi-associate practices and assurance that the associates' schedule will be evenly balanced among all of them. Pooling associate salaries, whereby the target is a multiple of the combined salaries then bonus pools are split is a mechanism to reduce competition. While research has demonstrated that associate salaries are higher when paid on production, associates should be sure to evaluate the realistic probability that they will hit their production targets and understand the formula for calculation of production-based compensation.[1]

Conclusions

Whatever the compensation formula, it is very important that both employer and employee are familiar with the calculations and methodology, as nothing causes an employer-employee relationship to deteriorate faster than a misunderstanding surrounding compensation issues.

The employment contract will be an important reference document and complementary guide for your personal financial and career planning. Both parties should prepare and prioritize when negotiating an employment contract, and perform their own due diligence in drafting and understanding the final written document.

References

1.   Ontario Veterinary Medical Association 2006 Report on Compensation and Benefits for Associate Veterinarians

Biography

For Dr. Tait's biography, please see the Section 1 Introduction on page 3.

4-5

Protecting Your Income

Brian Clegg, CFP, CLU, CH.F.C.
President, Marathon Financial Group Inc.,
Waterloo, Ontario

> *The time to repair the roof is when the sun is shining.*
>
> —John F. Kennedy

Introduction

As professionals, protecting your most valuable assets for you, your family, and your practice is a critical consideration requiring significant thought and due care. In order to approach this topic fairly, I feel it is essential to develop an understanding of the history and philosophy surrounding insurance and its use in various situations. This allows you to better see the correlation that may be drawn to today and your situation.

Insurance can trace its roots as far back as the second and third millennia BC, to the practice of Chinese merchants who redistributed their wears across many vessels when traveling treacherous river rapids, in order to limit the loss resulting from any single capsizing. Indeed, it would seem most of the principles of insurance as we know them today can trace their roots to marine insurance and the many hazards found throughout the ages traveling treacherous seas.

London, England is often pointed to as the cradle of modern insurance as a result of developing a Fire Insurance scheme in 1680 following the great London Fire of 1666, which destroyed over 13,000 houses. London was also a marine centre during this era and was considered the trading capital of the world. As a result, there was rising demand for Marine Insurance during this period. A popular haunt for ship owners, merchants, and ship captains was Edward Lloyds coffee house; as a result, it became known as a reliable place for shipping news and a meeting place for people wishing to insure both cargo and ship. Today, the famous Lloyds of London remains a leader in the market of Marine Insurance and other specialty types of insurance.

The single most important concept to understand with respect to modern-day insurance is the concept of indemnification, which is the practice of putting the party insured back in the same position they were prior to the loss. As an example, Fire Insurance is designed so that in the event of a fire, the policyholder is able to rebuild his or her home or practice, thus leaving the insured in the same situation as they were prior to the loss. However, in transferring this concept to protecting one's income, there are several challenges that often make this both complicated and confusing for individuals.

Insuring Your Most Valuable Assets

If a survey were taken and participants were asked to list their most valuable assets, typical results would include the house or principal residence, vacation property, automobiles, jewelry, antiques, and art. Other assets may include equity in a business and pension plan values. If the same group of individuals were then asked for what value these assets were insured, most would respond with "their full market value in the event of loss." In other words, if they were to sustain a loss, they would be indemnified (as previously discussed) for 100% of their value, thus leaving them in the same position as they were prior to the loss.

However, let's take a minute to think about what is truly our most valuable asset. When we review the list above and dig a little deeper, we find that our most valuable asset is, in reality, our ability to get out of bed each and every day and go to our practice and fulfill our role as a professional. We have spent years attaining the skills and credentials to do what we do, and, as a result, we generate a cash flow from which we derive an income for ourselves and our families. This income is used to provide food, shelter, transportation, and investments (including art and pensions). As a result of our ability to work, even if we had no insurance, our houses, vacation properties, cars, etc., could all be eventually replaced in the event of total loss. Conversely, it should be recognized that if we lost our ability to earn an income, even if we had insurance for these other assets, they would ultimately disappear, as it would become necessary to sell various assets and/or liquidate investments in order to replace lost income in the event of a long-term disability or death. Therefore, it becomes clear that, just as we protect material assets, it is crucial to protect one's income as well.

In addressing our protection needs, the concept of *Human Life Value* provides an excellent starting point. Simply stated, *Human Life Value* is the value, in today's terms, of all future income generated throughout our professional careers and adjusted for inflation. By doing a quick calculation, you can easily see this is a big number. As an example, if you begin to practice at age 25, earning $75,000 per year with an annual increase of 3% per year, and you practice for 40 years, you will earn $5,875,000 by age 65. In virtually every situation, this amount far outweighs the value of any other asset. As a result, it is critical that we have adequate protection to replace an appropriate amount of our *Human Life Value* in the event of a future disability or death.

From a risk-management standpoint, it is essential that professionals consider all forms of insurance that will protect against potential future liabilities. In this chapter, I will concentrate on insurance programs that protect income in the event of premature death or disability. With this is mind, I will focus on Life Insurance, Disability Income Replacement Insurance, and Critical Illness Insurance.

However, first let's start with a look at a process that you can employ in order to make informed decisions with respect to the ideal insurance solutions addressing your present and potential future needs. This process involves the analysis and answers to four strategic questions—all of which should be answered to your complete satisfaction prior to proceeding. The questions are as follows:

1. When should I buy insurance to protect my income?
2. How much insurance should I buy?
3. What kind of insurance should I buy?
4. From whom should I buy this insurance?

Once we complete our journey through these four questions, you will be armed with the information necessary to work with a professional financial advisor specializing in insurance and income protection programs, and you'll be able to build an insurance portfolio that is right for you, your family, and your practice.

When Should I Buy Insurance to Protect My Income?

First, let's review the assets previously discussed by introducing you to the *Priority Financial Planning Pyramid* (Figure 1), which is a widely accepted, simple tool for building a financial plan. It represents how the development of a sound financial plan progresses in an orderly fashion and is based on having a sound foundation. According to the experts, the areas of emphasis that

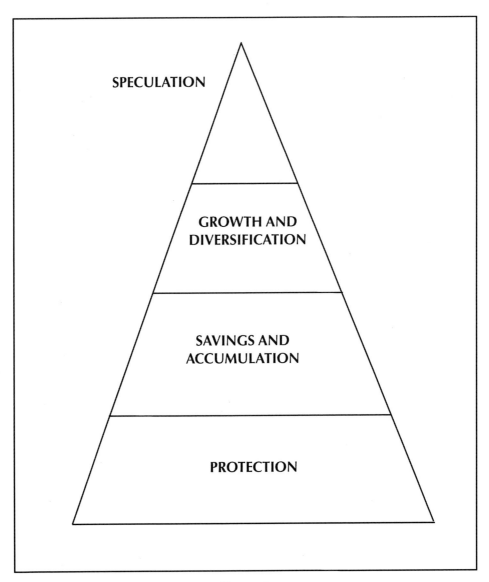

Figure 1

should be addressed first are life and disability insurance, followed closely by regular savings, the development of an emergency fund (generally felt to be three to six months' income), debt reduction, and an up-to-date will. This represents the foundation and protection component of the *Financial Planning Pyramid*. With time, one will move up the pyramid into asset investments that provide an opportunity for higher yields while increasing one's risk and often reducing liquidity. When we review the list of assets presented at each stage of the pyramid, you will note that, for the most part, they all share a commonality—the financial wherewithal to purchase that asset.

Why are various forms of income protection insurance dramatically from other types of asset insurance? Along with the ability to pay the premiums, there are other factors that must fall into place in order to secure an income protection insurance program, the most critical of which is health. Health combined with your ability to pay for the premium and your lifestyle make up the requirements that the insurance company and the underwriter assess prior to the issuance of a contract or policy. Insurance applicants who do not meet the requirements may find their ability to build a solid foundation and achieve financial success compromised. Keeping in mind the adage, "You only get what you pay for," contracts that do not have this requirement and are not underwritten in advance may present problems for the insured at the time of claim, and such contracts should be avoided. Similarly, contracts that do not provide guarantees and are not controlled and owned by you, the insured, should be avoided. Insurance contracts that are underwritten prior to issuance and are owned and controlled solely by you are known as unilateral contracts. The only person able to make changes to these contracts, once issued, is you the insured; thus, the insurance companies complete their due diligence (e.g., medicals, blood tests, attending physician statements, motor vehicle reports, etc.) prior to the issuance of the contract, thereby assessing risk.

Health considerations include anything within your medical history that may impact your overall life expectancy. Additionally, familial medical history (e.g., heart disease, cancer, and diabetes) can also impact on the issuance of certain types of insurance. For this reason, it is generally understood the best time to buy any insurance program is when you are young and healthy. It is further recommended that one purchase an amount of insurance adequate to cover one's needs today and add various contract riders or endorsements, which will allow additional insurance to be purchased, regardless of health changes in the future (thus insuring insurability on a go-forward basis). These endorsements are known as *Future Insurance Options* or *Guaranteed Insurability Options*.

Notwithstanding the above, other reasons are often cited for buying contracts at an early age, including the fact that insurance premiums are lower for those that are younger. However, this may not always be the case. While it is true that an applicant aged 25 will pay less than an applicant at age 35 for the same program, it should be noted that the individual who waits to purchase the insurance (assuming they can still qualify at some later date) will make a lesser number of premium payments as a result of waiting (i.e., 10 years of no premium payments in the above example). Therefore, and based on studies our company has done, we were able to conclude that the cost of all similar programs is the same whether one begins at age 25 or 35. However, this doesn't take into account the risk of developing health concerns during those 10 years, and this may make one ineligible for coverage. Therefore, from a risk-management perspective, why not have the coverage for one's entire lifetime, starting today, and eliminate the risk of not qualifying as a result of health or other considerations in the future?

Lifestyle factors also impact on insurability. Although smoking and its related risks are obvious today, in Canada it has only been since 1981 that insurance premium rates became based on smoking habits. Today, many insurers will offer contracts at preferred rates to people who do not use tobacco, who have sound family medical history, and who have blood pressure, height, weight, etc., within certain parameters. Beyond smoking, other lifestyle considerations may be assessed, such as one's habits and hobbies. Examples include alcohol consumption and/or driving record—either of which may be an indication of the overall risk resulting from lifestyle behaviour. Hobbies (including flying, climbing, race car driving, and skydiving to name but a few) may represent additional risk, depending on one's training in the activity, background in the activity, frequency of participation, and the location of activity.

It is clear that when all the facts are in, the answer to the question "When should I buy insurance?" is right now. For most individuals, statistics show that they will never be better positioned to qualify for an insurance program than they are today.

How Much Insurance Should I Buy?

This question may be slightly more complex than the previous one. The question is two-pronged, in that it raises questions with respect to both the amount of insurance as well as the price; as a result, this impacts on our next question regarding the type of insurance we should consider. From an earlier discussion, we determined that our hypothetical professional has a human life value of almost six million dollars; therefore, one might conclude that in the event of premature death, the individual's family or practice may require six million dollars to properly *indemnify* them for the loss. There are several generic rules of thumb (e.g., multiples of income) that can be employed to arrive at a dollar figure for one's insurance need. Although these rules of thumb can prove helpful as guidelines, they are not designed to address the unique needs of the individual, including immediate cash and long-term income needs. Although a homemade plan is superior without question to no plan at all, I recommend working with a professional advisor, as s/he will not only be able to provide you with various formulas to determine the correct amount of Life Insurance, Critical Illness Insurance, and Future Guaranteed Insurability Benefit, but s/he is also trained to tailor any contemplated program to your specific needs. In addition to this, a professional advisor will be able to direct you to types of insurance that are available at easily affordable price points, which is generally one of the key considerations in planning with young professionals.

Disability Income Protection, on the other hand, provides a unique and different set of challenges for many young professionals. *Human Life Value* projections, although interesting, may vary dramatically from one individual to another. This positive or negative variation, combined with the insurance company's requirement to understand clearly the risk they are insuring, directly impacts the amount of disability income protection one can purchase relative to one's current income. However, most insurers offer graduate programs—many of which are available during one's final year. For new practitioners, it is usually a flat rate during the first year of practice, which can be increased to reflect total revenues going forward. Since statistically the chances of experiencing a career-threatening disability at a younger age far outweighs the chance of death, a sound argument could be made for this being the most important consideration for a young professional.

As with Life Insurance and Critical Illness, overall budgetary considerations and cash flow are critical considerations. Working with a professional advisor, you will be able to determine and understand which of the key components of a plan are important in your situation. Considerations include:

- waiting period or the time before one is eligible for benefits
- benefit period or the length of time the contract will pay, usually measured in months
- definitions

Definitions can vary dramatically, and some clearly favour the insured. Definitions of disability or partial disability are critical and unique to these contracts. In the world of disability or income protection insurance, there exists a great deal of "grey zone," with only the definition to act as the determining factor.

As an overview, let's look at a few guidelines to assist in clarifying or outlining issues related to the three bullet points above. The appropriate waiting period before your monthly benefit for income protection begins is similar to the deductible on your automobile insurance. As an example, the higher an auto insurance deducible (i.e., the amount one personally pays in the event of loss before the insurance responds), the less the premium of that policy will be, since, in effect, one is self-insuring for the lower and typically more frequent accident occurrences. With disability income replacement insurance, the longer the waiting period (or period of self-insurance), the less will be the policy premiums. It is generally agreed that income replacement programs are long-term plans and not designed for short-term coverage (e.g., a couple of days or even a couple of weeks). If we review our priority pyramid, we know good financial planning recommends that we have three to six months of income available in the event of an emergency, and this may be used as a starting point for determining a suitable benefit waiting period. Longer waiting periods also generally allow for the purchase of more income protection for the long term, which is the real liability that needs to be protected against.

With regard to definitions, one wants to be insured by a contract that allows you to receive benefits if you cannot perform the essential revenue-generating activities of your job description, notwithstanding your ability to engage in other types of work, even if that work is within your profession (e.g., lecturing). Be aware that while you may be limited in the amount of coverage you purchase to protect your own income, you may be eligible for overhead expense coverage to protect your practice, allowing you to conserve the asset by being able to meet payroll, pay rent, or pay for other costs (e.g., locums) that may be incurred while you recover.

So, how much insurance should you buy? I have always recommended that you work with your advisors to determine your needs and build your insurance program, taking into consideration not only your insurance needs but the impact the premiums will have on cash flow, especially with respect to your overall cash flow needs. This will differ with each individual, and each individual will have different liabilities at different stages of his or her life that need to be insured.

What Type of Insurance Should I Buy?

For a brief overview of the types of insurance available to veterinarians, please review Chapter 4-6 entitled, *Understanding Insurance and Its Role in Risk Management*, by Claire Walker, in this section of the book.

From Whom Should I Buy the Insurance?

Insurance is a commodity, and, like most commodities, it is available and distributed in many different forms. One can purchase insurance from Alumni Associations or other Affinity type groups, from Professional Veterinary Associations, through the Internet, from insurance agents, and from financial advisors. Throughout this chapter, reference has been made to utilization of a professional financial advisor. For the same reasons individuals seek out your services as a professional, it only makes sense that when dealing with such a vital area of your financial well-being, you seek out the advice and direction of a professional financial advisor. I have always suggested to clients that they view their premiums as payment for the services I provide. If one recognizes that the premium payment will occur regardless of whether one purchases on-line or with a professional advisor, it makes sound financial sense to avail oneself of this value-added service. Consider the financial advisor as a valuable member of your team. Think of him or her as an employee of your practice, one whose job description it is to protect the future financial well-being of you, your family, and your practice. Your financial advisor will be available to provide updates on tax, product, and market changes that may affect your future plans, including your personal goals and objectives, and he or she will make corresponding recommendations for change. Finally, a professional advisor will represent several insurance company product providers and will be able to advise as to which one(s) are the right one(s) for you and ensure that your contracts are provided by established companies with solid financial standing, who will meet their obligations in the future, including good service along the way.

So what are the considerations when looking for an advisor? Let's start with professionalism. Look for the designations:

- Certified Financial Planner or CFP. This initial designation shows competence as a financial planner. It is general in nature; however, many good planners work successfully with a high level of consumer satisfaction without formally expanding their education further.
- Chartered Life Underwriter or CLU is a financial advisor with a specialty in life insurance and employee benefits.
- Chartered Financial Consultant or CH.F.C. is a financial planner with a specialty in wealth accumulation.
- Registered Health Underwriter or RHU is a financial advisor with a specialty in living benefits, including disability income replacement, office overhead expense programs, and critical illness insurance.

Guidelines in Choosing a Financial Planner

1. Know what you want. Determine your general financial goals, both short and long term.
2. Be prepared. Read appropriate information resources to maximize your familiarity with financial planning strategies and terminology.
3. Talk to others. Get referrals from advisors you trust or from colleagues and friends.
4. Look for competence. Many degrees and designations are held by individuals working in the financial planning and investment services.
5. Interview more than one planner. Ask them to outline their education, experience, and specialties; the size and duration of their practices; how often they communicate with clients; and whether assistants handle client matters. Make sure you feel comfortable discussing your finances with the individual you select.
6. Ask for references. Find out if the financial planner works with any other professionals in your field. Ask for other professional references, such as accountants or legal advisors, and follow-up with these individuals.
7. Know what to expect. Ask for a registration or disclosure document that details the method of compensation, conflicts of interest, business affiliations, and personal qualifications.
8. Get it in writing. Request a written advisory contract or engagement letter to document the nature and scope of services the planner will provide. You should also understand how the planner is to be compensated.
9. Reassess the relationship regularly. Financial planning relationships are quite often long-term. Review your relationship on a regular basis, making sure your planner understands your needs as they change and develop over time.

Numbers one through eight above are vital and a wise part of your personal due diligence; however, number nine is critical. In looking at the relationship, is this an individual with whom you feel comfortable? Do you feel you can trust this individual with confidential and sensitive information? Do you believe he or she understands your goals and directions? Choosing a financial advisor to become an important member of your team deserves your time and energy to ensure your decisions today and protect your income for the years ahead.

Biography

Starting his career in Hamilton in 1974, Brian held numerous positions in the financial services industry. Moving to the community of Kitchener-Waterloo in 1984, Brian built one of the most successful organizations in his company. Recognized as a leader in the development of others, Brian has also been committed to self-development and continuing education evidenced by his membership in the prestigious Million Dollar Round Table and Court of the Table as well as the attainment of CFP, CLU, and CH.F.C. designations. A noted public speaker, Brian is sought after by groups and organizations to speak on such topics as financial, retirement and estate planning.

Within the community, Brian has worked as a volunteer and coach for the past 20 years. Most notably, Brian's vision resulted in the annual St. John Marathon/Half Marathon for charity. His coaching credits are highlighted by the five years he spent as the assistant basketball coach with the University of Waterloo.

The driving force behind the formation of Marathon Financial Group Inc., Brian is committed to the belief that success is a by-product of what we give to others.

Understanding Insurance and Its Role in Risk Management

Claire E. Walker, BA, LL.B
Partner, Cassels Brock LLP,
Insurance Litigation Group

> *People who live in glass houses
> should take out insurance.*
>
> —Anonymous

Introduction

Appropriate and sufficient insurance coverage is the cornerstone of personal and business risk management. Without it, personal and business assets are exposed to legal costs and judgments arising from injuries to third parties or damage to their property. In addition, significant financial hardship can result from the loss of or damage to personal or business property through fire, water or wind damage, or theft. Lastly, adequate death and disability coverage must be in place to provide security in the event of serious illness or death.

The majority of insurance transactions are conducted not between the insured and the insurer directly, but between the insured and insurance agents or brokers. Although in some respects the terms "agent" and "broker" are interchangeable, there is one important distinction: agents are permitted to represent only one insurer, whereas brokers may sell the insurance products of a number of different insurers. Thus, an agent may be viewed as a virtual employee of the insurer he or she represents. A broker, on the other hand, is a true intermediary and can often provide a broader range of insurance products to choose from. Whether dealing with an agent or a broker, it is important to locate one with an expertise in the insurance needs of veterinarians. An experienced agent or broker can explain the types of coverage available and provide advice as to the coverage required.

Insurance can be roughly divided into two categories. The first pays a benefit directly to the insured and is often referred to as "first party insurance." The second, usually referred to as "liability insurance," protects the insured by providing and funding legal representation in the event of a lawsuit and paying any resulting settlement or judgment up to the limit of coverage under the policy.

First Party Insurance

Property Insurance
Property insurance policies insure against loss or damage to an insured's own premises and possessions. Property insurance policies provide coverage for losses either on a "replacement cost" or "actual cash value" basis. This is an important distinction, as replacement cost often far exceeds the actual cash value of property lost or irreparably damaged.

Homeowners' Policies
Although homeowners' policies vary somewhat, depending upon the insurance company providing them, the property coverage provisions usually insure the dwelling and any attached structures and the contents of the dwelling that are owned by the insured, his or her spouse, relatives of either, or persons under the age of 21 who are in their care. If coverage is required for a detached building on the same property, such as a storage shed, barn, or detached garage, those structures must usually be insured separately as "additional buildings." In most policies, the limit of contents coverage is a percentage of the limit of coverage on the dwelling. It is important to review both types of coverage regularly to ensure that they are sufficient.

Under all homeowners' policies, certain types of property are subject to special limits of insurance. These usually include money, business property, watercraft, utility trailers, jewellery, watches, stamp or coin collections, and bicycles. Because the special limit may be far less than the value of such items, it is recommended that persons with such property stored in their homes consider additional coverage for them in an endorsement or schedule to their policy.

Homeowners' policies also provide coverage for additional living expenses incurred as a result of damage to the dwelling, while the dwelling is being repaired or rebuilt.

A comprehensive homeowner's policy insures against "all risks" of direct physical loss or damage, subject to certain exclusions. Of particular importance to veterinarians who have an office or clinic adjacent to or in their homes is the "business use" exclusion. It excludes coverage for structures used for business purposes and, as stated above, usually contains a fairly minimal amount of coverage for business property. A veterinarian who practices out of his or her home, therefore, requires a separate business policy to ensure adequate coverage for buildings and property used in the course of his or her business. Other common exclusions from coverage include structures or property used for farming purposes, damage caused by sewer backup, theft by a tenant, and damage caused by insects or animals. It is imperative that the exclusion provisions be carefully reviewed in order to determine if the policy provides adequate coverage, or whether further coverage is required.

Business Premises Policies

Business premises policies provide similar coverage to homeowners' policies, but cover business premises rather than dwellings. Coverage often extends to equipment and stock. All such policies contain exclusions and, therefore, must be carefully reviewed to ensure that adequate coverage is being purchased. For example, theft by employees is normally excluded under a basic business policy, but an endorsement can be obtained that provides coverage for any losses resulting from employee theft.

Business insurance policies often do not cover the financial losses caused by the inability to conduct business due to property loss or damage. However, most insurance companies offer a business interruption endorsement that can be purchased for an additional premium. Because there are different levels of business interruption insurance, the options should be reviewed carefully with an insurance broker.

Automobile Insurance in Ontario

In Ontario, automobile insurance policies are prescribed by statute. They do not vary depending upon the issuing insurance company; therefore, automobile insurance policies contain the following types of first party coverage:

Direct Compensation

This coverage relates to damage to automobiles owned by the insured. The insured's own insurer pays for collision damage to the vehicle, to the extent that the insured is not at fault (i.e., No Fault insurance; see Glossary of Terms). If, for example, the other driver is 100% at fault, the insured's own insurer will pay 100% of the repair cost, even if collision insurance was not purchased. If the insured is 50% at fault, the insurer need pay only 50%.

If the insured purchased collision coverage, the insurer will pay the full cost of the repairs, regardless of fault. In addition, the insurer will also cover the reasonable cost of a rental vehicle while the insured vehicle is being repaired. If the insured was not at fault for the accident, the insurer will waive the deductible. If the insured was at fault, he or she will be required to pay the deductible. Fault is determined by the "Fault Determination Rules," which are contained in the Regulation 668 to the *Insurance Act.*

The decision regarding whether to repair or "write off" a vehicle involved in a collision rests with the insurer. The insurer is liable to pay only the lesser of the cost of repair or the actual cash value of the vehicle. Actual cash value is the price the vehicle could have been sold for in its pre-accident condition. If the vehicle cannot be repaired for less than its actual cash value, it will be written off. Thus, if a vehicle is old and its value is very low, it likely does not make economic sense to have collision coverage, as the premiums paid over very few years would exceed the amount paid out to the insured if the vehicle is involved in an accident and subsequently written off.

It is possible to buy a special endorsement for vehicles that are less than two years old. If the vehicle is destroyed within two years of the date of purchase, the endorsement provides coverage for the cost of replacing the vehicle, instead of the lower actual cash value.

Statutory Accident Benefits

All motor vehicle policies issued in Ontario provide for the payment of Statutory Accident Benefits to the insured in the event of injuries sustained in a motor vehicle accident. The benefits available include Funeral and Death Benefits, Income Replacement Benefits, Medical and Rehabilitation Benefits, Caregiver Benefits, and Housekeeping Expenses, to name a few. A number of coverages are optional and can be purchased for an additional premium (e.g., Optional Caregiver and Dependent Care Benefit; an Optional Medical, Rehabilitation, and Attendant Care Benefit; and Optional Death and Funeral Benefit).

It is important for high-income earners to be aware that a standard motor vehicle policy provides for the payment of Income Replacement Benefits of only 80% of pre-accident net income to a maximum of $400 per week.

The monetary limit can be increased by purchasing the Optional Income Replacement Benefit to a maximum of $1,000 per week, but the 80% of net income limit cannot be varied. Thus, high-income earners would be wise to consider obtaining adequate disability coverage under a separate disability policy.

Family Protection Endorsement
Insured individuals can purchase an optional coverage known as the Family Protection Endorsement (OPCF 44R in Ontario; similar endorsements exist in other provinces). The endorsement increases the amount of money available to compensate an insured individual who is injured in a motor vehicle accident caused by an uninsured or inadequately insured motorist. It pays the difference between the insured's own liability limit and the amount of liability insurance on the at-fault vehicle. The OPCF 44R Endorsement is an essential coverage that should be purchased.

Automobile Insurance Outside of Ontario
The automobile insurance systems in each of Canada's provinces are different, although they have similar features. A number of provinces have shifted over the years from a fault-based system to a no-fault-based system for compensating claims for bodily injury and death. However, the majority continue to base their systems on the fault model with modest first-party (i.e., no fault) benefits for bodily injury or death. Most provinces deliver automobile insurance by way of private insurers, whereas in British Columbia, Manitoba, and Saskatchewan automobile insurance is provided by government monopoly insurers. A synopsis of the automobile insurance schemes beyond that in Ontario is beyond the scope of this chapter. Persons requiring automobile insurance in provinces other than Ontario should discuss their automobile insurance needs with an insurance professional in that province or review an applicable reference textbook.

Life and Disability Insurance

Life Insurance
Life insurance policies vary greatly in the type of benefits that they provide.

- A standard life insurance policy confers payment to a named beneficiary upon the death of the insured.
- An endowment policy provides for payment to be made on a specific date, unless the insured passes away earlier.

- An annuity policy provides for payments to be made at periodic times during the insured's life. Such policies may or may not provide for payments for a fixed period, even if the insured passes away.
- Accidental death and dismemberment insurance policies pay a lump sum upon death or serious injury.

Given the myriad of options available with respect to the life and disability policies, it is recommended that an insurance broker be consulted prior to obtaining such coverage.

Disability Insurance

Disability insurance provides benefits to the insured or designated beneficiary in the event that the insured becomes disabled due to injury or disease. Such policies are often written on a "Short-Term Disability" basis, which provides specific benefits for a given period of time, with a companion "Long-Term Disability" coverage for persisting disabilities. Disability policies can be purchased on an individual basis or on a group basis if the insured is a member of a larger group that has obtained a disability plan. A number of different options are available, and a qualified broker can provide additional information.

Liability Insurance

Homeowners' Policies

Homeowners' policies provide coverage for certain claims brought against the insured arising from injuries to third parties or damage to their property. For example, if a houseguest slips and falls on ice while visiting the insured, the insurer will defend the ensuing claim and indemnify the insured for the amount of any settlement or judgment, up to the limit of third-party liability coverage under the policy.

Standard homeowners' policies exclude claims arising from business risks. Thus, for example, if a client slips and falls while bringing a pet to a clinic that is operated from the insured's home, the homeowner's policy will not respond. Appropriate business risk insurance must therefore be obtained.

Commercial General Liability

Commercial General Liability (CGL) policies protect owners of commercial premises and their employees from lawsuits by third parties, arising from bodily injury or property damage caused, or allegedly caused, by negligence of the owner or its employees.

While CGLs issued by the various insurance companies are quite similar, the contents are not mandated by statute. Thus, care must be taken to ensure that the policy purchased is appropriate to the individual's business interest. Before purchasing a CGL, any exclusions contained therein must be carefully reviewed. Sometimes an insured individual erroneously believes that the insurer will respond to any and all claims made against him or her that occur within the policy period. This is not the case. Although such policies contain a "blanket coverage" provision, they also exclude coverage for claims arising from certain causes. Common exclusions include claims arising from the use of watercraft or motor vehicles and environmental contamination. Almost all of these policies will exclude losses caused by professional services. Coverage for excluded claims should be purchased from the same insurer by way of an endorsement or under a separate policy issued by the same or another insurer.

Professional Liability Insurance

This type of insurance, also known as Errors and Omissions (E&O) coverage, covers the payment of damages that an insured becomes legally obligated to pay due to the performance or failed performance of professional services to others. Given that veterinarians perform professional services that could result in financial losses to animal owners, this is an essential type of insurance for veterinarians to carry.

While the writer is not aware of any negligence claim against a veterinarian succeeding at trial, it must be remembered that the legal costs incurred in defending a claim can be significant. Professional liability insurance covers such defence costs in addition to providing indemnity for any settlement or judgment. For veterinarians, it is also important that the coverage obtained includes payment of the legal expenses incurred in the event of being brought before the College Discipline Committee to defend a complaint.

Errors and Omissions policies are usually written on a "claims-made and reported" basis. That means that a policy only responds to claims that are first made and reported during the policy period. The definition of "claim" in these policies varies widely and often includes written and oral demands for compensation. It is accordingly very important to review and understand the reporting requirements in these policies. If the claim is not reported within the policy period, there will be no coverage.

Special care must also be taken when changing policies from one insurer to another. Some insurers limit coverage by including a "retroactive date" that precludes coverage for wrongful acts that took place prior to a certain time. Retroactive dates should be avoided if possible, or extended back in time as far as possible. When changing insurers or retiring, the insured should consider purchasing what are known as "extended reporting periods." Such periods provide an additional amount of time, from one to several years, after expiry of the policy to report claims that arise out of negligent acts or omissions that occurred during the policy period. By way of illustration, assume that an error occurred during the 2006 policy period, which will expire on December 31, 2006, and you retire on that date. Subsequently, a claim arising from that error is made in January 2008. Unless an extended reporting period was purchased, there would be no coverage, as the claim was not first made and reported during the 2006 policy period. If a two-year extended reporting period had been purchased, there would be coverage.

The insured can also be protected to some extent when changing insurers or retiring through a "notice of circumstances" clause. This clause permits the insured to report circumstances during the policy period that might result in a claim. If a claim subsequently arises out of the reported circumstances, it would trigger coverage even after the policy expires.

Workplace Safety Insurance

Employees of employers who are covered under the Workplace Safety and Insurance Act (the WSIA) cannot sue their employers for injuries they sustain in the course of their employment. In exchange, they are entitled to benefits paid by the WSIA insurance fund, regardless of fault.

While certain types of business activity are automatically covered by the WSIA, veterinary work is not. However, subsection 74(1) of the WSIA allows employers who are not automatically covered by the WSIA to apply to the Workplace Safety and Insurance Board for coverage. The employer will then pay premiums to the Board and be entitled to the same rights and be subject to the same obligations as those employers who are compulsorily covered.

Motor Vehicle Liability Insurance

In Ontario, all motor vehicles must be insured for third-party liability. Failure to have third-party liability coverage can result in a fine of $5,000 to $25,000 for a first conviction and $10,000 to $50,000 for any subsequent conviction. Other penalties include a driver's licence suspension for up to one year. In addition, if a person is injured in a motor vehicle accident while operating an uninsured vehicle that s/he also owns, that person is precluded from recovering for any loss or damage resulting from bodily injury. As well, the operator of an uninsured automobile may be denied certain first-party accident benefits, such as Income Replacement Benefits and Housekeeping Expenses.

In addition to an insurer being responsible only for damages up to the limit of third-party liability coverage, the insurer is also only responsible for legal costs until that limit is exhausted. In the event of serious injury, the insurer may surrender the policy limit to the injured party (i.e., an insurance company may pay the injured person the limit of coverage available under the policy, leaving the insured responsible for any judgment in excess of the policy limit and all ongoing legal costs).

The minimum limit of third-party liability insurance in Ontario is $200,000; most automobile policies issued in Ontario have a third-party liability limit of $1,000,000. In the case of a severe injury, this limit may not be sufficient. One would be well advised to consider coverage of at least $2,000,000. The cost of the additional $1,000,000 coverage from the issuing insurer is quite modest. Alternatively, one can purchase an excess or umbrella insurance policy from the same or another insurer for a fairly modest cost. An excess or umbrella insurance policy is a second layer of insurance coverage that is not triggered until the limit of coverage under a primary policy is exhausted.

How to Make a Claim

The first step in making a claim under an insurance policy is to provide the insurer with notice of the loss or damage that has occurred. The details of this obligation will be outlined in the relevant policy. Most polices require written notice within a certain period of time after the event occurs. In many provinces (including Ontario), there are statutory conditions for the insured's notice of loss obligations for fire, automobile and accident, and sickness insurance. For example, section 6.5 of the Ontario Automobile Policy states that the insured must notify the insurer in writing within seven days of any accident in order to make a claim for property damage. The Ontario Insurance Act provides that for claims regarding accident or sickness insurance, written notice must be provided to the insurer within 30 days of the date that the event or loss arose.

Following the giving of notice, the insured must also produce sufficient evidence that the loss occurred. Statutory conditions and the terms of the policy in question dictate the time limits to be honoured and the types of evidence to be provided.

How to React to a Claim or Potential Claim

It is always in the best interest of an insured to report a liability claim, or potential claim, to the insurer as soon as s/he becomes aware of it. Many policyholders hesitate to report potential claims promptly due to concern that reporting such a claim will adversely affect their premium; however, this is not necessarily the case. Prompt reporting of a potential liability claim allows the insurer to begin investigating the claim and gathering evidence while recollections of the events are still clear. On the other hand, failure to report in a timely manner may result in a loss of coverage. Thus, any incident involving personal injury, damage to the property of a third party, or allegations of improper treatment of a client's animal should immediately be reported—do not wait until you are served with a Statement of Claim.

What to Do if Your Insurer Denies Coverage

The law relating to insurance coverage is exceedingly complex. If your insurer denies coverage on a first-party claim or denies you a defence and/or indemnity with respect to a third-party claim, seek legal advice from a lawyer who specializes in insurance coverage issues. This should be done promptly, as many policies require that any claim against the insurer be made within a specific time after the denial of coverage.

Glossary of Terms

No fault insurance – a system of insurance whereby the insured receives benefits either from his or her own insurer or from a government fund, regardless of whether the injury in question resulted from his or her own negligence

Endorsement – an amendment to a policy by which the original terms are changed *Rider* – an addition to a basic policy that provides for benefits in excess of those contained in the policy *Indemnify* – to restore the victim of a loss, in whole or in part, by payment, repair or replacement. To compensate for a loss incurred.

Additional Recommended Reading

Insurance Law in Canada. Brown C, Brock C. Carswell (Toronto); 1999.
Liability Insurance Law in Canada, 4th Edition. Hilliker G. LexisNexis (Markham); 2006.
Business Interruption Insurance. Seigel, JS. Canada Law Book Inc. (Aurora); 2004.
Commercial General Liability Insurance. Sanderson, H. Butterworths (Toronto); 2000.
Disability Insurance – Canadian Law and Business Practice. Hayes, R. Carswell (Scarborough); 1998.

Biography

Claire E. Walker has an Honours BA in Economics from Glendon College, and she graduated from Osgoode Hall Law School in 1993. Following Claire's call to the Bar in 1995, she joined the Insurance Litigation Department of Cassels Brock LLP, becoming a partner in 2004. Claire's practice involves defending personal injury and property damage actions and advancing insurance coverage claims.

Claire has a particular expertise in claims relating to the horse industry. She defends claims against equestrian facilities and coaches and also acts on behalf of horse and equestrian facility owners whose insurers have denied coverage for fire loss, loss-of-use and mortality claims, and for third-party liability claims.

Claire has represented her clients in the Ontario Court of Appeal, the Divisional Court, and the Ontario Superior Court of Justice. She has also appeared before the Workplace Safety and Appeals Tribunal and the Financial Services Commission of Ontario.

Claire is a member of the Canadian Bar Association, the Toronto Lawyers Association, the Canadian Defense Lawyers Association, the Ontario Equestrian Federation, the American Quarter Horse Association, and the Ontario Federation of Agriculture.

Investing Strategies During Your Career

Jay Stark, CFP
Sutton Financial Group, Saskatoon, Saskatchewan

> *To invest successfully over a lifetime does not require a stratospheric IQ, unusual business insight, or inside information. What's needed is a sound intellectual framework for decisions and the ability to keep emotions from corroding that framework.*
>
> —Warren Buffet

Introduction

As a financial planner, I have had the good fortune to work with a number of veterinarians in my career. From these client relationships, I have come to a few conclusions about the profession, and I will provide three as a basis for what will be discussed in this chapter. First, veterinarians are not in it for the money; second, veterinarians have extremely demanding careers; and third (and in light of the first two), veterinarians tend to procrastinate when it comes to planning their finances. In the next few pages, I will try to show why one needs to make financial planning a priority and how one can do it in a demanding profession. My goal is to help start you off on the right road to a financially rewarding veterinary career, thereby enabling you to have a great work-life balance.

Is There a Need to Invest?

This is a great question that has a very easy answer. The answer is made up of the 10 most powerful two-letter words: "If it is to be, it is up to me." People can rely on the government to take care of them in the future through the Canadian Pension Plan (CPP). Having said that, will the CPP be the same after the "baby boomers" have utilized the plan? Will there be anything left for the rest of us? Well, it is not the type of thing any of us can afford to wait for to find out. So, you need to decide if you are going to wait or act. The consequences are significant either way. Even if the CPP is viable when retirement occurs, the question as to whether or not it will be able to sustain individual lifestyles remains.

What about my pension through work? This is great if you have one, and if you plan to stay with your employer for your whole career. However, the reality is that career goals have changed over the years, and in today's job market, job satisfaction is very important. If someone isn't happy, they are likely to make a change to find the right fit; it is less likely that they will work for only one employer for their entire career. People remark that this indicates a lack of loyalty; however, the opposite seems to be true. Employees *are* loyal, unless they find they are not in a good employment fit. They definitely should not stick it out just to get a good pension. The reality is that most employees don't stay in one place long enough to earn a good pension. In addition, most private practices do not provide pensions in the first place. Hopefully this will change; but until it does, the onus is on you to fund your own pension/retirement. Perhaps you are thinking you will own your practice and sell it when you are ready to retire. This is great in theory, but in reality, practices are selling for the real estate value and equipment. When it comes to selling, goodwill just doesn't have the value it once did. Selling your practice will fund part of your retirement; however, you need to fund the rest on your own.

Another reason you need to invest is that DVM graduates have the highest debt to income ratio of the professions. Meaning, as a new graduate, you have less income with which to pay your higher debts off than your colleagues in dentistry, medicine, or law. A pro-active approach is clearly in your best interest. While it may seem like a big hill to climb, with a little planning you will gain the confidence and peace of mind that comes from knowing you are on the right track financially.

So, Where Do You Start?

Start with a plan. There is only one way to ensure your success financially, and that is to have a financial plan. Your plan should be built to suit your unique needs and doesn't need to be complicated. Here is the simplest financial plan you will find: Live well below your means and save. In other words, pay yourself first. If you save a little off the top, enough to achieve your long-term goals, then you're able to live well on what is left. Sounds simple enough, yet there are many horror stories about people's finances later in their careers. The main reason people fail to achieve financial independence is procrastination. They do not set financial goals, nor do they have a cash management system, pay themselves first, have a tax savings strategy, or plan for unexpected events. It's not that they plan to fail—they simply fail to plan.

If procrastination is the enemy, how is it overcome? The hardest part of financial planning seems to be in getting started. What is easy to do is also easy not to do! You need to look for sources of motivation; often this can come from a book, a quote, a persistent friend, or an advisor. Below is an illustration that may change how you view motivation.

I was at a leadership seminar, and while discussing personal growth, John C. Maxwell (the presenter) talked about motivation. His message was clear: Don't wait to get motivated! He then went on to share an excerpt from a medical magazine, which he paraphrased as:

> We hear it almost every day: sigh, sigh, sigh.
> I just can't get myself motivated to…(lose weight, test my blood sugar, etc.)… And we hear an equal number of sighs from diabetes educators who can't get their patients motivated to do the right things for their diabetes and their health.
> We have news for you. Motivation is not going to strike you like lightning. And motivation is not something that someone else—nurse, doctor, family member—can bestow or force on you. The whole idea of motivation is a trap.
> Forget motivation. Just do it. Exercise, lose weight, test your blood sugar, or whatever (or how about investing??). Do it without motivation. And then guess what, after you start doing it, that's when the motivation comes and makes it easy for you to keep on doing it.
> Motivation is like love and happiness. It's a by-product. When you're actively engaged in doing something, it sneaks up and zaps you when you least expect it.
> As Harvard psychologist Jerome Bruner says, 'You're more likely to act yourself into feeling than feel yourself into action.' So act! Whatever it is you know you should do, do it.

If you are reading this book, then something has obviously motivated you to this point, and you should be commended. You are on the right track!! Good for you…now keep reading!!

The Plan

The planning process itself is beyond the scope of this discussion, although I can't stress enough its importance! (I refer you to *The Money Book*, by Kevin Cork[1]) Give some thought to where you see yourself in one, three, five, 10, or 30 years. Set some goals and then find a Certified Financial Planner (CFP) to help you develop a plan to achieve your goals. Especially if time is a scarce commodity, leveraging off the expertise of an advisor will make managing your finances a much less daunting task. It's not that you aren't intelligent enough to look after this yourself; quite the contrary. It's simply a matter of time and expertise. The biggest ally early in your career is time, because time is on your side. You want to insure your investment decisions benefit from good advice starting day one.

Clearly, you have invested a lot of time, energy, and money to earn your DVM degree—much like the advisor who works hard to earn his or her CFP. Finding an advisor can be a daunting task, so keep these points in mind when you are looking for someone to trust with your financial future:

1. Talk to your trusted colleagues. Get a referral from someone you trust to someone they trust. You won't get far if you don't trust the person enough to share your hopes and dreams. You can also check out the following link for a listing of qualified advisors in your area: www.cfpca.org/public/public_choosingaplanner.asp.
2. Demographics. What do you have in common with a potential advisor? Are you close in age or stage of life? Do you share the same beliefs and values?
3. Ask about the potential advisor's credentials (e.g., is s/he a CFP?), compensation (how does s/he get paid?), and references. Check out www.gettingadvice.ca for more detailed guidelines on what to ask.
4. Be open and honest and share your expectations. Trust is the most important aspect of any professional relationship. By being open and honest in your interaction with your advisor, you will set the foundation for a good long-term relationship. If your gut tells you it isn't a good fit, then move on.

Investing Fundamentals

Let's shift our focus to some key fundamentals that you should incorporate into your plan. First and foremost is time. Time and the magic of compound interest are in your favour as you start your career in veterinary medicine. Recent graduates often ask when they should start investing for retirement. The answer: with the first paycheck. Starting early allows you to take advantage of the magic of compound interest.

To illustrate, let's compare two recent graduates, Laurel and Grady. Both are 25 years old. Laurel is eager to start her retirement plan and contributes $500 a month to her Registered Retirement Savings Plan (RRSP). She takes her tax refund and applies it to her student debt. Good for her financially, but we'll ignore it for this comparison. If she continues to invest $500 a month, earning 8% a year, her investment will be worth $1,610,540 on her 65th birthday. Not too shabby.

Grady, on the other hand, decides to wait until he pays off his student loans, as his new SUV payment makes it a little tight for a RRSP contribution. On his 35th birthday (10 years later), Grady has finished paying off his student loans and starts contributing to an RRSP with $500 a month. Amazingly, he earns the same 8% a year, and on his 65th birthday, he will have $704,275. Again, not too bad. Yet he has over $900,000 less than Laurel. In fact, to save up the same amount as Laurel, Grady would need to invest $1,143 a month from his 35th birthday. Grady will have invested $411,480 compared to the $240,000 Laurel invested. Clearly, compound interest and time give you a huge advantage when it comes to investing.

Point made – you need to start investing right away, but how much should you invest? If invested properly, you need to set aside 10% of your gross income each month into a retirement account. As a recent graduate, you should seriously consider contributing between 5% and 10% of your income from your next paycheck. Start with a minimum of 5% and work your way up to 10%. You will never go wrong in paying yourself first, and you will find yourself able to adjust your lifestyle to live well on what's left—the same way you adjust to income tax being taken off your paycheck and/or paying off your student loan. It's not easy, but it does work. In the same way a goldfish grows to its surroundings, you can grow into your income. Give it a try! You will be surprised how it works and how quickly your investments will grow.

Behaviour

Successful investing has a lot to do with your behaviour. How you react to the short-term fluctuations in your investment account will have a significant impact on how well you do in the long term. While I will discuss risk in more detail later in this chapter, one of the key lessons that needs to be learned about investing is called "myopic loss aversion." This concept is important to understand so you can save your investments from your own good, but often misdirected, intentions.

Myopic loss aversion is actually a combination of two behaviours. The first is a greater sensitivity to losses than to gains. In other words, investors are more afraid of losses than they are excited about profits. The second behaviour is the tendency of investors to continually re-evaluate their performance. A related tendency is to focus on investment holdings individually instead of treating the portfolio as an integrated whole. These myopic behaviours greatly increase the likelihood of an investment loss.

To gauge whether you may be prone to myopic loss aversion, consider whether you would be willing to play the following game of coin toss. You would win $200 if a coin toss comes up heads and lose $100 if it comes up tails. While the odds of winning with either heads or tails are 50/50, if you are like most people, you would decline to play. Why? Because you would feel more badly about the $100 loss than you would feel excited about the $200 gain. (The author of this famous example is Paul Samuelson, the 1970 Nobel laureate in economics.)

Now imagine that you are given 100 chances to play the same game. Now you are probably willing, because the odds are excellent that you will come out a winner after so many coin tosses. The key to being willing to play is focusing on all the tosses as one game rather than as 100 individual games.

This coin-toss game is not unlike investing in the stock market. The sooner you start to invest, the sooner you will experience these emotions and learn how to properly react to them. For this reason alone, I always encourage new veterinarians to invest something into their long-term account, regardless of their debt levels.

In What Should You Invest?

While it is beyond the scope of this chapter to develop a portfolio for you, there are some fundamental investment principles that will form the basis of your investment philosophy.

First, only invest in what you understand. This does not mean that you must investigate every investment to the nth degree. It means that when an investment is recommended to you, it should make sense before you write the cheque. For example, when I look at my watch, I can tell what time it is and often realize how late I am in picking up my kids. Having said that, I have absolutely no idea how my watch actually works, how that second hand knows how to tick exactly 60 times a minute. The key is, I don't need to know how the watch works in order to tell time.

Second, be wary of risk tolerance questionnaires. Given a novice investor's innate fear of losing money or possibly an innate willingness to let it ride (I've found more of the former in the veterinary industry), coupled with a lack of understanding of investment jargon, it is easy to get slotted in some ultra-conservative portfolio that may or may not be a wise investment. Don't get me wrong; questionnaires are good educational tools for confirming understanding. However, questionnaires in and of themselves are not enough to correctly determine your investment portfolio.

Let's compare them to similar questionnaires used in your role as a veterinarian. Your client Tom comes in with his dog, Jasper. You hand Tom the questionnaire that asks a number of things about Jasper: his diet, his amount of exercise, or any past health concerns. Tom fills out the questionnaire and hands it back to you. You review his answers—some of which look more like questions for you than answers—and before you even look at Jasper, you give Tom your diagnosis. Is this what would be expected of a professional? Clearly this would not happen. While the answers will provide you with some useful information, they wouldn't be enough to allow a professional diagnosis or recommendation for treatment.

Unfortunately, in the investment world, that is how questionnaires are used. Your answers are put into a computer and out pops a recommended portfolio. Clearly this is not in your best interest, and it is not what you would expect from a professional. Be encouraged if you are asked to fill one out, as it shows that your advisor wants to know where you are on the investment learning curve. But be very concerned (enough to keep searching for the right advisor) if a recommendation comes from your answers alone.

Risk

Let's focus on risk. While there are two types of risk you need to be concerned with, most of the attention goes to the risk of losing the principal, or your initial investment. When it comes to investing in the stock market, there is a very real risk of losing your principal in the short term. Day to day, the fluctuations

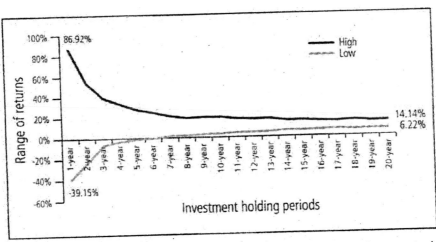

Figure 1—Range of returns over different investment holding periods (S&P composite index 1957-2004). Source: Bloomberg

in the markets can make even a seasoned investor dizzy; however, as your time period lengthens, something strange happens. The risk of losing money fades. As illustrated in Figure 1, the range of possible returns reduces dramatically and becomes predictable in the long term.

On the flip side is a risk that doesn't get much attention: the risk of losing purchasing powers. This is measured by inflation and is almost negligible day to day. The cost of a bag of Doritos doesn't change every day, week, or even month; however, as time goes on, inflation will affect the cost, and prices will rise—so much so that in 40 years, the cost for a $.99 bag of Doritos today will inflate to more than $5.00. The risk that was negligible in the short term is significant in the long term. When you take both risks into consideration, it becomes evident that as your time horizon increases, the risk changes. Ultimately, you need to know the length of your time horizon in order to determine how much risk you are willing to place your principal or purchasing power under.

In other words, one needs to match their investment goal with their time horizon. If you are investing for your retirement, usually there is a long time horizon which allows you to expose yourr investments to the stock market or an equity mutual fund. If you are building an emergency fund, you could need your money any day and should therefore invest in a money market or cashable GIC. This makes sense, but the potential to lose money in your retirement account in the short term could take you out of your comfort zone. However, it is better to do what is right and learn to become comfortable with it over time, than to do what is comfortable now and find out in 25 years that it was a mistake. Let's look at some ways to manage that risk so you are comfortable from the beginning.

So How Do You Manage This Risk?

First, you want to reduce the risk as much as possible. To do this, you must diversify your assets through the use of a mutual fund. Instead of owning a single company, you will own a professionally managed mutual fund that invests in 30 to 100 companies. If one company does very well or goes completely bankrupt, you will be insulated from significant gain or loss, because you only have 2% of your money invested in the company instead of all your money. Diversification is a fundamental investment concept that reduces risk.

I will further define how you can apply diversification to your portfolio in an effort to optimize risk. Let's use the sport of soccer as an analogy to understand how you can optimize your risk. Suppose you were going to a tournament where four soccer teams were playing. Each team was composed of the best players from their defined territory: the Red Deer Hopefuls, Alberta Strikers, Canadian North Stars, and the World All-Stars. Who do you think would win the tournament? Clearly, the World All-Stars of course. They can choose the best players from around the world—the best of the best. When it comes to investing, the same philosophy holds true. The mandate of a Global Mutual Fund is to find the best companies to invest in from around the world. While some of those companies will be in Canada, many of the top companies in any industry are located in other countries. A portfolio that is globally diversified provides you with the best of the best.

Finally, you need to invest on a regular basis—ideally, the same frequency as you get paid (i.e., weekly, biweekly, or monthly). This allows you to get your money working for you as soon as possible and allows your investments to benefit from dollar cost averaging.

Dollar cost averaging is a method of investing the same amount of money on a regular schedule, regardless of the market price of the investment fund. Your money buys more shares when the price is lower and fewer shares when the price is higher. If you're investing on a regular basis, you'll actually start hoping for a down market. Those times are the best times to buy, but it will be extremely difficult to continue when everyone and their dog is screaming about the sky falling. For this reason, it is recommended to set up an automatic investment plan with your advisor. A set amount will automatically be withdrawn from your bank account each month and invested in the globally diversified portfolio of mutual funds you've chosen. Then you can just sit back and relax, knowing that regardless of the short-term bounces in the markets, you are benefiting and will be rewarded in the long term.

Summary

Investing is like any other endeavour. At first, it is scary, because you don't know what to expect. However, what you don't know can hurt you. Therefore (and like most other endeavours), the more you understand and educate yourself about investing, the more comfortable you will be in getting started.

A lot of information has been covered in this chapter, and yet it is a mere tip of the iceberg. I hope your appetite has been whetted for what lies ahead. So, take the next step. Think about the goals you would like to achieve, seek out the assistance of a qualified advisor, make a financial plan, and start your investment journey. And remember, someone is sitting in the shade today because a seed was planted many years ago. Start planting your seeds today and watch them grow.

References

1.   *The Money Book: A Survival Guide for Canadians Under 35*. Cork K. Key Porter Books, Toronto, ONT; 2001.

Additional Recommended Reading

The Wealthy Barber: The Common Sense Guide to Successful Financial Planning. Chilton D. Stoddart Publishing, North York, ONT; 2002.
Simple Wealth, Inevitable Wealth. Murray N. The Nick Murray Company Inc, Mattituck, NY; 1998.

Biography

Jay Stark is a Certified Financial Planner with Sutton Financial Group in Saskatoon, Saskatchewan. He began his career in the financial services industry as a personal financial officer at a chartered bank in 1997. His desire to work more closely with clients to achieve their financial goals motivated him to move into independent financial planning. Jay has an uncanny ability to explain complex financial ideas in simple-to-understand ways, and he gets great satisfaction from helping his clients fulfill their true potential.

Jay has had the good fortune to work with many veterinarians and has developed a keen sense for the issues they face early in their careers. Veterinarians now form a significant part of his practice, and he attributes that to his shared values, his low-key approach to business, and a focus on doing what is in his clients' best interests. Jay believes that if he is able to help his clients become successful, he too will be successful.

When not working, Jay enjoys spending time with his lovely wife Sheri and their two adorable daughters, Alexandra and Sydney. As a family, they spend as much time as they can outdoors, and they especially enjoy their camping trips to the mountains.

The Move to Practice Ownership

JJohn Tait, BSc, DVM, MBA, DFP, ADR
Managing Partner, Ontario Veterinary Group,
Toronto, Ontario
Assistant Professor, Ontario Veterinary College,
Guelph, Ontario

> *Before everything else, getting ready is the secret of success.*
>
> —Henry Ford

Introduction

One of the biggest steps a veterinarian will take is the move to practice or business ownership. Succession or transition planning is a process highlighted by a series of events. By definition, succession planning for a practice is the transfer of both the physical assets and management of an existing practice from one practitioner, or group of practitioners, to another. The process of complete succession planning involves a number of stages, including initiating, negotiating, and closing a practice sale. There are four phases to the completion of a successful transition. The negotiation phase is the period during which the parties agree upon the terms of sale of the practice. The inheritance phase happens quickly and is the formal transfer of a business that occurs at closing. The actual succession phase is the cultural shift, whereby a new owner or owners assume control and impart their leadership, views, and cultural philosophy. Finally, the withdrawal phase is the departure of the former owner or owners; this may happen coincidentally with the inheritance phase, during the succession phase, or after the succession phase.

The Process

The process of succession planning can take years to complete, or it may happen very quickly, depending on the life stage status of the parties involved and their level of motivation and commitment to move the process along. No matter how long the process takes, smooth succession planning is important for a number of reasons. It maintains the continuity of the practice and the goodwill—generally where the most value lies in a purchase. For both buyer and seller, the transition into and out of practice facilitates a key step in their career planning. According to a Scotiabank survey conducted in 2001, over 50% of companion animal practice owners already are or will be at retirement age in the next 10 years, placing a greater number of practices in the marketplace for sale. As professionals, we move through a series of life stages when our actions with respect to acquisition versus divestiture of businesses complement our particular life stage, as shown on the next page in Figure 1. A significant group of practice owners, on or near the leading edge of the baby boomer generation, are moving into the pre-retirement stage. It is during this stage that individuals will often seek to reposition their assets to be more liquid, or available to them in cash, and will therefore be more motivated to divest themselves of non-liquid assets such as veterinary practices.

On the surface, it often appears that buying a practice is about legal documents, practice values, debt, and control. In fact, buying an existing practice (which is more common than establishing a new practice) is more about establishing and changing a relationship, letting go, and altering life roles.

The inherent personality of an owner will affect his or her approachability when it comes to selling a practice. A very controlling, micromanaging owner may never be able to let go of the hospital, whereas an owner who enjoys seeing the practice transition to the next generation will take the lead in driving the process. Motivation always plays a significant role in moving the process along. Buyers should assess the nature of the vendor(s) with respect to their personalities and willingness to move the process of succession along.

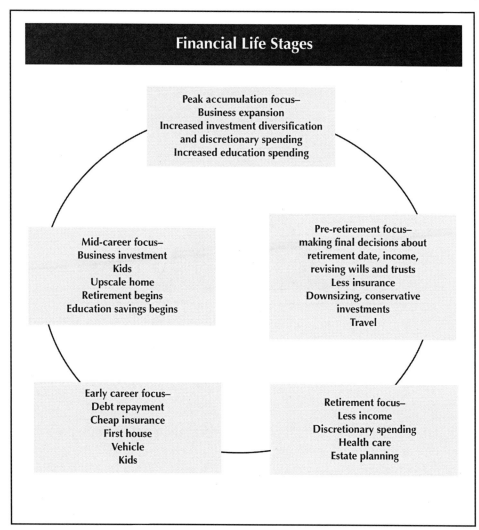

Figure 1 – Financial life stages.

Start Up Versus Buy In

Numerous underlying decisions need to be made on both sides of a practice transition prior to the initiation of discussion and commencement of required due diligence. One decision a potential purchaser must make is whether to start up or buy into an existing practice. Both options always carry an element of risk. Whether you are planning on starting a practice or assuming partial or total ownership of an existing practice, an over-riding goal should be to reduce

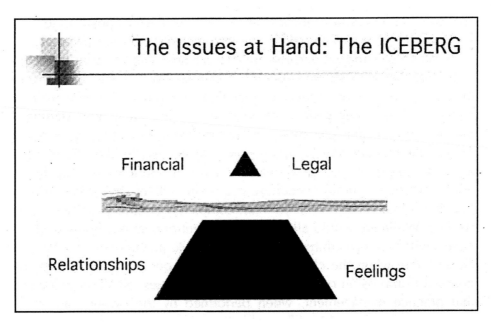

Figure 2 – The various issues involved in buying a practice, using an "iceberg" analogy to illustrate their individual "weight."

uncertainty and risk as much as possible; to help accomplish this, proper due diligence and informed input are necessary.

Start-ups carry unique risk, in that all new staff must be hired, no client base per se exists, and you are "jack of all trades" when it comes to ownership, practicing veterinary medicine, conducting facility maintenance, and assuming general management duties. Of course, starting a practice also means you may not be borrowing or spending as much money; the practice can be set up exactly as you would like and be managed as you prefer; you can control whom you hire from your applicant pool; and you can build the culture you desire. Often a belief in starting a practice is that as an owner, you can completely control your own hours worked. While we would all like to have control over our hours worked, clients will have something to say about that! As practitioners, we have to be available when the clients can best access our practice. Further, the national Commission on Veterinary Economic Issues (NCVEI) has tracked that practice management, when performed by the owner, can easily occupy an average of 15 additional hours or more per week.

If you are thinking about starting a new practice, your business plan becomes a very important guide in the process. In terms of the process, the first step is to secure your occupancy arrangements and find a suitable location.

A feasibility analysis for the particular region you are considering is recommended before committing to a location, because if an area is statistically "saturated" with veterinarians, you will need to rely more on getting clients to transfer from existing practices. An area saturated with veterinarians means that a new practice is less likely to grow as quickly. The facility should be large enough and designed adequately to support the level of practice activity, services, and amenities you desire for the short- and long-term as the practice grows.

If the feasibility analysis is to your satisfaction, the occupancy terms should be factored into a set of financial projections that include the expected revenues from all sources in a best- and worse-case scenario for the first three to five years of the practice. Included in your expense projections will be assumptions on your staffing levels, fixed costs for the size facility you have chosen, and variable costs (including equipment costs, leasehold improvement costs, marketing costs, etc.), and the interest and principal payments to satisfy the total debt.

Once facility arrangements are secure, a business plan is prepared that includes the above projections. Confirmation of financing is sought prior to entering into any formal, irreversible commitments with contractors, landlords, real estate agents, staff, etc. Terms of any financing arrangements should be such that the interest and principal are repayable over a reasonable period of time, and some access to credit should be available for operating cost volatility in the early period of the new practice.

Various debt financiers structure "term sheets" that outline the full cost of borrowing, including ongoing transaction and monitoring fees, and the terms of their loans are based on their assessments of risk. It's a good idea to shop around for term sheets, as some institutions may have specific programs aimed at small-business professionals (like veterinarians), and, as such, they often have a better-informed frame of reference to facilitate financing. The same principle applies to a contractor building a practice; a frame of reference on building a practice helps in addressing the nuances of veterinary hospitals. With financing in place, formal arrangements can be initiated for building, obtaining equipment, and planning for opening.

Buying into a practice or completely buying out an existing owner or owners has certain advantages. For example, a client base already exists, with a management structure in place and immediate cash flow available. Often some transition support is available from existing owner(s), experienced staff personnel are in place, and the practice is an established entity with proven systems. A marketing infrastructure is set, and a presence in the community is already known, thereby reducing the risk of failure. Depending on the amount of money being borrowed for the buy-in, debt financiers or banks often prefer existing businesses, as they have proven cash flow and capacity to handle debt. Buy-ins carry their own form of risk, however. If you have never worked in the practice, and you are unfamiliar with the culture, standards, and philosophy, you may have difficulty adjusting to or changing the culture without investing a considerable amount of time in the process and in managing staff changes.

A credible reason should explain why the business is for sale. Is there an upcoming retirement, or is the business in trouble because of the health or death of the owner? Is the area already saturated? Is the facility not able to deliver the services? Is the business poorly run and having cash-management problems? Prior to buying into or buying out an existing business, it often helps to create your own vision or profile of the practice you want, taking into account the location, style of practice, price, and timing.

The Details

The planning and executing of a buy-in or complete buy-out should follow an orderly process. The ultimate legal transfer of a practice will proceed through a number of steps. First are the data gathering and initial discussions, and then the confirmation of main objectives, primary agreement items, and any remaining details of the agreement. Lastly, the agreements are formalized into legal language, followed by closure. Assuming both the vendor (i.e., seller) and buyer (i.e., purchaser) are motivated and considered to be compatible, they will proceed in parallel with the creation of a purchase and sale agreement to further detail the terms of their partnership agreement if the transaction is a buy-in, or they will proceed with the assessment of value and commence negotiating on the terms of the sale.

Financing an existing practice almost always requires a fair market value assessment or practice evaluation. Unless a purchaser has close to two dollars for every one borrowed, a debt financier is going to request some justification of the value and expect assurance that the practice is able to generate enough cash flow to support the purchaser's living costs and debt repayments.

A practice evaluation can be commissioned by vendor and purchaser jointly, by one party or the other, or by each separately. Certainly a jointly agreed-upon assessment reduces the risk of variance or the need for extensive, further discussions on the price. It is highly advisable to utilize an appraiser who has some background in the veterinary industry and is well-versed in evaluating veterinary practices. The inherent risk factors evident in a veterinary practice are not as obvious to an inexperienced assessor who has not had exposure to the industry, and this introduces the risk of the assessor arriving at a final value that is considerably different from the actual transactions and price points in the marketplace.

A practice appraisal is much more than a document to facilitate a purchase price. An evaluation will provide input into a new purchaser's adjusted cost base for a share sale and the subsequent calculation of capital gains when part or all of the practice is sold. The appraisal may be required in the case of an estate sale or for the owner's own estate planning and wealth management. It will be required in the case of a marital dissolution and may be required when a practice owner is seeking to borrow additional capital as security. Practice evaluations created and updated over time can be vehicles to monitor the owner's return on investment. An appraisal can also help identify what areas of the practice need additional resources or time to positively affect the profit and future value of the business.

Once an appraisal price is agreed upon, it may be subject to adjustments based on whether the sale is an asset or share-based sale. Prior to arriving at a final price, advice from an accountant and/or lawyer on the tax consequences and structure of the deal is recommended. Accountants and lawyers and other consultants (in addition to the appraiser) form a key part of the primary resource base for buying a practice. These individuals can be facilitators who often aid in streamlining the process, reducing unnecessary costs and time, and bringing an informed perspective to expedite the process. While you are still the ultimate decision-maker, a facilitator can provide a different perspective.

A vendor always retains the right to ask more than an assessed price for a practice. The purchaser must then decide to accept the vendor's asking price, negotiate on the price, or walk away from the deal. Psychology, desire, and motivation will always play a role on both sides of the transaction in these circumstances. People will overpay when they are highly motivated to possess a specific asset or business in a specific area, and vendors with an urgent sense of timing to divest themselves from the business may sell under an assessed price, while those with multiple offers and who are in no rush to sell can wait and/or bid up a purchase price. It is often difficult to practice emotional detachment in such situations, but decisions should not be rushed and should be based on sound information and a solid financial perspective.

There are various techniques to evaluate practices. Ideally, an evaluation should use a combination of techniques, and the evaluator should have a frame of reference on the veterinary industry in order to properly assess the risk and better project future earnings. The relative and absolute markets play a role in determining the calculated fair market value of a practice. A practice should be evaluated as though it is being sold to an arm's length, unaffiliated person. No change in the calculated value should occur if a purchaser already works at the practice, nor should the calculated value change in case of a marital dispute or other external circumstances. The relative market is gaining in popularity among practice evaluators and operates similar to the real estate market, where practices are priced relative to how much other practices actually sold for. This technique is more of a secondary technique for justification, and should not be relied on solely to determine a fair market value. Other techniques are more absolute in sense the formulaically calculate fair market values. The discounted cash flow or excess earnings technique uses the incremental income an owner or owners of a practice earn and capitalize (or multiply) those earnings according to risk and within multiples consistent for our industry.

Armed with a practice evaluation and an informal agreement on timing and joint operating philosophies (if that is necessary), a vendor can now proceed to seek financing; without financing, the deal is less likely to proceed as there is a greater degree of uncertainty surrounding the terms and timing (unless there are further negotiations). A financier is going to be seeking information (either included with the evaluation or separately as part of the business plan or other document) regarding the borrower and his/her financial status and history; the practice, the facility, the services, the amenities, and history of the business; the amount requested and possible financial projections; and personal guarantees on amounts borrowed. If a financier agrees to provide a loan, the borrower or purchaser of the practice will be provided with a "term sheet" that will outline the conditions. Term sheets are generally subject to some negotiation with a bank.

While there are a number of items to negotiate and agree upon, three are critical: the practice purchase price and timing of closure, the occupancy status, and the role of the outgoing owner. The facility will be either leased or owned. If the facility is leased, a purchaser should ensure a long-term lease is secured, with predictability in current and future rental costs. If the facility is owned by the practice owner and not being purchased along with the practice, a lease should be arranged, and an option and/or first right of refusal for purchase should be created at a future date if that is an opportunity.

The role for the outgoing owner after the sale can be a sensitive issue if the owner wishes to stay with the practice. The time to arrive at this agreement is in advance of the sale, not afterward. As a new purchaser, if you don't wish to keep the outgoing owner around, then a plan should be formalized for his/her gradual withdrawal from the practice. If the outgoing owner wishes to remain, and you are in agreement, then an employment agreement and new job description should be part of the closing documents. Seller's remorse is not unusual for someone who has spent his/her career building up a practice, and after selling the business, it can be difficult to relinquish control. It is important for a new owner to display some empathy, but ultimately to establish the prior owner's role as one that is more "behind the scenes." You as the new owner should recognize and accept that the prior owner simply had a different way of doing things, and you should not let that bias your own thinking.

During the balance of negotiations when potentially sensitive issues arise (including such topics as the transfer of staff and any terminations, inheritance of current liabilities, accounts receivable, and other commitments), a facilitator can continue to play a role in providing input, advising on current market norms, and bringing forward suggestions for resolution.

The issue of inheriting employees and dealing with the human element in buying into/out a practice can be sensitive and emotional. Prior to committing to the purchase of a practice, it is a good idea to be familiar with employee-related issues, including the current compensation, role, and status of each employee (including any disciplinary actions). Employment standards in Canada dictate that unless employees are terminated with the vendor paying severance amounts owed based on seniority and then subsequently immediately rehired, a new purchaser will be liable for all future severance payments based on the employee's total seniority within the practice, dating back to the original hire dates. Therefore, if there are employees to be terminated, it is best to settle the discussion on timing and who is liable for severance prior to the closing date.

In the case of purchasing only part of a practice, you must share in decision-making and ensure that you are compatible with the other partner who will share in the authority. Partnerships or buy-ins that happen gradually and proceed through a partnership stage until one owner has control over the entire practice, should be approached with attention to the due diligence of issues that can potentially cause future disagreements. There should be synergy between partners and compatibility with respect to goals and philosophies. Sometimes partners at different stages in their financial life cycle will have different priorities with respect to the capital investment they are willing to put into the practice.

Below is an extensive, but not exhaustive, list of other partnership issues requiring discussion and agreement:

- How will the decision-making be done? Will each partner make decisions only within his/her own area? Will there be discussion and consensus, or will decisions be made by the majority if there are more than two of you? It is important to know how much your vote weighs, especially in non 50:50 partnerships.
- How will you determine hours of operation and work hours/vacation/statutory holidays, and time for continuing education?

- Who will handle staffing decisions, and how will they be handled (e.g., hiring, promotions, wage increases, dispute resolution)?
- What if another associate wants to buy in? What about their pay and hours? When is it time to add another partner? Do you decide unanimously or by percentage of holdings?
- What will target staffing levels be, and how will you decide on staffing complements?
- Who will make decisions regarding the facility, leasehold improvements, and major equipment purchases? More importantly, how are they to be financed or paid for (e.g., lease, buy, etc.)?
- What kind of marketing budget will you have, and what will the marketing plan be? Who will be in charge of it? How will you choose or pick which marketing techniques to use?
- Who will deal with industry representatives? Who will deal with vendors and approve deals and promotions?
- Will there be a strategic plan for the next three to five years, or will you "fly by the seat of your pants"? Who will lead? How will the plan be implemented, and who will do what?
- Will you have a yearly budget? Who will create, manage, and monitor it?
- How often will the partners meet? Who will keep a record and/or minutes?
- How will information technology (IT) decisions be made?
- Will your vehicle be expensed through the practice, and what other write-offs will you put through? How will they be tracked? Will you allow income splitting? If so, how much?
- Who will your professional advisors be?
- What will the mechanism for dispute resolution be?
- What kind of non-competition agreement do you want in place?
- Will you allow sidelining or "moonlighting" outside of the practice?
- What will your formula of action be if someone wants out or a new veterinarian wants in?
- What if somebody dies—how will the spouse of the deceased be compensated (i.e., how much life insurance)? What if someone divorces—how will the partnership and practice be protected?
- What will your fees be, and how and when will they be changed? Will the fees be set by consensus, by one individual, or by a third-party fee guide?
- What financial reports and bookkeeping records do you and your own personal accountant want and need? Who will be your accountant?

- What protocol will you follow in case of an opportunity to expand the business (e.g., retained earnings, gross, or mutual decision)?
- What happens in the case of a downturn? What will you do about decreasing staff and your draws?
- Can you take a loan from the business?
- Will you agree to expand your corporate structure?
- How long will you collect a salary in case of personal disability?

Due Diligence and the Business Plan

While the relationship between the outgoing and incoming owner must be successful to facilitate a smooth transition, considerable due diligence must happen on the part of the purchaser to prepare for a practice purchase.

In some cases, financing institutions may request for a business plan to be prepared. This document will be a must in the case of a start-up venture. A business plan, by definition, is a comprehensive written analysis that demonstrates your business will succeed. It is a visioning piece, a guide, a reinforcement tool, and a road map for a new business owner. A business plan provides such features as an overview on the industry sector; the history and identifying features of the business; an environmental scan or analysis of current economic, legal, and demographic issues and competitive presence; financial projections; management structure; service analysis; and a detailed operational plan for the business.

A number of functional operational issues for the practice must be considered by a new owner. Each issue involves choosing a particular direction and strategy, which can be summarized in the business plan.

1. *Financial plan.* Is the goal of the business going to be to increase revenue, decrease expenses, make capital improvements, or minimize debt?
2. *Marketing plan.* Is the goal of the marketing plan to increase the number of new clients, get existing clients to visit more often and spend more, bring new products in, or maximize the appearance of the facility for marketing purposes?
3. *Human resource plan.* Staff will be a significant, challenging aspect of management. Is your intent to increase staff satisfaction, create formal policies and procedures and job descriptions, or enhance teamwork?
4. *Operations plan.* This plan addresses operational issues, such as hours of operation, fees, discounts, product choices and inventory levels, and scheduling within the business day.

5. *IT plan.* In this era of increased technology, a computer system can be used for everything from a giant cash register to a marketing and client education tool—all of which have varying costs associated with them.
6. *Facility plan.* All facilities age and wear out, and this business plan must consider the feasibility of staying in the current location, making potential improvements, expanding, making the best use of rooms, and applying decorating schemes.

Potential Barriers

Buying a practice or starting one and going through the transition or succession into practice ownership are processes with many potential barriers and obstacles. Be aware of the following key barriers that can threaten a successful outcome.

1. *Lack of current information.* Financiers will want to see current information on the business, and it must also be available for the practice evaluation anyway. If the financial and other record-keeping is sloppy, and numbers, purchases, and transactions are not able to be verified and traced (or are not reported accurately), a successful deal will be threatened. The vendor, in particular, should be able to provide answers to key questions, and if this cannot be done, then adequate due diligence is difficult to perform.
2. *Staff exodus.* If the staff of an established practice follows the exiting owner(s) out the door, it will mean rehiring and retraining. This can have a detrimental effect on the practice and possibly jeopardize the ability to finance the purchase. If key personnel head to a competitor, the risk increases.
3. *Inappropriate rumors.* If word leaks out prematurely, and—even worse—incorrectly, that a change in ownership is pending, clients may choose to leave the practice, feeling the quality of care they have received will no longer be guaranteed. A more effective, subtle approach is to have planned announcements, so the transition appears seamless and the service standards are maintained or improved. With effective planning, no loss (above the normal turnover of clients) should occur, and revenue and profits should not be affected.

You as a new owner should be assertive in effectively establishing yourself when taking over a practice. The staff under you will be looking for direction and assessing your leadership qualities. Ask lots of questions, participate at a ground level, and avoid demonstrating the position of power you have as an owner. It is important early on to establish goals, create a mission statement collaboratively with staff, decide on your values, and thereby signal that you are creating a supportive environment of open communication where everyone will function as a team.

Additional Recommended Reading

Building the Successful Veterinary Practice, Volume 1,2,3. Catanzaro T. Iowa State University Press; 1998.

Total Business Planning: A Step-By-Step Guide. Burton E, McBride W. John Wiley & Sons, 1998.

The Best Laid Business Plans: How to Write Them, How to Pitch Them. Branson R, Barrow P. Virgin Business Guides, London, UK; 1991.

Tips and Traps When Buying a Business. Balanko-Dickson D. McGraw Hill, New York, NY; 2006

Biography

For Dr. Tait's biography, please see the Section 1 Introduction on page 3.

4-9

Developing Your Banking Relationship

Mike Feaver, BA (Economics), MBA
National Manager,
Health Care Professionals,
RBC Royal Bank,
Toronto, Ontario

> *Annual income, twenty pounds; annual expenditure,
> nineteen six. Result: happiness. Annual income, twenty pounds;
> annual expenditure, twenty pound ought and six.
> Result: misery.*
>
> — Charles Dickens (writing in *David Copperfield*)

As you make the transition from student to working professional, your banking relationship will evolve too. At the outset, you might require advice on managing student debt. Next, you might need guidance to develop a business plan and eventually gain access to capital to start or acquire a practice. Eventually, you will be faced with many decisions around managing that capital to best serve your personal and business goals. What you need from your financial institution, and the support you require from your banker, will change depending on the stage of your life and the career you are entering.

Success in any profession can be measured in many ways—job satisfaction, career development, and a sense of accomplishment, to name a few. One way to ensure financial success is to start off with the right bank and clear expectations.

Choosing the Right Bank

Make that "choosing the right banker." The products and services offered by various banks are usually similar, if not identical, in terms of accounts and credit, for instance. But that doesn't mean that all banks are alike.

Your dealings with a bank will hinge in large part on the working relationships that you develop with individual banking professionals. In order to meet your business and personal needs, you might encounter two types of relationship managers: personal and business advisors. A personal financial advisor will be able to provide products like a mortgage to purchase a new home. A business advisor could provide financing for a new practice. Some banks may have relationship managers who can offer both services, while others may refer you to the appropriate person internally. Having all of your banking needs provided by the same bank is often beneficial. Not only does this mean that your banker has a complete picture of your finances, but it can also provide an opening for a conversation around preferential rates.

Even if all you require at this point are basic banking services, you want to set the foundation for a relationship that serves your needs as they change. To find the right relationship:

- Talk to your current bank, peers, friends, family, working veterinarians whom you know, and other advisors to get recommendations. Who do they trust? You may be relocating after school, so being introduced to a new bank in a new city becomes especially valuable.
- Decide if you want a banker that has specific experience in dealing with veterinarians. Some banks have specialists in this area, which could be particularly important to you if you're looking to go into business for yourself.
- Talk to or meet with a few bankers to get a feel for the best fit. You want someone who seems eager to learn about your career and life goals, and one who is interested in helping you think of what you will need (in terms of finances) to accomplish those goals. Treat each meeting as if it were a business meeting: dress appropriately, come with questions, and bring any necessary documentation (ask in advance when you make your appointment).
- Learn if the banker will be your relationship manager (i.e., will he or she always be the person you can call on for service or questions?). You

want a relationship that's comfortable and gives you confidence. If you experience a change in your account manager, don't be afraid to ask for someone new if he or she is not meeting your needs.

What Should You Expect From Each Other?

Your banker isn't just there to open an account, complete a transaction, and handle paperwork. To have a truly productive relationship, each of you should be meeting certain expectations. Consider what you should be providing each other:

From Your Banker

- Referrals as needed, whether inside the bank (e.g., other professionals who can bring to bear their areas of expertise, from financial planning to mortgages) or outside (e.g., an accountant or lawyer).
- Information that adds value—not just information about bank products and services, but information regarding your career opportunities. If your banker specializes in the field, then he or she may have valuable market intelligence (e.g., information on equipment and trends in veterinary practices, and data on how you're performing and progressing compared to other veterinary practices).
- Advice on what you need to reach the next stage, in terms of your life goals. If you want to own a practice, for instance, your banker needs to be able to tell you if you're in a position to do so. If so, how do you do it? And if not, what do you need to have in place to make this happen?
- Invitations to financial seminars and briefings, and other resources (e.g., on starting a business, budgeting, financing, etc.) that can expand your knowledge and understanding. Also, obtaining links to local groups and associations that can expand your network is also helpful.
- Periodic discussions, regardless of your needs at the moment, to discuss your financial and career status and goals.
- Information on your credit rating and how this can be maintained (or improved).

From You

- Open discussions about your short-term and long-term goals, so your banker can shape the best possible advice and direct you to the most appropriate products and services. Your relationship is based on an ongoing dialogue.

- A willingness to seek advice that helps you to think about your future. Your banker can be a sounding board for your ideas well before you implement them (or need specific assistance), and he or she can offer new ideas to manage your finances and maximize your financial potential.
- If you're seeking credit, a complete picture of your financial affairs and plans (e.g., assets, liabilities, income, business plans, etc.).

Handling Debt

Before you even start thinking of taking on debt to buy into or start a practice, it's prudent to get your personal debt in order first (e.g., any student loans).

Your banker and accountant can help you review strategies to eliminate the personal debt that isn't offering you any taxable benefit, and replace it, as needed, with debt that can be beneficial. So talk about the most efficient and workable repayment terms and time frame, and how you can retain enough financial flexibility to pursue your career opportunities. As for knowing how much debt you can reasonably handle, you and your banker (along with your accountant) need to discuss:

- Your overall financial obligations (personal and professional)
- Your financial projections (i.e., revenue and expenditures)
- Your short and long-term plans

The challenge is to successfully juggle your debt and your other immediate financial needs, while retaining enough financial freedom to plan for more distant objectives. A trusted source like your banker can help you achieve the right balance, so that you can meet all of your career and life financial goals.

Access to Capital

Banks use their own objective criteria to make money-lending decisions; but one thing that will definitely count in your favour is a business plan. Writing it forces you to think about the requirements and goals of the practice, lets you fine-tune your ideas, and helps your banker assess whether you have positioned yourself to succeed.

The chapter on *The Move to Practice Ownership* (see Chapter 4-8) touches on business plans, which cover topics including the market and demand; your positioning and objectives; trends; management; marketing; costs; capital equipment; operations; and your financial plan. That's the written plan, but when talking to your banker, it's also wise to discuss topics including your credit history, references, reputation, any equity/personal capital you have at risk, and security or collateral (i.e., inventory, equipment, real estate, personal assets).

What's the best time to approach a bank? Well before you have a borrowing requirement. This gives you and your banker sufficient time to talk through financing solutions.

What Types of Capital Are Available?

The right credit solutions can help you establish your practice and ensure its continued success. A key part of your banking relationship is talking to your account manager about the credit that best suits your needs and time frame, as well as customized and flexible solutions. In general, you can think of credit in terms of how you will use the capital.

Short-term Debt
Any practice has short-term expenses (e.g., supplies, payroll, and rent) until the business generates real revenue. You may also need capital to get through your start-up phase or slower periods.

- An operating line of credit (LOC) extends your cash resources. If you're short of funds, you can access the pre-approved limit in the LOC, usually with minimal or no cost. You can pay down an LOC as cash comes in and pay interest only on the amount outstanding.
- Business overdraft protection also allows you to extend your cash resources when necessary, for greater control over your day-to-day cash flow. This gives you peace of mind while helping to protect your business' reputation and credit rating.
- Another option for short-term expenses is business credit cards. Again, you gain easy access to cash, can track expenses for planning and record keeping, and can make purchases interest-free until the payment is due. You also have the option of separating your business and personal expenses by having two cards. Some banks will even allow you to consolidate points that can be put toward future purchases.

Long-term Debt

To operate and grow your practice, you need hard assets such as equipment, vehicles, and buildings. Consider several options:

- Term loans can be ideal for buying new or used capital assets, or for business expansion and acquisitions. With a term loan, you can pay off the amount borrowed over a longer period, to avoid tying up your credit line/cash flow. Regular payments (whether variable or fixed-rate loan) make it easy to forecast cash flow, and you can match the term of the loan to the life of the asset it's paying for.
- When you lack the cash flow to buy hard assets outright (or don't wish to buy), leasing can make sense. Some advantages: up to 100% financing; you often require little or no cash up front; the lease can match the useful life of the equipment; and monthly payments may be tax deductible. End-of-term options also give you the flexibility to buy the equipment or let the leasing company keep it.
- If you're interested in buying real estate, another possibility is a commercial mortgage. You can find competitive options for long-term financing, with fixed or variable interest rates.

Using Your Capital Wisely

Rent or buy space? Lease or own equipment? These are age-old questions for any veterinarian, and there's no right or wrong answer. Many variables should be considered, including cash flow, the stage of your practice and your plans for it, the necessity of equipment and its life span, and tax implications. Often decisions come down to personal choice; but your banker can help you sort through the options. Here are some questions to consider:

Rent or Buy Space?

- Do you want to reduce your risk by renting? Renting can be especially important in the early years of setting up and operating a practice, given the number of other unknowns.
- Do you want to invest more in your practice right off the bat, by buying your location and building up equity instead of seeing the money you pay in rent disappear?
- Where will you get the greatest return on your capital? You only have a certain amount of capital. Should you invest it in a property as equity? In equipment? What kind of cash flow do you generate to service your leasing costs and/or debt? You need to look at the return on your core

business—your practice—which is where your banker and accountant can help.

- Are indirect expenses associated with managing a property (e.g., your time)?
- Are you considering perhaps the most important single factor that will impact your bottom line—location?
- Have you thought through your plans for your practice? Do you want to be able to modify the office as needed? Do you have room to expand? Do you have the flexibility to move easily?

The costs of commercial property and leasing rates in different markets, the stage of your practice, your comfort with risk, your overall financial picture, and many more variables can influence your decision. These issues are rarely black and white. With a trusted relationship in place, you can rely on your banker to help you make a fully informed decision.

Lease or Own Equipment?

Many veterinarians assume that having sound technical skills will keep them atop their field. In fact, part of staying on the leading edge involves making the right decisions about equipment—not just what to get and when, but also whether to buy or lease, and from whom. Such deals can have a huge impact on both your practice and finances. Again, use your banker to help you weigh the options, and consider all of these questions:

- Will the equipment last long? Is it something you might want to change sooner rather than later? Technology changes fast, so deciding to lease or buy can come down to whether the equipment is stable over time.
- Do you want to use part of your LOC for a purchase, decreasing your available cash flow? Or do you want a lease that establishes an alternative LOC and keeps your financial cushion intact?
- What are the terms (e.g., maintenance, upgrades) and buy-back options?
- What type of flexibility do you want? Do you want to lease equipment to try it out, or would you rather buy something that you could be free to sell in the secondary market if need be?
- Do you know the tax implications? With a standard term loan, you pay all the taxes (i.e., GST and PST) at the front end. With an equipment lease option, you may be able to finance up to 100% of the costs, which provides some relief on cash flow, preserves your working capital, and lets you pay taxes as you go. Leasing can be tax advantageous too, as 100% of the lease payments are usually deductible. When you own,

you only get to write off the interest and depreciate the asset over a set time frame (which depends on the asset).

All sorts of tax and other financial issues need consideration, so it's always best to talk to your accountant and banker in advance of making decisions.

Summary

A multitude of financial products and services exist to help you build and manage your veterinary career. These are pivotal in reaching your professional and personal goals. Yet the right advice—the kind of independent and expert advice you should expect from the best banking relationships—can be just as essential to realizing your dreams. Developing that relationship early in your career is critical. Find a banker that:

- Understands your short and long-term needs and goals
- Offers sound guidance when it's needed most
- Gives you insight into your field and the factors for success
- Sorts through your financial options and solutions, to find the ones that are best for you
- Helps you see the big picture
- Links you to other expert resources
- Helps you anticipate and plan for your career and life stages

You have already made an investment in your education, and in the years ahead you will make important investments in your career. Nurturing a banking relationship that's filled with mutual trust and respect is another investment that will help your goals and dreams become reality.

Biography

Mike Feaver's banking career spans 15 years as a Commercial Account Manager and VP Commercial Banking. As National Manager, Health Care Professionals for RBC Royal Bank, he is responsible for supporting the bank's service to doctors, dentists and veterinarians.

CHAPTER 4-10

Selecting a Trusted Business Advisor

Andrea Chan, CA
Partner and Regional Professional Services Leader, Eastern
Canada
MNP LLP

Introduction

Ready to launch your new veterinary career and begin realizing your dreams for the future? You'll likely have many questions and decisions along the way, such as:

- How do I pay off student debts as quickly as possible?
- Should I be an associate of a practice? On what terms? When and how do I buy-in?
- Should I start my own practice? What kind of business plan do I need? How do I finance a purchase or start-up?

These questions point out the value of having a trusted advisor—a capable, reliable professional who can help you understand your options so you make the choices that best fit your situation and goals.

Since achieving success is increasingly challenging in today's marketplace, veterinarians often look to their accountant—a professional with extensive business experience and industry insight—to be their "go to" advisor. But how do you find an accountant who has the ability and integrity you trust?

Consider the following advantages of working with a trusted advisor so you achieve your personal and business goals.

What an accountant, as your trusted advisor, can do for you

Admittedly, some veterinarians may look to an accountant solely for tax advice or for bookkeeping and preparation of financial records. But for those who wish to build a thriving practice while also increase their personal assets, having access to an advisor who has extensive insight and knowledge about today's complex world is essential.

In numerous surveys, accountants emerge as the top choice of business owners as their trusted advisor because they bring broad and deep experience drawn from working with diverse people and organizations in a range of industries. Typically, no other advisor— lawyer, banker, personal financial advisor or insurer—knows a client's business and personal situation better.

While the capabilities of a professional accountant vary widely from one individual to another and from one accounting firm to another, here are some of the specific ways that your trusted advisor can make valuable contributions to your business and personal success.

Assist with practice purchase and/or set up

If you plan to purchase a practice, you'll encounter a wide variety of issues, ranging from what price to pay, to how to finance the purchase and how to negotiate the best deal. If you intend to launch your own practice, there will be other considerations such as how to develop a business plan, forecast revenues, determine capital requirements, establish a budget, and set up an accounting and financial reporting system. An experienced accountant can provide guidance on all of these issues and can also assist with:

- Determining the most tax-efficient business structure
- Advising on partnership and shareholder agreements
- Preparing financial forecasts and helping to monitor progress
- Developing a plan to secure financing
- Bookkeeping support
- Developing compensation strategies

Optimize practice performance

Once your practice is up and running, it will be important to build revenue, cash flow and profits. Your trusted advisor can add significant value by helping you establish performance benchmarks and interpret results to assist with planning and decision-making. Other ways your advisor can help, include:

- Budget, profit and cash flow forecasting and break-even analyses
- Suggestions for effective management of finances, inventory and pricing
- Developing fraud prevention strategies
- Planning to minimize business taxes
- Devising solutions for specific financial challenges

Support business growth

If you have ambitious intentions to expand your practice, you'll need to develop a strategic growth plan. A trusted advisor can offer an objective perspective and provide needed information as well as support with:

- Advising on a reorganization
- Conducting valuation and due diligence of a potential acquisition
- Advising on property and equipment leasing and purchase
- Determining loan requirements

Advise on compliance requirements

Few veterinarians like having to spend time complying with financial, tax and government regulations. Your accountant can therefore serve a valuable compliance role by helping you determine appropriate financial information needed for internal and external requirements, manage regulatory obligations, meet reporting and filing deadlines and even negotiate with tax authorities. Other compliance requirements your advisor can help with include:

- Auditing, reviewing or compiling financial statements
- Preparing personal, partnership and corporate tax returns and other tax and information returns
- Providing commodity tax advice

Assist with retirement/succession planning

Should you set up an Individual Pension Plan? Do you have an exit strategy? A retirement plan? An estate plan? Realizing your vision for the future requires planning today—even though exiting your practice or retirement may be decades away.

Your advisor can help you achieve future success by working with you to address these issues today. When the day comes when you decide to sell your practice, your accountant can also help you maximize the proceeds from a sale by:

- Conducting a valuation of the practice or goodwill
- Providing pre-sale tax planning and profit improvement advice
- Negotiating price and structure for a sale

Protect and build personal assets

As a veterinarian, your business and personal financial goals are intertwined. That's why it's important to choose an advisor who will focus on protecting and building your business assets while doing the same for your personal assets. As your practice evolves and changes occur in your personal life, your advisor can also assist with:

- Advising on structuring family assets, distribution of income earning assets and ownership of property
- Planning to minimize personal/family taxes
- Personal tax planning for individuals with international source income or investments
- Addressing family trusts and income splitting strategies to minimize tax
- Preparing personal and trust tax returns
- Developing an estate plan

Depending upon the accountant's education, experience, capabilities, interests and the resources available within his or her firm, this professional may also offer other specialized services. These can range from market analysis, to workforce planning, payroll services, litigation support, succession management and more.

What type of accountant do you need?

Professional qualifications

Before considering what services an accountant may be able to offer you, it's important to determine whether the individual has the appropriate qualifications. In Canada, the term "accountant" has broad meaning; there are no restrictions on anyone wishing to refer to themselves as an "accountant." There are, however, three recognized professional accounting designations in Canada:

- Chartered Accountant (CA)
- Certified Management Accountant (CMA)
- Certified General Accountant (CGA)

A new, unified designation is in the planning stages. The Canadian Institute of Chartered Accountants, the Certified Management Accountants of Canada and the Certified General Accountants of Canada are currently working toward establishing a common designation that will be known as Chartered Professional Accountant (CPA).

An accountant having any of these designations must meet certain education, training and ongoing professional development requirements. This individual must also deliver services in accordance with standards established by his or her respective accounting body and is bound by a code of ethics.

While a non-designated accountant may have all the expertise you are looking for, it is important to know that if you experience any problems, you have no protection from a governing body.

Personal traits

Of course education, experience in your industry and professional qualifications are only part of what contributes to the trustworthiness of an advisor; character and personality are equally important. Just as clients choose you to be their trusted veterinarian for their beloved pet because you are not only professionally competent but also attentive and caring, you want a similar level of comfort with your trusted advisor. Ideally you will have a close, long-term relationship with this individual, which is why it is important to look for the following personal traits.

- Friendly—approachable and easy to work with
- Objective—sees the big picture and helps you view situations from new perspectives
- Proactive—offers timely ideas, suggestions and solutions
- Reliable—consistently delivers quality work
- Accessible—easy to reach in a timely manner
- Helpful—responsive to your questions and requests
- Knowledgeable—familiar with veterinary practices and the areas where you most need support
- Informative—educates you on relevant issues and provides you with the information you need to strengthen your business
- Honest—holds similar values and acts honourably
- Loyal—always has your best interests at heart

Size of firm

When choosing an advisor who can meet your needs, it's also important to consider the size of the firm with which the accountant is associated.

Sole practitioner/small firm: If your accounting requirements are relatively simple, a sole practitioner or small accounting firm specializing in veterinary practices may offer the experience and knowledge that you need. Since overhead tends to be lower in smaller firms, clients can benefit from lower pricing. At the same time, small firms do not typically offer a wide variety of services and you may experience slower service or gaps in service when your accountant is on vacation or ill.

Mid-to large-size accounting firm: If your needs are sophisticated or complex or you have ambitious plans for the future and would like strategic counsel on a range of issues, a larger accounting firm may be a better fit. Often, partners in mid-size to large firms will specialize in certain industry sectors while also working with other professionals across the firm, thereby sharing knowledge and insights from a broad client base. Larger firms also offer a wider variety of specialized services and expertise so it's less likely that your needs will exceed the firm's capabilities.

How to identify prospective advisors

By now, you may have a good sense of the kind of advisor you are seeking; so how do you find this person?

Referrals from respected sources are a good place to start. Ask fellow veterinarians who are in similar situations to yours or whose type of practice you aspire to achieve about their experience with their accountant.

Other good sources of referrals could be your banker, lawyer or veterinary practice broker. Describe your goals and the services and support you want from an advisor and then ask if they might recommend an appropriate accountant.

You can also contact the provincial/territorial institutes of the professional accounting bodies and ask which members in your local area have experience with veterinary practices.

Your provincial/territorial veterinary association may also be another source of referrals.

How to determine if you've found the right advisor

Once you have a few names, schedule a meeting with two or three accountants who appear to be the most promising. Since you'll be establishing a close, long-term relationship, it's important to meet face-to-face to assess your comfort level with each person. Schedule sufficient time to discuss your needs, meet with any other staff members with whom you might be working and to get a sense of the firm's culture. You might want to start the meeting by articulating your goals and asking how the accountant would assist you. The following questions may help to guide your discussion.

Experience and results

- How long have you been in business? Who are your main clients?
- What experience do you have with veterinary practices; how many clients like me do you have?
- What are some typical challenges that you've solved for them?
- In what ways do you help clients like me protect and build their business and personal assets?

Services and capabilities

- What services do you offer? Do you have access to other specialists if I have needs beyond your area of expertise?
- How do you stay up-to-date with tax and business legislation?
- What is your tax philosophy?
- Are you qualified to represent me for a Canada Revenue Agency audit?

Client service

- How do you work with clients? Would I also be working with other staff members? What is their experience? Can I meet them?
- How often do you meet with clients? How would you prefer that I communicate with you? How quickly do you usually respond to client questions?
- What accounting system do you recommend for clients like me; why?
- What processes and technologies do you use to work efficiently?
- Based on what we have discussed, what would you estimate typical annual fees for someone like me?
- Why should I choose to work with your firm?
- How would you suggest we begin a working relationship? What would be next steps?
- Do you have any questions for me?

If you have any specific tax or financial concerns, this is a good opportunity to ask the accountant how he or she would handle these situations. Listen carefully to assess how comfortable you are with the answers.

You should also ask for the names of a few clients in the veterinary sector whom you can contact for references. Then be sure to follow up.

How to start an effective working relationship

Once you've identified the accountant you would like to work with as your trusted advisor, schedule your first working meeting. Ask what information and documents you should bring. Be sure to discuss your immediate priorities and raise any specific concerns or problems you may have.

Going forward, meet often enough that your advisor can stay current with your personal life and your practice, its progress and challenges. The frequency of meetings will depend upon what services your accountant is providing, but quarterly is a good starting point. Use these check-ups to resolve problems and generate ideas for improving your practice and identifying beneficial opportunities for your overall financial situation.

As you and your advisor start to build a trusting relationship, you now have a strong foundation in place to build your personal and business success.

Biography

Andrea Chan, MA, CA, is a Partner and Regional Professional Services Leader, Eastern Canada for MNP LLP.

Andrea works with veterinarians, doctors, dentists and other professionals to enhance the profitability of their practices and to achieve personal financial wellbeing for themselves and their families.

With extensive expertise in financial management, personal and business taxation and business performance, Andrea develops customized strategies for professionals who are starting, purchasing, growing or selling their businesses. She also devises retirement and succession plans to help individuals realize their dreams.

Section 5

LEGAL AND ETHICAL ISSUES IN VETERINARY MEDICINE

Introduction

In this section, we have assembled a mix of legal and ethical issues frequently encountered by veterinarians in their daily lives. The goal of each chapter is to provide you with the tools to develop a preventive approach to issues you want to avoid as well as some insights on how to deal with these challenges if and when they arise in your life.

In addition to the insights that I have gained in my role as lawyer to the veterinary community, we have been fortunate enough to have some world-class contributing authors, chosen for their expertise and experience. Each author has provided an essential core of factual information as well as correcting popular misinformation surrounding their topic of focus.

As veterinarians we sometimes forgot that the public expects us to be animal advocates. The chapter introducing veterinary ethics challenges you to face the hard questions in dealing with ethical issues in both companion animal and farm animal practice. I encourage you to step up to the plate when it comes to animal ethics and advocacy.

The chapter on veterinary risk management planning provides sound advice as a starting point on how to practice proactively from a legal and risk management perspective.

The equine pre-purchase examination is one of the riskiest activities you will engage in as a veterinary practitioner. This chapter takes you though the steps to allow you to perform this essential function without unduly exposing yourself to liability. I encourage you to build on this approach and to incorporate it as standard operating procedure in your practice.

Of course an integral part of risk management is insurance. This chapter demystifies and takes the "snake oil" out of insurance. You are given the essential details of what you should know and what the insurance jargon really means – all from an expert who is not trying to sell you any insurance products. With this base of knowledge you can become an informed consumer and intelligently use insurance as an integral part of your risk management strategy.

When I give lectures to veterinary students, one of the issues that I get the most questions about is non-competition agreements. When I speak with my clients - whether they are owners or employees - this is one of the "hot buttons" and also one of the fields where I find students and graduates alike have the most misconceptions. Read this chapter for the real facts and a win-win approach to negotiating a noncompete agreement.

As a professional you may be required to testify, advocate, or comment as an expert. Review the chapter on *Being an Expert Witness* for guidelines to become more professional and credible in this role, minimize your liability, and reduce the stress that often accompanies such activities.

We have also include a chapter on pets and wills to detail you on the importance of making adequate provisions to take care of your own pets if you are not able to because of death or disability. It will also prepare you to deal with questions your clients frequently ask when making plans to care for their pets.

Our goal is that this section will provide you the reader with the tools to develop, along with your professional advisors, a preventive approach to dealing with the challenges and opportunities you face in your personal and professional life.

Brian Ausman, BSc (Agr), DVM, MBA, LL.B
Real Estate & Business Broker, Lawyer, and
Practice Co-Owner, Guelph, Ontario

For Dr. Ausman's biography, please see Chapter 1-3, pages 25-26.

An Introduction to Ethics in Veterinary Medicine

Bernard E. Rollin, PhD
Professor of Philosophy, Professor of Biomedical Sciences,
and Professor of Animal Science,
Colorado State University,
Fort Collins, Colorado, USA

> *We seem to be in the place of God to [animals], to be His Viceregents and empowered to receive homage from them in His name. And we are obliged by the same tenure to their guardians and benefactors.*
>
> — David Hartley

Introduction

Given the centrality of ethics to the veterinary profession, it is surprising how little attention veterinary medicine has devoted to ethical issues. A study of veterinary practice conducted in the early 1980s showed that veterinarians spend more time managing ethical issues than in any other single activity (Dr. Marvin Samuelson, personal communication). It is also arguable that the major challenges facing veterinary medicine in North America are societal ethical questions:

- What should be done about the welfare of food animals raised in intensive confinement systems?
- Ought the legal status of animals as property be modified, and if so, how?
- Given the strength of the human-companion animal bond, graphically illustrated during Hurricane Katrina, ought the value of companion animals be raised from mere market value?
- How should veterinarians respond to the magic thinking underlying increasing public demand for non-evidentially-based "alternative medicine"?
- How does one determine and weigh considerations of animal quality-of-life in medical decision-making?

Organized veterinary medicine and veterinary educational institutions have exhibited little understanding of or formal training in dealing with ethics. Historically, veterinary ethics amounted to little more than veterinary etiquette, with "ethical" codes addressing issues like advertising, the size of one's sign, and the sending of Christmas cards. Important issues were ignored, such as the teaching of surgery by multiple use of animals in sequential procedures, or the regulation of the use of animals in research, or the lack of analgesia use in veterinary teaching and practice.

This cavalier disregard of genuine ethical issues came from a variety of sources, including the historical subordination of veterinary medicine to agriculture and the general failure of science and medicine to embrace ethics, captured in the mantra that science is "value free." But as society has become more concerned about animal welfare issues and animal treatment, and has grown more litigious, ethics is ignored by professions at their own peril. It is thus imperative for nascent veterinarians to enjoy at least a rudimentary understanding of the "logical geography" of ethics.

Ethics1 and Ethics2

At the outset, it is essential to distinguish between Ethics1 and Ethics2. Ethics1 is the set of beliefs about right and wrong, good and bad, just and unjust, fair and unfair, which all persons acquire in society as they grow up. One learns Ethics1 from a multiplicity of sources, including parents, friends, church, media, teachers, and so on. For most people, these diverse teachings are haphazardly stuffed into one's "mental hall closet" and are not critically examined or discussed much. Yet the chances of them forming a coherent whole are negligible. As an example, consider what parents teach about sexual ethics versus what one learns from friends, college roommates, and films.

Ethics2, on the other hand, is the systematic study and examination of Ethics1, addressing such questions as whether the beliefs in question are consistent, why and if one must have ethics, whether there is a coherent way to affirm that some ethical views are better than others, how one justifies Ethics1 statements, etc. One learns to do Ethics2 from philosophers, since philosophy is the branch of knowledge where the purpose is to critically examine what we take for granted.

Some further distinctions must be made. Under Ethics1, we can distinguish three subclasses: social ethics, personal ethics, and professional ethics. A moment's reflection makes one realize that, if we wish to avoid a life of chaos and anarchy where, as Hobbes put it, life is *"nasty, brutish, and short,"* there must be ethical notions binding on everyone in society. That is what I call the social consensus ethic, which is most clearly reflected in the legal system and the Constitution or Charter of Rights upon which it is based, providing someone with a broad overview of what that society views as right and wrong.

However (and fortunately for the freedom humans seem to love), the social consensus ethic does not dictate all ethical decisions. Much is left to an individual's personal ethic—his or her own beliefs about right and wrong and good and bad. Such ethically charged issues as what one eats, what one reads, what charities one chooses to support are, in western democracies, left to the personal ethic, with the proviso that the societal ethic trumps the personal on matters of general interest.

Both the purview of social and personal ethics evolves over time. In the 1950s in the United States (US), for example, the social ethic forbade abortion, homosexuality, and pornography, and allowed institutionalized discrimination against black people and the discipline of children to be up to the discretion of the parent. To whom one rented or sold one's property was a matter of personal ethics. All this, of course, has changed, with abortion and sexual behavior reverting to personal ethics (with the exception of rape or child molestation) and renting and selling of property taken over by the social ethic. In general, personal ethics change to social ethics when leaving them to individuals is seen as generating widespread injustice and unfairness. As we shall see, animal treatment—once paradigmatically the purview of personal ethics—is increasingly falling under a societal umbrella.

Professional Ethics

What is professional ethics? A profession is a subgroup of society entrusted with work that society considers essential, and which requires specialized skills and knowledge. Examples include law, medicine, veterinary medicine, and accounting. Loath to prescribe the methods by which a profession fulfills its function, society in essence says to professions: "You regulate yourselves the way we would regulate you if we understood in detail what you do. If you fail to do so, we will hammer you with draconian regulation." Not to respect this charge is to risk loss of autonomy, as has occurred in the US with accounting.

Some years ago, Congress became concerned about excessive use of antibiotics in animal agriculture, both as growth promotants and as a way of masking poor husbandry, since such overuse led to the evolution of dangerous antibiotic-resistant pathogens. When it became clear that veterinary medicine was partly responsible, Congress considered withdrawing the privilege of extra-label drug use from veterinarians. Had this indeed transpired, veterinary medicine as we know it would have been dealt a mortal blow, since veterinary medicine relies on human drugs used in an extra-label fashion.

Every area of ethics is subject to being rationally criticized; otherwise, one could make no moral progress. For example, US societal ethics was criticized during the Civil Rights era for segregation being logically inconsistent with the fundamental principle of American democracy. In particular, Martin Luther King and Lyndon Johnson utilized Plato's dictum that, in dealing with ethics in adults, one could not teach, one needed to remind. Thus, Johnson realized that the vast majority of Americans, even Southerners, would accept the following two premises: all humans should be treated equally, and black people are human. But they did not draw the logical conclusion that black people should be treated equally, and when it was "written large" in law, they acquiesced to it.

Similarly, although most people don't realize it, personal ethics is also subject to rational criticism. For example, I sometimes ask my lecture audiences how many of them are Christians and for Christians to hold up their right hands. I then ask the same audience how many of them are ethical relativists (i.e., people who believe that good and bad vary from society to society or individual to individual) and for the relativists to hold up their left hands. I am faced with many people waving both hands, due to their failure to realize that one cannot logically be a Christian and a relativist, as being a Christian commits one to some moral absolutes, and being a relativist denies any such absolutes.

Finally, professional ethics can be rationally criticized, as when Congress was about to "spank" veterinary medicine for indiscriminate dispensing of antibiotics despite its commitment to assuring public health.

Individual veterinarians in all areas of practice and organized veterinary medicine face countless ethical issues that must be adjudicated and resolved. But before one can deal with an ethical issue, one must realize that it is an issue and identify all relevant ethical components—even as in medicine, one must diagnose before one can treat. However, identifying all ethically relevant components of a situation is not always easy, as we perceive not only with our sense organs, but also with our prejudices, beliefs, theories, and expectations.

The famous Rosenthal effect in psychology provides a nice scientific example. Researchers studying rat behavior were told that one of the groups of white rats they would be working with was a special strain of highly intelligent rats. In subsequent studies, the researchers found that the bright rats did better than the ordinary rats in learning trials. In fact, they were all "ordinary" rats—the "brightness" came from the researchers' expectations. Often we experience the same "halo" effect with students in our classes, when we are told by other instructors of a particular student's brightness.

Another amusing example is provided by a "paradox" that used to perplex people in the 1960s and 1970s called, "The Boy with Two Fathers," which was presented as follows:

> A father and son are involved in an automobile accident. Both are seriously injured and are rushed to separate hospitals. The son is immediately readied for emergency surgery; at the first sight of him, however, the surgeon says, "I can't operate on this patient—he's my son!" How is this possible?

Twenty and 30 years ago, one could perplex almost everyone in a class with this case. Today it falls flat as everyone sees the answer immediately—the surgeon is the boy's mother. Nothing in young people's expectations today precludes the possibility of a female surgeon.

Finally, let me cite a very poignant example from veterinary medicine. In the mid-1980s, I was team-teaching a veterinary ethics course with a prominent surgeon. I was discussing the tendency in veterinary medicine (and in science in general) through most of the 20th century to ignore animal pain. In the midst of my lecture, the surgeon stopped me. "My God," he said. "I was trained in the mid-sixties and was taught to castrate horses using succinylcholine chloride (a curariform drug). This is the first time it ever dawned on me that the animals must have been hurting!"

Specialists are extremely prone to perceive with the theoretical biases and predilections of their specialty. Examples abound: A physician friend of mine told me of a world-renowned cardiologist serving in the emergency room on a Saturday night, when a patient was brought in complaining of severe abdominal pain. The cardiologist immediately ran every conceivable test of cardiac function and was perplexed when no diagnostic clues were forthcoming. It took a first-year resident to point out that the patient was showing all the classic signs and symptoms of acute appendicitis!

Professional Ethics: An Example

An excellent example of a case where veterinarians were blind to many ethical dimensions of a situation occurred some years ago. A man brought a small, comatose dog with a head injury to his veterinarian. The owner freely admitted, and even boasted, that he had struck the dog on the head with a frying pan because it barked too much. It was only when the dog did not regain consciousness and the man's wife became upset, that he sought veterinary attention. His veterinarian advised him to take the dog to the veterinary school hospital. The dog died there, and the animal's body was brought to necropsy and presented as a case to a group of students by a pathology instructor. Coincidentally, one of the veterinary students in that class was an animal control officer, among whose duties was investigating cruelty complaints. With the instructor's permission, the student took the client's name from the file and began to investigate the case, phoning the client's home and speaking with his wife. The client became irate and complained to both the referring veterinarian and to the veterinary school clinician who had taken his case that his right to privacy had been violated. The private practitioner and the veterinary school referral clinician in turn were furious with the student. The student was frightened, worried about the effect of the incident on his academic status and subsequent career, and sought help.

What moral conflicts and problems does this case raise? Initially, the referring practitioner, the veterinary school clinician, and some administrators saw only one issue—the betrayal of client confidentiality by the student. As the case evolved, administrators were also troubled by the involvement of the pathologist who had "betrayed" the identity of the client. Only after much dialogue with an ethicist, the pathologist, and the student did the parties begin to realize that there were many other concurrent issues.

First, there was an animal welfare issue—the client should not be allowed to fatally beat an animal with impunity. In addition, there was a social or moral obligation to report the occurrence of a crime—the same sort of moral obligation (now also a legal one in human medicine) that exists for health care professionals to report suspected child abuse. Furthermore, there was the moral (and legal) question of whether one could invoke confidentiality in a public teaching hospital, where it is implicit that cases will be discussed with students as part of their learning process. Lastly, the pathologist argued that, as a veterinary teaching institution, the school had a high moral obligation not to condone that which society as a whole has recognized as immoral and illegal.

Some veterinarians argued that the pathologist was within his rights to reveal the name, but that the student ought not to have acted upon the information. To this point the student replied that, as a law officer, he had a sworn duty (a moral obligation) to enforce the law. Some veterinarians hypothesized that if confidentiality isn't strictly observed, abusers of animals will not bring animals in for treatment. A controversy also arose over the fact that the school clinician had at least obliquely threatened the student with recriminations when he came to the clinic. Others worried that the information about the case and these issues had not been sent back to the referring veterinarian for that party to handle. The issue of a conflict of interest between being a veterinary student and serving with animal control was also raised.

Ultimately the situation was resolved (at least for future cases) by the university's drafting of a formal policy that suspected abuse cases of this sort would automatically be reported to the school and government authorities. One of the noteworthy features of the case was its dramatic teaching value in demonstrating just how complex a single ethical problem or case can be.

Meeting Your Ethical Obligations

How does a veterinarian assure that he or she does not miss some morally relevant dimension of a situation? One excellent approach is to maintain a diverse array of conversational partners with whom to discuss situations that seem to be "ethics laden." For example, suppose you encounter a situation where you worry that there might be an animal welfare issue present that you are unable to articulate. Having an animal liberationist as someone to engage in dialogue with will help assure that the issue emerges with clarity. The fact is that most of us tend to seek friends that share our views, and this is particularly true of veterinarians who, as students, are physically isolated from the rest of the university where they are educated.

Dialoguing with others not sharing your views is a fine way of keeping yourself honest. When I wrote a book on the ethics of genetic engineering, I gave the manuscript to some of my genetic engineer colleagues to garner criticism, which they were collegial enough to provide—particularly since they tended to see ethics as only peripherally relevant, if at all, to science. In that way, I made sure that I would get a researcher's perspective on my ideas.

Ideal though such dialogue may be, most people will not seek it out. I have therefore developed a heuristic device to help veterinarians hone in on all ethical aspects of a case. This involves reflecting on the ethical vectors relevant to veterinary practice and applying the ensuing template to new situations.

Veterinarians have moral obligations to animals, to clients, to peers and the profession, to society in general, to themselves, and to their employees. Ethically charged situations present themselves where any or all or various combinations of these obligations occur, and they must be weighed. In every new situation, the veterinarian should consider each of these ethical vectors and see if they apply to the case at hand. In this way, he or she can maximize the chances of not missing some morally relevant factor through the sort of blindness illustrated in the case of the dog struck with the frying pan, described above.

In addition, some veterinary associations meet on a regular basis to discuss difficult ethical issues. The *Canadian Veterinary Journal* is an excellent resource in this area; since 1990, I have written a regular monthly column on ethical issues and situations submitted by readers. In the 190+ columns we have done so far, one can find virtually any combination of ethical vectors mentioned above. Over 100 of the columns are reprinted in my *Veterinary Medical Ethics: Theory and Cases* (Blackwell; 2006).[1]

The Fundamental Question of Veterinary Ethics

The astute reader probably will have realized that far and away the most difficult cases one encounters concern moral obligations to animals, since the social consensus ethic is virtually silent on animal treatment (with the exception of proscribing deliberate deviant cruelty, as we will discuss shortly). Yet the question of a veterinarian's moral obligation to animals is so important to veterinary medicine that I have called it "The Fundamental Question of Veterinary Ethics." The issue, of course, is to whom does the veterinarian owe primary obligation—owner or animal? On the "Garage Mechanic Model," the animal is like a car, where the mechanic owes nothing to the car and may or may not fix it, depending on the owner's wishes. On the "Pediatrician Model," the clinician owes primary obligation to the animal, just as a pediatrician does to a child, despite the fact that the client pays the bills. When I pose this dichotomy to veterinarians, the vast majority profess adherence to the Pediatrician Model as a moral ideal. As we shall see, though animals are property, society's ever-increasing concern with animal welfare is putting increasing limitations on what one can do with animals, as seen in recent laws restricting the treatment of research animals in the US and research and agricultural animals in Europe.

Ethics and the Pet Owner

Leaving obligations to animals aside for the moment, how does one deal with ethical questions regarding people, assuming one has "diagnosed" all the relevant ethical components? In the simplest cases, the answer is dictated by the social consensus ethic (which prohibits stealing, assault, murder, etc.), so that throttling an obnoxious client (however tempting) is not a real option. However, in most cases, the ethical issues confronting the veterinarian are not so simple.

We all grow up with a toolbox of moral principles in our Ethics1: don't lie, don't steal, give to charity, help others, keep your word, don't hurt people's feelings, etc. Difficulties arise when a given case evokes two contradictory principles. For example, the principle of "don't lie" may often conflict with the principle of "don't hurt people's feelings" (as when a friend gets a new dress, nose, or husband, and asks, "How do you like it [or him]?"). Or when one is approached by a beggar and feels a conflict between "Help the needy" and "Don't encourage shiftlessness." In such cases of competing principles, one needs to appeal to a higher-order principle to weigh them. Therein lies a major role for ethical theory.

Ethical Theory

Construction of such ethical theories has occupied philosophers from Plato to the present. It is beyond the scope of this discussion to survey the many diverse theories that have been promulgated. On the other hand, it is valuable to look at two significantly different systems that nicely represent extremes in ethical theory and that have been synthesized in the theory underlying our own social consensus ethic.

Ethical theories tend to fall into two major groups: those stressing goodness and badness (that is, the *results* of actions) and those stressing rightness and wrongness (or duty; that is, *the intrinsic properties of actions*). The former are called *consequentialist* or *teleological* theories (from the Greek word *telos*, meaning "result," "end," or "purpose"). The latter are termed *deontological* theories (from the Greek word *deontos*, meaning "necessity" or "obligation"); in other words, what one is obliged to do. The most common deontological theories are theologically based, wherein action is obligatory because it is commanded by God.

The most well-known consequentialist theory is *utilitarianism*. It has appeared in a variety of forms throughout history, but it is most famously associated with 19th century philosophers Jeremy Bentham and John Stuart Mill. In its simplest version, utilitarianism holds that a person acts in a given situation according to what produces the greatest happiness for the greatest number, wherein *happiness* is defined in terms of pleasure and absence of pain. Principles of utilitarianism would be generalizations about courses of action that tend to produce more happiness than unhappiness. In situations where principles conflict, decisions are made by calculating which course of action has the best likelihood of producing the most happiness. Thus, in the trivial case of the ugly hairstyle mentioned previously, telling a "little white lie" will likely produce no harm, whereas telling the truth will result in hostility and bad feeling; so one ought to choose the former course of action.

There are many problems with this sort of theory, but they lie beyond the scope of this discussion. The only point here is that adherence to such a theory resolves conflict among principles by providing a higher-order rule for decision-making.

Those of us who grew up with very liberal parents will quickly recognize the utilitarian approach. Suppose you approach such parents in a quandary. You are thinking of entering into an adulterous relationship with a married woman. You explain that she is terminally ill; she is despised and abandoned by her vile, abusive husband who does not care what she does, but who nonetheless sadistically blocks a divorce; and she is attempting to snatch a brief period of happiness before her demise. These parents might well say, "Adultery is generally wrong, as it usually results in great unhappiness. But in this case, perhaps you both deserve the joy you can have together…no one will be hurt."

On the other hand, those of us who grew up with German Lutheran grandparents can imagine a very different scenario if one approached them with the same story. They would be very likely to say, "I don't care what the results will be; adultery is always wrong! Period!" This is, of course, a strongly deontological position. The most famous rational reconstruction of such a position is to be found historically in the writings of the German philosopher Immanuel Kant. According to Kant, ethics is unique to rational beings. Rational beings, unlike other beings, are capable of formulating universal truths of mathematics, sciences, and so on. Animals, lacking language, simply do not have the mechanism to think in similar terms. As rational beings, humans are bound to strive for rationality in all areas of life. Rationality in the area of conduct is to be found in subjecting the principle of action you are considering to the test of universality, by thinking through what the world would be like if everyone behaved the way you are considering behaving. Kant called this requirement "the Categorical Imperative;" that is, the requirement of all rational beings to judge their intended actions by the test of universality. In other words, suppose you are trying to decide whether you should tell a little white lie in an apparently innocuous case, like the ugly hairdo dilemma. Before doing so, you must test that action by the Categorical Imperative, which enjoins you to "act in such a way that your action could be conceived to be a universal law." So before you lie, you conceive what would occur if everyone were allowed to lie whenever it was convenient to do so. In such a world, the notion of telling the truth would cease to have meaning, and so too would the notion of telling a lie. In other words, no one would trust anyone.

Thus, universalizing a lie leads to a situation that destroys the possibility of the very act you are contemplating, and therefore it becomes rationally indefensible, *regardless of the good or bad consequences in the given case.* By the same token, subjecting your act of adultery to the same test shows that if one universalizes adultery, one destroys the institution of marriage and would thereby in turn render adultery impossible! Thus, in a situation of conflicting principles, one rejects the choice that could not possibly be universalized.

While Kant's theory also is open to some strong criticisms, these too need not be discussed here. The point is that both personal and social ethics must be based in some theory that prioritizes principles to assure consistency in behavior and action. Having such a theory helps prevent arbitrary and capricious actions.

Whatever theory we adhere to as individuals, we must be careful to assure that it fits the requirements demanded of morality in general: treating people equally who are relevantly equal; treating relevantly similar cases the same way; avoiding favoring some individuals for morally irrelevant reasons (such as hair color); being fair and not subject to whimsical change.

Ethical Theory and Society

Obviously, a society needs some higher-order theory underlying its social consensus ethic. Indeed, such a need is immediately obvious as soon as one realizes that every society faces a fundamental conflict of moral concerns— the good of the group or state or society versus the good of the individual. This conflict is obvious in almost all social decision-making, be it the military demanding life-threatening service from citizens or the legislature redistributing wealth through taxation. It is in society's interest to send you to war, but it may not be in yours, as you risk being killed or maimed. It is in society's interest to take money from the wealthy to support social programs or, more simply, to improve quality-of-life for the impoverished, but it arguably doesn't do the wealthy individual much good.

Different societies have, of course, constructed different theories to resolve this conflict. Totalitarian societies have taken the position that the group, or state, or Reich, or however they formulate the corporate entity, must unequivocally and always take precedence over the individual. The behavior of the Soviet Union under Stalin, Germany under Hitler, China under Mao, and Japan under the emperors all bespeak the primacy of the social body over individuals. On the other end of the spectrum are anarchistic communes, such as those of the 1960s, that give total primacy to individual wills and see the social body as nothing more than an amalgam of individuals. Obviously, societies along the spectrum are driven by different higher-order theories.

In my view, western democratic societies have developed the best mechanism in human history for maximizing both the interests of the social body and the interests of the individual. Although we make most of our social decisions by considering what will produce the greatest benefit for the greatest number (a utilitarian/teleological/consequentialist ethical approach), we skillfully avoid the "tyranny of the majority" or the submersion of the individual under the weight of the general good. We do this by considering the individual as, in some sense, inviolable. Specifically, we consider those traits of an individual that we believe are constitutive of his or her *human nature* to be worth protecting at almost all costs. We believe that individual humans are by nature thinking, speaking, social beings who do not wish to be tortured, want to believe as they see fit, desire to speak their mind freely, have a need to congregate with others of their choice, seek to retain their property, and so forth. We take the human interests flowing from this view of human nature as embodied in individuals and build protective, legal/moral fences around them that insulate those interests even from the powerful, coercive effect of the general welfare. These protective fences guarding individual fundamental human interests even against the social interest are called *rights*. Not only do we as a society respect individual rights, we do our best to sanction other societies that ride roughshod over individual rights.

In essence, then, the theory behind our social ethic represents a middle ground or synthesis between utilitarian and deontological theories. On the one hand, social decisions are made and conflicts are resolved by appeal to the greatest good for the greatest number. But in cases wherein maximizing the general welfare could oppress the basic interests constituting the humanness of individuals, general welfare is checked by a deontological theoretical component: namely, respect for the individual human's nature and the interests flowing therefrom, which are in turn guaranteed by rights.

The practical implications of this theory are manifest. Consider some examples. Suppose a terrorist has planted a time bomb in an elementary school, placing the lives of innocent children in jeopardy. Suppose further that there is no way to defuse the bomb without setting it off, unless the terrorist, whom we have in custody, tells us how to do so. But he refuses to speak. Most of us would advocate torturing the terrorist to find out how to neutralize the bomb; after all, many innocent lives are at stake. Yet, despite the enormous utilitarian costs, our social ethic would not allow it, because the right to be protected from torture is so fundamental to human nature that we protect that right at whatever cost.

This is a sketch of our underlying social ethical theory. One may choose any personal ethical theory, but it must not conflict with the precedence of the social ethical theory. Thus I may choose to limit what I read by virtue of my adherence to some theological ethical theory, but if I am a librarian, I cannot restrict what *you* read. We shall shortly return to the social consensus theory just discussed, as it is highly relevant to the new ethic emerging in society about animal treatment—an ethic that is, in turn, highly relevant to veterinary ethics.

Societal ethical theory and personal ethical theory function to resolve conflict of principles. If one wishes to be morally consistent, it is valuable to articulate one's personal ethical theory and apply it uniformly.

Ethical Theory and Animals

A fundamental question of veterinary ethics still exists, because the societal ethic has historically been silent with regard to the moral status of animals and our obligations to them. And few people have bothered to develop a consistent personal ethical theory for animal treatment.

However, as society has developed an increasing concern for animal treatment, a characterizable ethic has begun to emerge. Anyone attending to cultural history over the last three decades cannot have failed to note a crescendo of societal concern about animal treatment across the western world. This is clearly evidenced in multiple ways. During that period, laws and regulations constraining the use of animals in a variety of areas (including biomedical research and agriculture) have proliferated worldwide. In the US, two pieces of landmark laboratory animal legislation passed in 1995, despite vigorous and powerful opposition from the research community (who also publicized the claim that such laws would threaten human health). In the European Union (EU) increasingly stringent regulations pertaining to both toxicological testing and animal agriculture have been promulgated (for example, that sow stalls must be abandoned within a decade and that in vitro cosmetic testing must replace animal testing). In Sweden in 1980, the Parliament passed, "virtually unopposed" according to the *New York Times* (October 25, 1988), a law eliminating confinement agriculture (what is colloquially known as "factory farming").[2] Recent years in the US have witnessed numerous examples of federal bills floating in Congress that pertain to animal welfare. Areas of concern have been as diverse as protecting marine mammals from tuna nets to preventing duplication in research. In 2003, approximately 2100 bills were introduced in state legislatures relevant to animal treatment. Most notable, perhaps, was the successful California law making shipping horses for slaughter a felony and knowingly selling a horse to someone who will ship the animal for slaughter a felony. This bill is now being pursued in Congress.

Historically, both the laws protecting animals and the societal ethic informing them were extremely minimalist; in essence, they were forbidding deliberate, willful, sadistic, deviant, extraordinary, and unnecessary cruelty not essential for "ministering to the necessities of man," or outrageous neglect. This ethic is found in the Bible and in the middle ages, when St. Thomas Aquinas, while affirming that although animals were not direct objects of moral concern, nevertheless presciently forbade cruelty to them on the grounds that those who would be cruel to animals will inexorably "graduate" to people (an insight buttressed by decades of research). Beginning in roughly 1800, the anti-cruelty laws were codified in the legal systems of most western societies.

The question naturally arises as to why, if the anti-cruelty ethic and laws sufficed for most of human history, did the past three decades call forth a demand for a new ethic and new laws? In contract research I undertook for the United States Department of Agriculture (USDA), I identified five factors:

1. Demographics have changed, as well as the consequent paradigm for animals. Whereas at the turn of the century, more than half of the population was engaged in producing food for the rest, today only about 1.5% of the US public is engaged in production agriculture. One hundred years ago, if a person were to ask another person on the street (urban or rural) to state the words that come to mind when hearing the word "animal," the answer would doubtless have been "horse," "cow," "food," "work," etc. However, for the majority of the population today, the answer is "dog," "cat," or "pet." Repeated studies show that almost 100% of the pet-owning population views their animals as "members of the family." And virtually no one views them as an income source. Divorce lawyers note that custody of the dog can be as thorny an issue as custody of the children!

2. We have lived through a long period of ethical soul-searching. For almost 50 years, society has turned its "ethical searchlight" on humans traditionally ignored or even oppressed by the consensus ethic: blacks, women, the handicapped, and other minorities. The same ethical imperative has focused attention on our treatment of the non-human world (i.e., the environment and animals). Many leaders of the activist animal movement have roots in earlier movements, such as civil rights, feminism, homosexual rights, children's rights, and labor.

3. The media has discovered that "animals sell papers." One cannot channel-surf across normal television programming without being bombarded with animal stories, real and fictional. (A *New York Times* reporter recently told me that more time on cable TV in New York City is devoted to animals than to any other subject.) Recall, for example, the extensive media coverage a decade ago regarding some whales trapped

in an ice floe and freed by a Russian icebreaker. It seems someone in the Kremlin realized that liberating the whales was a cheap way to win credit with western public opinion.

4. Strong and visible arguments by philosophers, scientists, and celebrities have been advanced in favor of raising the status of animals.

5. Of highest significance is the precipitous change in animal use occurring in the mid-20th century.

Traditionally, society's major use of animals was agriculture—for food, fiber, locomotion, and power. The key to agricultural success was good husbandry, which meant taking great pains to put one's animals into the best possible environment one could find to meet their physical and psychological natures (which, following Aristotle, I call *telos*). Also of importance was augmenting the animals' ability to survive and thrive by providing them with food during famine, protection from predation, water during drought, medical attention, help in birthing, and so on. Thus, traditional agriculture was roughly a fair contract between humans and animals, with both sides being better off in virtue of the relationship. Husbandry agriculture was about placing square pegs into square holes, round pegs into round holes, and creating as little friction as possible in doing so.

Welfare was thus assured by the strongest of sanctions—self-interest— and the anti-cruelty ethic needed only to deal with sadists and psychopaths unmoved by self-interest.

The rise of confinement agriculture, based in applying industrial methods to animal production, broke this "ancient contract." With technological "sanders" (e.g., hormones, vaccines, antibiotics, air handling systems, mechanization, etc.), we could force square pegs into round holes and place animals into environments where they suffered in ways irrelevant to productivity. If a 19th century agriculturalist had tried to put 100,000 egg-laying hens in cages in a building, they all would have died of disease in a month; today, such systems dominate.

At the same historical moment, animals began to be used on a large scale in research and testing—again, causing new and unprecedented degrees of suffering.

The amount of suffering arising from these sources far outweighs what is produced by deliberate cruelty. Further, the anti-cruelty laws do not cover these new uses and cannot be twisted to fit anything like steel-jawed trapping, sow stalls, or toxicology, since these exemplify "ministering to human necessity." Thus a demand was called forth for a new ethic.

Summary

In Western societies, human ethics balances utilitarian considerations (the greatest good for the greatest number) against concern for individuals by building "protective fences" around essential features of human nature; these fences are called rights. Rights are a moral/legal notion designed to save essential features of an individual's human nature (e.g., the desire for free speech) from being submerged for the general welfare. The logic of this notion is being exported to animals. Society wishes to ensure that their basic interests, flowing from their *telos*, are not submerged, and that farm animals live decent lives, and laboratory animals have pain controlled.

Direct rights for animals are, of course, legally impossible, given the legal status of animals as property. To change this would require a constitutional amendment in the US. (Many legal scholars are working to elevate the legal status of animals.) But the same functional goal can be accomplished by restricting how animal property can be used. Thus, the laboratory animal laws require that pain and distress be controlled, repeated invasive uses be eliminated, exercise be mandatory for dogs, etc. Some European laws have forbidden sow stalls. This mechanism is the root of what I have called "animal rights as a mainstream phenomenon." This also explains the proliferation of laws pertaining to animals as an effort to ensure their welfare in the face of historically unprecedented uses.

This new ethic is good news for veterinarians, as they can now expect increased social backing for their priority commitment to animals (what I have called the Pediatrician Model). Veterinary medicine must engage and lead in providing rational answers and laws to protect animal well-being in all areas of animal use. Not only will job satisfaction increase, but as the status of animals rises in society, so too will the status of those who care for them.

References

1. Bernard E. Rollin, *Veterinary Medical Ethics: Theory and Cases* Blackwell; Ames, Iowa; 2006).

2. *Irish Examiner*, June 25, 2001: "EU ministers agree to ban sow stalls for pregnant pigs" http://archives.tcm.ie/irishexaminer/2001/06/25/story6387.asp accessed May 24, 2006.

Biography

Dr. Rollin is Professor of Philosophy, Professor of Biomedical Sciences, and Professor of Animal Science at Colorado State University. Rollin's scholarly interests include both traditional philosophy and applied philosophy. In addition to numerous articles on the history of philosophy, philosophy of language, ethics and bioethics, he is the author of 14 books, including *Natural and Conventional Meaning* (1976), *Animal Rights and Human Morality* (1981, 1993, & 2006), *The Unheeded Cry: Animal Consciousness, Animal Pain and Scientific Change* (1988 &1998), *Farm Animal Welfare* (1995), *The Frankenstein Syndrome* (1995), *Science and Ethics* (2006), *Veterinary Medical Ethics: Theory and Cases* (2nd edition, 2006), as well as over 400 articles. He has edited a two-volume work titled *The Experimental Animal in Biomedical Research* (1989 & 1995) and *Harley Davidson and Philosophy* (2006). He is one of the leading scholars in animal rights and animal consciousness and has lectured over 1000 times in 28 countries around the world. Rollin developed the world's first courses in veterinary medical ethics, ethical issues in animal science, and biology combined with philosophy. The winner of numerous US and international awards, he is a weight-lifter, horseman, and motorcyclist.

The Proactive Veterinary Practitioner: Veterinary Risk-Management Planning

Douglas C. Jack, BA, LL.B
Douglas C. Jack, Solicitors,
Fergus, Ontario

> *The soul of a nation can be judged by the way it treats its animals.*
>
> — Mahatma Gandhi

Introduction

All of us in Canada live in an increasingly litigious society. Canadians have become very much aware, through various media, of their ability to enforce legal rights whenever they feel they have been wronged. This phenomenon has manifested itself in a plethora of lawsuits against professionals on the basis of negligent performance of their skills, leading to damages suffered by their unfortunate clients. In my opinion, effective practice management includes avoidance of claims of this nature, so as to ensure continued profitability of the firm and relief of undue anxiety for the professional staff. In this regard, one of the fastest growing areas of veterinary jurisprudence relates to societal recognition of the enhanced status of animals. With this enhanced status comes increased exposure for liability for their primary healthcare providers.

A topic of great importance in the medico-legal world is the issue of informed consent to treatment. It is comforting to note that few actions have been brought against veterinarians for professional negligence, relative to other professions; however, the profession and its governing body readily have accepted that obtaining informed consent to treatment now is rooted firmly in veterinary medicine as well.

This article will provide basic understanding of the legal principles affecting veterinary malpractice claims and the current legal impact of the human-animal bond (HAB). Finally, some helpful tips will be presented to avoid liability through a thorough understanding of the concept of informed consent to treatment. The practitioner and his/her employees may avoid claims arising out of problem cases through the implementation of strict policies within your business relating to this important issue.

Veterinary Malpractice Theory

In recent times, many veterinary practitioners use adjectives such as "demanding," "assertive," "knowledgeable," and "forceful" to describe common characteristics of their clients. The consumer age has brought with it a client base that readily is willing to assert its legal rights. In some cases, Canadian laws have made the court system more accessible for clients to pursue legal remedies in the event they feel that the veterinarian has acted inappropriately in the care of their companion animal or in the management of herd health. In the small-animal context, the growing importance of and research into the HAB creates deeper legal pitfalls for the practitioner. In the large-animal context, the absolute need for completely safe food products has created new avenues for liability related to the transmission of parasitic zoonotic disease.

The Law of Negligence

The Law of Negligence is grounded in the common Law of Torts, which has as its objective the need to compensate victims of inappropriate conduct. Negligence arises when the practitioner is found to have breached his/her duty of care to a client and, as a result thereof, the client has suffered damages.

It can be assumed that the veterinary practitioner in North America today implicitly holds himself/herself out to have special expertise and skill in veterinary medicine, upon which members of the public are entitled to rely. As such, no doubt exists that a duty of care is owed to the public as soon as you make yourself available to perform veterinary treatment. The breach of that duty arises when something goes amiss; a diagnosis is incorrect, a treatment regime is unsuccessful, or some other unanticipated result occurs.

The Standard of Care

All veterinary practitioners are obliged to exercise the care, skill, and diligence provided by a reasonable practitioner in similar circumstances. This is the objective test of the standard of care that you must discharge to each and every client in your practice. Your actions will be judged in reference to your colleagues in hypothetical situations in which they would be called upon to exercise care in the same or similar circumstances.

Proximate Cause

In every jurisdiction, the negligence complained of must have caused the damages claimed, in order for them to be recovered. Proximate cause is a legal doctrine that dictates that some clear causal connection must be demonstrated between the acts complained of and the actual damages that resulted—it is an artificial line drawn to cut off the natural consequences of an act at some point. This concept is made more difficult in cases where two events, the first being the cause of the underlying condition and the second being the act of negligence complained of, occur closely together in time. In these cases, it can be argued that the first event may have lead to the same result in any event.

The Veterinarian's Role in Society

The veterinary profession has participated in society as health-care professionals; that is, the profession has been involved in preventive medicine, comparative medicine, food hygiene, control and elimination of zoonotic disease, and other public-health issues. Perplexing is the apparent lack of understanding by private veterinary practitioners of their roles, responsibilities, and obligations in public-health concerns. The consumer's increased awareness of the apparent benefits of pet-assisted therapy in human health, the move towards preventive veterinary medicine, and the intolerance of tainted products from food-producing animals could lead to a much greater role for the veterinary practitioner in the health-care sector. The veterinarian will be faced with new legal obligations to owners, employees, nursing-home residents and the public generally.

With this health-care role comes legal exposure for malpractice, heightening the need for the veterinary professional to practice preventively. New opportunities for practitioners to expand their practices may be available in providing advice on matters relating to human-health concerns and matters of public health.

The Calculation of Damages

Damage awards for veterinary malpractice are either compensatory or punitive in nature. Until recently, compensatory damages when patients were either injured or killed were straightforward. The general rules dictate that, since animals are in law property, the calculation of damages was based on the market value of the animal. Claims for emotional suffering of owners were not successful. This has been the case in a small-animal context. In equine and food-producing animal contexts, the animal has a market value that can be established based on cost comparison with other similar animals. However, damages could be significant for a valuable racehorse or a herd of dairy cattle.

The fact that veterinarians are not immune from the rigours of litigation is evident in the reported cases. In 1989, the Court of Queen's Bench in New Brunswick dealt with damages to be awarded to an owner of a standardbred horse that had undergone unsuccessful cryosurgery undertaken by the veterinarian. In fact, in this case, the veterinarian admitted negligence so the only issue to be dealt with in *Ryan v. Avenue Animal Hospital Ltd.* was the correct amount of damages to be awarded. The value of the horse at the time of the surgery was $16,800; accordingly, the award of damages was in that amount. In these cases, expert evidence is necessary to determine the value of the particular animal, so as to determine the correct damages. You should be aware that the plaintiff (i.e., owner) must prove such evidence in each case.

Calculation of compensatory damages also was made in *Murray v. Mouris*, a 1980 decision of the Nova Scotia Supreme Court. In that case, the defendant veterinarian had advised a farmer that a heifer could not reproduce. The farmer then arranged for the animal's slaughter and, in the rendering process, it was determined that she was five-months pregnant. The damages were set at $10,000, including the sum of $2,500 for the value of the unborn calf.

Punitive damages are awarded rarely, except if the conduct of the practitioner has been particularly distasteful or malicious. In the United States, one court has indicated that punitive damages would be awarded only where the conduct of the practitioner was evidenced by "an evil hand guided by an evil mind."

The Impact of the Human-Animal Bond

The most controversial area in the calculation of damages appears to be in a small-animal context for the emotional distress of pet owners whose pets have been injured or killed through negligence. The importance of the HAB has been advanced in support for new heads of damages (reasons for damages with no history in jurisprudence) for this distress; damages in a case in Florida in 1964 were contemplated on this basis. In *LaPorte v. Associated Independents, Inc.*, the defendant was a corporation engaged in the garbage collection business. The plaintiff was a customer of the defendant. One morning, Mrs. La-Porte was preparing breakfast while her miniature dachshund was tethered outside, beyond the reach of her garbage cans. She observed a garbage collector, employed by the defendant, empty the garbage and then hurl the empty can in the direction of the dog, striking it. The dog was injured and eventually died from its injuries. Having witnessed the incident, the plaintiff became quite distraught to the point of marked hysteria and sought the assistance of her family physician, who later testified that he had been treating Mrs. La Parte for a nervous condition. The court reviewed these facts and indicated that the plaintiff could recover damages for the alleged mental suffering and awarded the plaintiff $2,000 in compensatory damages and $1,000 for punitive damages. The defendant then appealed this decision arguing that the plaintiff's ability to be compensated for nervous suffering was improper.

The Florida District Court of Appeal held that while the general rule in cases of injury or destruction of a companion animal is that the market value of the animal should be used to determine the amount of the pecuniary loss, this was not applied in this case stating:

> *The restriction of the loss of a pet to its intrinsic value in circumstances such as the ones before us is a principle we cannot accept. Without indulging in a discussion of the affinity between 'sentimental value' and 'mental suffering', we feel that the affection that a master has for his dog is a very real thing and that the malicious destruction of the pet provides an element of damage for which the owner should recover, irrespective of the value of the animal because of its special training such as a seeing eye dog or sheep dog.*

As a result and beginning over 40 years ago, courts started to give some credence to the HAB and were prepared to award damages to a bereaved owner in certain circumstances.

In *Nicholls v. Sukaro Kennels*, the owner of a seven-year-old toy poodle claimed damages against a kennel operator when the operator's own dog "tore off" the left front leg of the poodle. In that case (Iowa, 1996) the plaintiffs claimed special damages for the "intrinsic value" or "special value" of the dog to them. In rejecting the claim for special damages, the court noted that the plaintiffs did not produce any evidence of the "special purpose, or intrinsic value other than his value as a family pet."

Following the previously described *LaPorte* case, the Florida District Court of Appeal allowed damages for mental anguish in a veterinary malpractice case involving the death of a dog during routine treatment for a dermatological condition. The dog's remains were disposed of contrary to the owner's instructions, thus making necropsy impossible.

In 1978, the Florida District Court of Appeal in *Knowles Animal Hospital v. Wills* allowed a jury to consider mental anguish caused to an owner in negligent veterinary care when a dog was left unattended on a heating pad and sustained severe burns.

Other jurisdictions have not been as willing to accept the award of damages for mental suffering of the owner. In New York, an appeals court rejected such a claim in *Jason v. Parks*. Similarly, in 1996 the Iowa Supreme Court made its ruling in the previously described *Nicholls* case, rejecting the plaintiffs' claim that they had a "humanistic" relationship with their pet. Such claims have been rejected in Illinois in *Jankosi v. Preiser Animal Hospital Ltd.*, where the court held that the loss of companionship of the animal did not stand as an independent cause of action.

Volumes of materials have been written analysing many aspects of the HAB. In particular, the use of animals in pet-assisted therapies in a human-medicine context is well documented. On a daily basis, veterinarians continue to underscore the importance of the bond in offering preventive medical advice and "wellness" therapies on the basis that the companion animal is truly a "part of the family." Advertising campaigns are mounted by veterinary interest groups and veterinary suppliers that direct the consumer to consider the importance of the animal's well being in the owner's life. Effective marketing for the small-animal practitioner includes embracing the pet as a "family member;" this is particularly true in practices that offer grief counselling for owners.

Damages for loss of income can be awarded. This is often the case for performance horses rendered unable to compete at the same level as prior to the negligent conduct. Expert evidence is necessary to prove such claims.

In addition, a number of revealing studies draw direct causal links between the health of a human patient and the presence of a companion animal. Geriatric human patients often are presented with pet-assisted therapies. A recent study presented at the 7th International Conference of Human/Animal Interactions in Geneva suggests that heart-attack victims who own pets, particularly dogs, are nine times more likely than their non-pet-owning counterparts to be alive one year after an attack.[1] Dr. Ian Robinson, pet-ownership studies manager of Waltham and the primary sponsor of the event, suggests that this "...*study is somewhat of a landmark in the growing field of human-animal interaction research because it directly links pet ownership with longevity."* The study involved one-year survival data of more than 350 cardiac patients; 19 of 282 study patients who did not own dogs died while only one of 87 dog-owning patients died. The study was presented by Dr. Erika Friedman, who suggested, *"one could argue that because they exercise their animals, dog owners are, in general, healthier than non-dog owners. However, when we compared physiological profiles of dog owners and non-dog owners, there were no significant differences, suggesting that the relationship itself with the animal was a predictor of survival rates."*

The veterinary practitioner must appreciate that as scientific studies continue to provide results that draw causal links between human health and continued good health of companion animals, the risk and exposure of greater damage awards is a reality in negligence cases. In my view, it will become increasingly difficult to argue that the appropriate damage award is restricted to the value of the animal; as a result, veterinary malpractice insurers will require payment of higher premiums to reflect increased exposure. In addition, litigation involving pet owners likely will increase, as greater damage awards will be at stake.

Statutory Evolution

Clear evidence indicates that the HAB is now the subject of statutory recognition in various forms. Municipal ordinances relating to animal-control issues in both San Francisco and Boulder have been amended in recent years to change the words "animal owners" to "animal guardians." With all due respect, I suggest that the term "guardian" has a distinctly different connotation than that of "owner," suggesting a level of care is required because of the dependency of the animal. As well, the States of Maryland, Tennessee and Oregon each have placed bills before their respective state legislatures to limit damage awards that might be made available by a court to an animal owner. In the Oregon bill, the quantum of damages is proposed to be limited to $250,000 for non-economic losses. As such, I respectfully suggest that this represents further evidence of the recognition of the importance of animals to their owners and, indeed, the influence of the HAB.

Malpractice Avoidance

With the increased exposure the veterinary professional has to claims of malpractice, it is critical that s/he implement effective strategies within the clinic to avoid as many claims as possible. In this regard, it is important that the practitioner have a thorough understanding of the principles of informed consent to treatment and effective records management.

Informed Consent—"What Is It?"

It is clear that veterinary medical treatment cannot be provided without first obtaining the consent of the owner of the animal. Failure to obtain consent could result in an action by the pet owner or farmer in trespass (as animals are deemed to be property under law, this is an alternative action to a veterinary malpractice claim). In addition to ensuring that the person consenting to treatment is mentally and legally capable of granting consent and that such consent is voluntary, the courts have (at least in the human-medicine context) required that such consent be informed. It is this latter requirement that potentially causes the greatest difficulty in day-to-day management of a busy practice. The threat of annoyed clients suffering from lengthy waits prior to undertaking an examination too often can lead to proceeding with a particular treatment without properly obtaining and providing evidence of obtaining informed consent, in the interest of saving time.

The Supreme Court of Canada has determined that in obtaining the consent of a human patient for the performance of treatment, the practitioner must answer any specific questions posed by the patient as to the risks involved. The practitioner should, without being questioned, disclose to the patient the nature of the proposed treatment, its gravity, any material risks, probable risks and any special or unusual risks attendant with the procedure.

PRACTICE POINT

In a busy practice, all members of the firm should be aware of the necessity to obtain informed consent. While the legal obligation rests with the veterinarian, it is incumbent upon hospital managers and lay staff to ensure that no treatment proceeds until such time as informed consent has been obtained.

Presumably the veterinarian must disclose the type of risks to the owner, as they relate to the welfare of the animal. The determination of whether or not these issues have been addressed properly is to be determined with reference to the circumstances of each case. What then are the tests to be applied to each of the probable or material risks?

The need to discuss these matters is set out in the statutory Code of Ethics for Veterinary Surgeons in Quebec. The Code dictates that the practitioner must reveal to his or her client in a complete and objective manner, the nature and scope of the problem, which, in the veterinarian's opinion, results from the facts presented to him. Further, the practitioner must not express his or her opinion based on incomplete advice.

Probable Risk

It will appear trite to state that probable risks are to be contrasted with mere possibilities; however, this is the manner in which courts will view the discharge of obtaining informed consent. The risk of death though, even if only a possibility, must be disclosed. As such, the prudent veterinarian must call upon all of his professional resources to provide reasonable disclosure of probable risks to the animal.

Material Risk

Possible risks, for which consequences would be grave, also need to be disclosed as being material risks. In human medicine, it has been determined that the risk of death must be discussed insofar as the proper information to be given to a client. Once again, an objective test of materiality is to be employed in determining whether or not any particular risk of treatment is material.

As many risks as possible should be discussed. It is proper, depending on the circumstances, to advise the client that the risk of adverse consequences is small; however, the important point is to ensure that the discussion took place and is well documented.

The determination of the court is based on whether a reasonable person in the client's position would have consented to the procedure if proper disclosure of the attendant risks had been provided. The main point is that the courts have determined that you are not to determine whether or not sufficient information has been given, based on a standard of what a reasonable veterinarian would provide in the circumstances. Rather, the test would appear to turn on whether you have provided enough information to the client based on what a reasonable client would want to know in the circumstances. The prudent practitioner will err on the side of providing too much information as opposed to too little.

PRACTICE POINT

A periodic review of files by the clinic manager is a valuable exercise to ensure that all necessary treatment forms have been executed properly by the pet owner. Through the form of a management meeting, a report on case files where proper consent may not have been obtained should be reviewed and remedied.

Emergency Treatment

Each of you will experience the occasion when a pet is brought to your clinic in very poor condition and requires immediate assistance. Although not determined by the courts in a veterinary context, the law appears to be that in circumstances where treatment is necessary to preserve the life or future health of a patient and it is impossible to obtain informed consent, then a veterinarian would be privileged to proceed.

Providing the Evidence of Informed Consent

As in many lawsuits involving professional negligence, a key difficulty is the veterinarian proving what was said and discussed with the animal owner. This difficulty then is subject to being determined by the court, based solely on the credibility of the witnesses—the poor, bereaved pet owner against the professional who took their pet from them through negligence. To this end, it is essential that clear, written, documented evidence be available and made mandatory throughout the practice as part of the standard practice management.

It is likely that some standard form for obtaining consent is being used in your practices; if it is not, a form should be developed immediately and implemented by the hospital manager. At minimum, the form should state that the client has been informed of the probable and material risks associated with the treatment and further, it should set out the very risks discussed. The failure to set out specific discussions reduces the credibility of the form to a self-serving statement from the professional.

A specific form may be developed for certain routine procedures (e.g., neutering an animal), which sets out all of the usual probable and material risks of that procedure. If such specialized forms are used, members of the firm should be cautioned against relying solely on them in the event that the particular animal presents itself in a condition that would give rise to other risks not spelled out already.

The form usually will be presented in a pre-printed format for the owner to sign. It is important that specific provisions on the form be pointed out and that the client be advised to read the document prior to signing it. Failure to do so could result in the form losing its credibility as being a standard-form contract, which have suffered greatly in the courts in other contexts.

In addition, the practitioner should be reminded that liability is invited if certain risks are not disclosed in fear of the owner not consenting to the treatment, which is required in the opinion of the practitioner. Ultimately, failure to act in circumstances where you have been so instructed will not attract liability in the usual case.

The prudent veterinary clinic manager will implement policies within the firm to ensure that every client entering the practice provides informed consent prior to treating his or her animal. The failure to do so will result in lost time, poor productivity, and potentially great expense for the practice.

Limitation Periods

Any action against a veterinarian for negligence is subject to the client bringing the lawsuit within certain time periods, known as "limitation periods," which can be found in some of the provincial statutes. The failure to initiate the proceedings prior to the expiry of these dates effectively bars any claim against the veterinarian.

The Veterinary Medical Act of Newfoundland and Labrador provides a relatively short limitation period; Section 53 of this Act states no action can be brought against a practitioner for negligence or malpractice unless such court action is taken within six months after the matter in question occurred.

Section 51 of the New Brunswick Veterinarians Act provides a limitation period for actions against a veterinarian or professional veterinary corporation for negligence, malpractice, or breach of contract of two years from the date the matter in question occurred.

The limitation period in Manitoba is two years from the date that the damages were sustained.

Under the Saskatchewan Veterinarians Act, any such action for negligence against a veterinarian in that province must be commenced within twelve months of the date that the matter in question occurred.

Conclusion

The prudent veterinary practitioner will have an understanding of the principles of veterinary malpractice in order to ensure appropriate strategies are implemented to avoid claims. Far too often, the practitioner approached the obtaining of informed consent to treatment in a cavalier manner, which can expose the clinic to unacceptable levels of risk. One must be diligent and take proactive steps in order to establish an effective system of risk management within the veterinary hospital.

References

1. Friedmann E, Thomas SA. Pet ownership, social support, and one-year survival after acute myocardial infarction in the cardiac arrhythmia suppression trial (CAST). Proceedings, 7th International Conference of Human/Animal Interactions; Geneva, 1995.

Biography

Douglas C. Jack conducts his own law practice in Fergus, Ontario dedicated to the law as it relates to the veterinary profession in both general commercial law matters and veterinary malpractice defence. He is a charter and founding member of the American Veterinary Medical Law Association and the only Canadian to have served as its President. Mr. Jack is the author of two books on legal aspects of veterinary practice management and has written numerous published articles in veterinary journals throughout North America. He is regularly invited to speak at veterinary conferences throughout the United States and Canada and often lectures on matters of Veterinary Jurisprudence at the Ontario Veterinary College and Atlantic Veterinary College. Mr. Jack is an affiliate member of the Ontario Veterinary Medical Association, the Veterinary Hospital Managers' Association, and the American Animal Hospital Association.

The Equine Pre-Purchase Examination: Standard of Care and Legal Tips

Catherine E. Willson, BA, LL.B
Founder and Partner, Willson Lewis LLP,
Toronto, Ontario
With thanks to Aimee Coyler LL.B, articling student at
Willson Lewis LLP

> *An ounce of prevention is worth a pound of cure.*
>
> — Anonymous

Introduction

With horses, cattle, and some other animals, the sale of an animal will usually not take place unless and until a veterinarian has examined the animal and pronounced the animal sound for the purposes of the prospective purchaser. With horses, purchasers are primarily concerned about issues of lameness, respiratory conditions, or other conditions or diseases that will render the horse (either now or after purchase) unfit for riding or use in whatever way the purchaser has in mind. With cattle and other animals, purchasers are most likely concerned with fertility issues and capacity to breed.

In both situations, a veterinarian will be called upon not to treat the animal, but to examine it for the purpose of sale. The purpose of the prepurchase examination is to obtain as much information as possible about the health of the animal so that an educated decision can be made regarding whether to purchase the animal. The prepurchase examination is the purchaser's opportunity to detect any physical defects in the animal that could negatively affect the purpose for which the animal is intended.

Given the price of some animals these days, especially horses and cattle, the veterinarian is assuming a huge responsibility when rendering a prepurchase opinion to a prospective purchaser. If the veterinarian is negligent in the provision of that opinion, and the animal proves to be unsound after purchase, the veterinarian could be found responsible by the courts for all of the purchaser's damages, including the sale price of the animal, transportation costs, veterinary bills, boarding and other maintenance costs, and even such abstract claims as damages for the pain and suffering of the purchaser and lost opportunity costs. For a prepurchase examination fee that runs between $500 and $1,000, a veterinarian assumes a significant risk.

Standard of Care

There is limited case law on the general standard of care imposed on veterinarians. The authority in *Wheeler v. Muri*[1] adopted a physician's standard of care for medical malpractice cases in relation to veterinarians. The standard of care was based on a reasonable degree of learning and skill ordinarily possessed by practitioners in similar communities in similar cases.

The authority in *Hihn v. Schaeffer*[2] held that a veterinarian is not a guarantor of results but must provide services in a reasonably efficient manner. The court in *Brettell v. Main West Animal Hospital, Ltd.*[3] accepted testimony from a veterinary surgeon and professor of veterinary medicine at the Ontario Veterinary College that a veterinary surgeon is not expected to be an expert in every instance.

It is not enough to conclude that a veterinarian has followed the usual practice in any particular area; the duty is fulfilled only if the veterinarian acts in accordance with a practice rightly accepted as proper by a body of skilled and experienced veterinarian practitioners. The next step is to consider whether the veterinarian conducted the "adequate tests adequately" (*Southwhite Stables, Inc. v. Ingram Veterinary Services, Ltd.*[4]).

As a rule of thumb, a veterinarian's standard of care for a prepurchase examination is to perform the examination with reasonable care and skill. The reasonableness will be determined by "industry standards"—that is, the usual degree of care and skill exercised by veterinarians in similar cases in similar communities.

It should also be noted that the *Veterinarians Act*, R.S.O. 1990, c.V.3, section 5.5 mandates that the professional, fiduciary, and ethical obligations of a member to a person on whose behalf the member is practising veterinary medicine

1.   are not diminished by the fact that the member is practising veterinary medicine through a professional corporation; and
2.   apply equally to the corporation and to its directors, officers, shareholders, agents, and employees.

Legal Tips

As a lawyer, I cannot comment on the scope of a prepurchase examination or the tests considered suitable or adequate. No doubt these will vary considerably, depending on the type and purpose of the animal. In the horse world, a physical examination of a horse can be accompanied by ultrasounds, radiographs, drug testing, and many other tests, depending on the value of the horse to the purchaser.

A new veterinarian should obtain the advice of several respected veterinarians in the jurisdiction to determine the methods and scope of any prepurchase examination; however, I can provide the following legal recommendations:

1.   Always produce for the client a written report of the prepurchase findings. Deliver this report to the client prior to purchase of the animal. From a business perspective, it gives the client something concrete for the money spent. From a legal perspective, it protects you, the veterinarian, in the event that an unsound animal is purchased by a client who didn't hear, didn't understand, or chose to forget your professional opinion. With no written report, a court may very well believe the client's version of the facts over your version of the facts. Because you are the professional, the court may expect you to know better than to render an oral report.
2.   Avoid situations of possible or perceived conflict. If you work for the vendor of an animal, don't perform the prepurchase examination on behalf of the purchaser. In the haste of the sale, a prospective purchaser may assure you that he trusts you and is not concerned that you work for the seller; however, the purchaser's attitude may change if the animal later develops problems. If you have treated the animal for an injury or disease for a previous owner, consider whether you should act

for a prospective purchaser in a prepurchase situation. Do you have an obligation to disclose to the purchaser your knowledge of the past injury or disease? Can you disclose it without breaching your obligations of confidentiality to the previous owner of the animal? The answer to these questions is facts specific and a question of veterinary ethics.

3. Ask your client, the purchaser, to detail the purpose for which s/he is buying the animal, and incorporate a reference to this purpose in your report. This is important for two reasons. Courts have indicated that a proper prepurchase opinion takes into account the purpose intended by the buyer. Further, the purpose of purchase may dictate the types of tests used in a prepurchase examination and the degree of exploration required. For example, the purchase of a competitive show horse may require the addition of ultrasounds and radiographs to the usual physical examination performed by the veterinarian. The purchase of a broodmare requires other tests.

4. Inform your client of the less standard tests available to him as part of the prepurchase examination, in addition to the tests you usually perform or recommend. In so doing, you give the client the choice of a more detailed examination (obviously for a greater price) if it is desired.

5. Due to the fact that certain animal injuries or illnesses can come on suddenly and without notice, the ideal time for vetting should be as soon before closing the sale as possible. While you, acting as the veterinarian, may not be able to make this decision, make your client aware of the time implications in vetting an animal too far in advance of closing the sale.

Examples From the Courts

The best way to appreciate the standard of care applicable to a veterinarian performing a prepurchase examination is to consider some examples.

Southwhite Stables, Inc. v. Ingram Veterinary Services, Ltd.[5] *In this 1984 Alberta case, the plaintiff purchased a horse that went blind in one eye from a cataract a year later. The plaintiff/purchaser sued the vendor of the horse for* misrepresentation and also sued the plaintiff's veterinarian for negligence in the prepurchase veterinary examination and the report to the purchaser.

The veterinarian had treated the horse three years earlier, on behalf of the vendor, for an eye injury. The horse presented with some watering of the right eye, some inflammation of the eye, a disturbance of the eye's conjunctiva, an abrasion or laceration of the cornea, cloudiness of the cornea, some inflammation of the interior chamber, and considerable pain. The horse was treated for seven days, and treatment was apparently effective. Three years later, and because of his previous experience with this animal, the veterinarian took special attention with respect to the eye test portion of the prepurchase examination. The veterinarian performed the usual tests on the eye that he performs in a prepurchase examination: a menace test, a papillary response test, and a three images test. He did not perform any additional tests on the eye, such as an examination using a direct ophthalmoscope. The veterinarian did not disclose to the purchaser his previous experience with the horse.

The court stated that it is not enough to conclude that a veterinarian has followed the usual practice in any particular area. The duty is fulfilled if the veterinarian acts in accordance with a practice rightly accepted as proper by a body of skilled and experienced veterinarians. In this instance, the test would be: Is reliance by most veterinarians on the three-phase eye test accepted by the veterinary profession as an adequate test for equine opacity of the lens? The court answered this question in the affirmative.

The court then went on to consider whether the veterinarian in this particular case should have used the ophthalmoscope, given his previous knowledge of the eye injury. The court said "no," as the evidence did not suggest that the use of a direct ophthalmoscope necessarily provides benefits in identifying opacities. It is merely an alternate technique and one in which this veterinarian was not trained or comfortable in using. Further, the one clear advantage of the direct ophthalmoscopic examination is its ability to view the fundic area. In this case, nothing appeared to be wrong with either the retina or the optic nerve of the eye, so there was no causal link between the failure to examine the fundic area and the eye condition. Finally, given the three-year period between the previous eye injury and the prepurchase examination, it could be expected (based on expert evidence) that the eye would be stable.

Having concluded that the tests themselves were adequate, the court then considered whether the veterinarian conducted the "adequate tests adequately." The court answered this in the affirmative; the veterinarian took the proper degree of care in performing the tests.

On the issue of reporting the results of the prepurchase examination, the court suggested that the veterinarian wrongly failed to report the corneal scar on the right eye to the purchaser, but this failure was not considered significant as the purchaser apparently already had knowledge of the corneal scar before purchase. The veterinarian's vetting of the horse as sound for the purpose of a green hunter should be understood in the context of the existence of the corneal scar, which was acknowledged by all parties.

Finally, the court did not answer the question of whether the veterinarian had a duty to report his earlier involvement with the horse to the purchaser, suggesting that this was a matter for discussion in veterinary ethics. In this case, the court considered the veterinarian's prepurchase opinion to be sound, and this was enough to end the discussion.

I would recommend that you not perform a prepurchase examination on a horse that you previously treated for an injury or disease. If you must, I would suggest that you first obtain your client's permission to disclose your previous involvement with the horse to the prospective purchaser before performing the prepurchase examination.

Murray v. Mouris[6]

This is a 1980 Nova Scotia court decision in which two veterinary defendants were found liable for breach of contract and negligence in conducting a medical examination of a heifer.

The plaintiff had purchased a Limousin heifer with a sterility guarantee, by which the vendor agreed to indemnify the plaintiff in the event that the animal manifested apparent total and permanent inability to breed. After the heifer failed to show any signs of heat, the plaintiff had his veterinarian examine the heifer for pregnancy. The veterinarian reported that the animal seemed to have very under-developed ovaries, that the uterus was small, and that it was unlikely the animal would be capable of breeding.

The plaintiff subsequently wrote to the vendor, advising that the heifer had not exhibited a regular heat cycle since arriving at his farm, and stating that he had recently had the heifer examined by a veterinarian who gave the opinion that it was unlikely the animal would ever conceive. In response, the vendor sent the purchaser a form to be completed by the veterinarian and returned. The veterinarian completed a portion of the form, indicating no deficiency of the vulva, that the cervix of the uterus was normal, that tonicity of the tissues was normal, and that the condition of the mucous membranes was normal. The veterinarian further indicated that rectal examination demonstrated the main part of the uterus was normal; that examination of the uterine cornua showed they were normal; and that examination of the oviducts showed they were normal. However, in the case of the ovaries, the veterinarian stated that they were under-developed and less than one centimeter in diameter.

The vendor replied, asking for a more detailed, recent report on the examination of the ovaries. The vendor requested that the veterinarian check again for evidence of any corpus luteum and any increase in the size of the ovaries since the last veterinary appointment. The plaintiff asked the veterinarian to perform a further examination and provide a report for the vendor. The veterinarian sent his associate (also a veterinarian and an employee of the original veterinarian) to perform the examination and provide a report.

The defendant (associate DVM) submitted a written report to the plaintiff, stating that the animal was physically under-developed for a cow of her age and size and that the cow was unable to reproduce. The plaintiff forwarded this report to the vendor, who replied that in accordance with the infertility guarantee, the cost of the heifer, less 15%, would be refunded. However, before the refund would be given, the vendor required an official slaughter certificate. The plaintiff arranged for the slaughter of the heifer, and in the report of same, it was disclosed that the animal was carrying a heifer calf at the time of death.

The court concluded that the defendant's (associate DVM) failure to diagnose the pregnancy and the giving of the opinion that the animal would never reproduce, resulted from a failure to exercise the care that a reasonably prudent doctor of veterinary medicine would show in conducting such an examination. The associate DVM was found liable to the plaintiff for negligence in the performance of his duties as a practitioner. Furthermore, based on the court's finding that there was a contractual relationship between the plaintiff and the original veterinarian, and the defendant (associate DVM) acted as his agent, the original veterinarian was found liable for breach of said contract.

References

1.   [1997] 3 W.W.R. 287
2.   [1987] O.J. No. 2025
3.   [1992] O.J. No. 2767
4.   [1984] A.W.L.D. 449
5.   *Ibid*
6.   [1980] 40 N.S.R. (2d) 637

Biography

Catherine Willson was called to the Ontario Bar in 1989, and she is the founder of the law firm Willson Lewis LLP, located in Toronto, Ontario. Willson Lewis LLP is a litigation boutique firm, practising in the areas of civil and commercial litigation, employment law, and construction, tax, family, and equine law. Catherine is an executive member of the Canadian Bar Association (Ontario) – Civil Litigation section; Chairman of the Risk Management Committee – Royal Agricultural Winter Fair; and a member of the Association of Trial Lawyers of America, The Advocates' Society, the Toronto Construction Association, and The Equine and Animal Lawyers' Association. She is a regular speaker at legal conferences and writes on legal issues for *Horsesport* magazine and other publications. She has owned and shown her horses on the hunter-jumper circuit. Her involvement with horses spans the last 28 years, and she is well recognized in the horse industry for her knowledge and experience in equine law.

Non-Competition Agreements: Walk a Mile in Another's Moccasins

Brian Ausman, BSc (Agr), DVM, MBA, LL.B
Real Estate & Business Broker, Lawyer, and
Practice Co-Owner, Guelph, Ontario

> *I believe in courtesy, in kindness, in generosity, in good cheer, in friendship, and in honest competition.*
>
> — Elbert Hubbard

Introduction

The issue of non-competition agreements is a highly charged subject, upon which both employees and employers have predictable opinions. When you begin your career as an employee, you will have one outlook that is likely to change when you become a practice owner and hire your first associate. Therefore, perhaps fairness is what is needed in these dealings, and a willingness to see the other person as an individual—not as an adversary— and a person who has legitimate interests to protect. To achieve this level of understanding, I invite you to review the following scenario, which is based on a real case.

The Employee's Perspective

"Hi, I'm Dr. Joe. I've just graduated from veterinary school, and I am about to accept my first job. I was born and raised in the prosperous community of Pleasantville and hope to return home. I have deep roots in Pleasantville; my great grandfather was one of the first settlers here, and my extended family has lived here ever since. My wife has been offered a job with the local school board and will be leaving the private school where she currently teaches. We are planning to move in July, so our children—ages six and eight years—will be able to change schools and make new friends at the beginning of the school year.

"I'm excited about the job. Dr. Susan, the hospital owner, has offered a generous salary, time off, and benefits. She recognizes how important my family is to me, and we have worked out an on-call schedule that works well with my personal life. The hospital is well equipped with a top-notch staff, and they practice good medicine. Most importantly, the practice takes good care of the patients, and they genuinely care about their well-being. I feel Dr. Susan's hospital will be an exciting and rewarding place to practice. Furthermore, Dr. Susan is approachable and patient. She is the type of practitioner I feel I really need as a mentor my first few months out of school.

"I have only one big concern. Dr. Susan is insisting I agree to, and sign, a non-competition agreement. She explained that she has a big investment in her hospital and has heard horror stories from other practice owners about their past employees. Indeed, some past employees have set up their own hospitals literally across the road from their former employer. Furthermore, her lawyer has told her to stand her ground on this point.

"I understand that Dr. Susan has a big investment in her practice. But what if things don't work out? I want to be fair. My wife is changing jobs, and my children are changing schools. My whole family is being uprooted to move here for my career. For whatever reason, if things don't work out with Dr. Susan, I just can't ask my family to pack up and disrupt their lives all over again."

The Practice Owner's Perspective

"Hi, I'm Dr. Susan, the owner of Pleasantville Animal Hospital. I've been in Pleasantville for 25 years. My husband and I moved here two years after I graduated. My husband's family is from this area, and it's been a great place to raise our own family. I'm very proud of my practice. The hospital exceeds the highest AAHA standards with a staff of three technicians, two receptionists, and three kennel assistants. I have all the latest equipment and spend a lot of time and money on continuing education for both the veterinarians and the staff.

"I'm very excited about Dr. Joe coming to work with me. For a new graduate, he has great medical and surgical skills, and he is absolutely dynamite with people. The staff is keen to work with him, and during the two weeks he spent with me in the practice, I received numerous phone calls and cards from clients telling me how much they hope Dr. Joe will continue to work in the practice.

"There's only one problem. He doesn't want to sign the non-competition agreement. I can understand his family is from Pleasantville and that he has a right to make a living too. But I feel very vulnerable without that non-competition agreement. My greatest fear is that Dr. Joe will spend a year or two in my practice, getting to know all my clients, and then simply open up a hospital across the street. My other associate had no problem signing the agreement; although I recognize that she's single, her family is in Toronto, and she could easily leave town tomorrow since she has no real roots in the community."

The Problem

Veterinary employers will often attempt to protect their market position by insisting that potential or existing employed veterinarians sign contracts that restrict their freedom to compete or assist others to compete against the employer in the future. Unfortunately, too often down the road the matter ends up as a motion before the courts, with the employer veterinarian asking for an injunction to enforce this covenant against the former employed veterinarian. So how can this be prevented at this stage in the dialogue between Dr. Joe and Dr. Susan?

A Win-Win Solution

Dr. Joe's lawyer asked him to consider his next best career option if he decided, for whatever reason, not to practice with Dr. Susan. Well, it turns out that Dr. Joe's other veterinary passion is equine practice, and there is a very large, local horse population that no veterinarian is currently serving. Dr. Susan's practice is limited to dogs and cats. Moreover, government contract work is routinely available in this area.

In identifying other viable employment and career options, Dr. Joe was able to agree to a non-competition agreement limited only to small animal practice. Even if things didn't work out with Dr. Susan, both Dr. Joe and his family could still live in the community, and he would still have career choices. Because Dr. Susan's practice does not include horses or government contract work, she was not threatened at all and felt that her core small animal clientele were protected from any potential unfair competition from a former employee.

The purpose of this dialogue is to show how developing an understanding of the other party's viewpoint will permit the parties to enter into non-competition agreements that take into account the legitimate needs of both parties. Taking the time to develop a non-competition agreement that is fair to all will result in agreements that are not only more enforceable but, most importantly, will likely be honoured.

Advice for Potential Employees

1. *Know Your Obligations*
   Remember that every employee has obligations when it comes to competing with a former employer. Even without a written agreement, it is best not to solicit clients of a former employer.

2. *Keep Your Word*
   Only agree to a non-competition agreement if you are prepared to honour it. Don't sign an agreement assuming that the courts will not enforce it.

3. *Know Yourself*
   In evaluating a proposed non-competition agreement, decide what is truly and realistically important to you. For example, if you are moving your family to a practice in a remote town where you have deep roots and hope to stay forever, any commitment to restraint of trade may seem totally unacceptable to you. On the other hand, if you have other viable employment or career options such as an interest in an alternative species, you may be able to commit to a restrictive covenant that both you and your potential employer find acceptable.

Advice for Practice Owners

1. *Be Realistic*
   Analyse whether the nature of the employment really justifies a non-competition agreement. The onus is on the former employer to prove the restraint is not more than necessary to protect a legitimate proprietary interest that it enjoys.

2. *Be Reasonable*
   The covenant must be reasonable between the parties. Reasonableness

is determined not only from the employer's perspective, but also from the employee's perspective. To be enforceable, the courts have said a non-competition provision must be reasonable as to time and area. In deciding what is a reasonable distance from the employer's practice, one often looks to define the trading area of the practice by looking at such factors as where the majority of the clients are coming from (e.g., by examining client addresses and postal codes). The result is that a reasonable distance is likely to vary dramatically between rural and urban practices. In deciding on a reasonable length of time for the non-competition agreement, one is guided by the principle that it must be long enough to disrupt the client-doctor relationship held by the departing associate so it can be replaced by a new one. In practice, the length of time varies as low as one year for someone working with less than two in a practice and is typically five years for long-term practitioners, practice sellers, or departing partners. The type of practice is also part of the reasonableness principle. For example, if you are working in a strictly small animal practice, it is unreasonable to be restricted to other types of veterinary practice, such as equine medicine.

3.   *Be Proactive*
It is highly recommended that an arbitration clause be included in most agreements to prevent a potentially long and expensive court battle if you have a disagreement in the future. Regardless of the outcome, adversarial legal procedures are costly in terms of time, money, and emotion to all concerned.

Conclusions

A well-thought-out and fair non-competition agreement is good preventative medicine. This article is intended to make veterinarians aware of the issues surrounding employment and restrictive covenants in employment agreements. This article is not intended to replace legal advice that, by necessity, is dependent on the specific facts of every case.

Biography

For Dr. Ausman's biography, please see Chapter 1-3, pages 25-26.

Being an Expert Witness

Ian Stauffer, LL.B
Partner, Tierney Stauffer LLP,
Ottawa, Ontario

Maura Kehoe
Law Student, University of Ottawa Faculty of Law
(Common Law),
Ottawa, Ontario

> *An expert is someone who knows some of the worst mistakes that can be made in his subject, and how to avoid them.*
>
> — Werner Heisenberg

Introduction

Professionals with specializations in fields such as veterinary medicine or toxicology may be asked to provide expert opinion evidence in a legal context. For the purposes of this chapter, we are assuming that you have been called upon by a lawyer who has asked you for a professional opinion. Typically, the lawyer will be acting for a plaintiff or a defendant. A common case would involve someone who has taken his purebred dog into a clinic for an operation, and the owner feels that the operation has not been successful.

Perhaps the dog has died. The owner retains a lawyer to be counsel for the plaintiff. From the defense side, a counsel will have been retained by the veterinary clinic's insurer. Both lawyers will need an expert's report dealing with the issues of standard of care and causation.

The Veterinarian's Role

Veterinarians are asked to participate in giving expert evidence when the legal system is faced with "scientific, technical, or specialized knowledge that is outside the sphere of expertise of" a judge or jury. In jury trials especially, the veterinarian as witness faces the challenge of explaining technical matters to lay people, who are charged with being the "triers of fact".[1] The jurors are the ultimate judges of the evidence. An expert veterinarian may be called upon to express an opinion, in an unbiased manner, on such diverse topics as animal health, welfare, and the value to the animal's owner. Common examples include cases of intentional or negligent abuse of animals (including claims regarding negligence in an agricultural setting), cases of feed poisoning, vandalism, farm safety and fire liability, and even negligent machinery design or installation.

There are two situations when a veterinarian may become involved with a legal proceeding. The first is when the veterinarian is the treating doctor, and the second scenario involves being called upon to give expert opinion evidence.

The Treating Veterinarian

The first scenario of being the treating veterinarian often involves cases of animal abuse. When animals are found in circumstances of abuse, authorities will report to the clinic or hospital that is located closest to the incident. In these situations, veterinarians generally have no control over what legal issues accompany the circumstances of a treated animal. It is for this reason that it is of utmost importance that clear, complete, and identifiable records be maintained at all times. Should a claim against you go to court, the trier of fact may prefer the owner's recollection of events to your own, especially if no notes exist to back up a conversation and/or mode of treatment. This applies to all treating veterinarians, regardless of reason that the animal has been presented for treatment.

In the role of treating veterinarian, it is always advisable to fully inform the animal's owner of the potential risks in a surgical procedure and have the owner sign a consent form, acknowledging the information you have provided. Additionally, keep in mind that all notes and working materials are subject to disclosure in court. A professional will feel more comfortable testifying in Court if he or she can refer to fulsome, readable notes. Remember that an animal's owner's recollection of events may be preferred by a Judge versus a veterinarian's unrecorded memory.

Veterinarians as Expert Witnesses

Veterinarians may be called upon to give opinion evidence. Some veterinarians genuinely enjoy the experience of preparing reports for lawyers and going to court to testify. They may even advertise themselves as legal experts, and, for some, giving expert testimony may become a substantial part of one's practice. Certainly, lawyers rely heavily on the expertise of veterinarians in a wide range of cases.

What do you need to know to prepare and feel comfortable in giving expert opinion evidence? First, you should realize that your type of evidence is unusual; it is only a recognized expert who can give an opinion about the standard of care and causation issues. A "layperson" cannot give opinion evidence. It is considered hearsay and unreliable. Therefore, before commencing a lawsuit, the lawyer seeking to retain an expert looks for someone with certain attributes. These include the expert's credentials (both academic and field-related experience) and prior courtroom experience. The latter qualification is important, but do not feel you can't help if you have not testified in court before. Some of the "best" experts are first-timers, if for no other reason than the judge has no preconceived notion of "bias" from testimony in prior cases. Lawyers seek to obtain humble experts who can communicate intelligently and can remain calm and professional under the pressure at trial. Essentially, the first role of the expert veterinarian is to educate the trier of fact about the case, including specialized terminology and procedures.

Once a lawyer has located a suitable expert, an engagement or retainer agreement between the lawyer and expert should be signed. This agreement sets out various terms of the relationship, such as the hourly rate of the expert and other billing arrangements, a written confidentiality agreement, the procedural outcome of the relationship if a conflict of interest arises, and specifications regarding the return or exchange of relevant materials.[2] This agreement is very important, particularly for the expert.

Before writing your report, remember that the credibility of an expert witness (initially with the lawyers and their clients, and later with a trier of fact) is based on the veterinarian's objectivity and impartiality. You must, for example, consider whether you have any potential conflict of interest (e.g., is the veterinarian whose techniques you are being asked to critique an old friend or a former business associate?). You should not give an opinion about the case if you have treated the animal in question, either pre- or post-incident.

When being asked to provide an expert's report, it is most important for the expert to understand the desired scope of investigation. The lawyer must discuss with the expert exactly what is to be examined and on which specific issues an opinion is to be provided. The lawyer should also specify what type of opinion is required. For example, if a veterinarian were providing an opinion on an injured animal, the required opinion could range from suspected cause of injury to future effects on the animal's health or resale value. While it is the lawyer's responsibility to acquire the desired evidence, it is important for legal experts to be self-motivated and enthusiastic in understanding the relevant questions. This kind of approach can solidify an expert's reputation in the legal community. Once the relevant questions are clearly identified, the expert examines the issues and provides a report.

In a case involving the care of an animal, it is critical to have all relevant information regarding the treatment history of the animal before you begin writing your report. If, for example, you give an opinion on the assumption that the animal was symptom-free before the incident in question, and records subsequently reveal similar pre-incident symptoms, your opinion will be weakened through cross-examination at trial.

After an agreement is reached with counsel, it is strongly recommended that you have a face-to-face meeting with the lawyer who has retained you (if time and geographical circumstances permit). Frequently, you will need to educate the lawyer on the scientific or technical aspects that are relevant to the issues identified. The lawyer will learn specifically what can and cannot be proved using the objective, impartial opinion of you as the expert. This allows the lawyer to complete further collection of evidence, if required.

Most lawyers will ask that you speak with them before putting your draft opinion in writing. You must realize that the lawyer needs certain questions answered, and it is best to have a discussion before writing your opinion, to be sure both of you know what your comments will be. One area of importance is the use of the words "possibility" and "probability." Triers of fact will be swayed more by something that is "probably" going to occur (for example, the future functioning of an animal) versus a "possible" outcome.

A legal action will not always proceed to trial. In Canada, in both the criminal and civil systems, legislation has mandated various pretrial processes to encourage settlement. Your report will be a critical factor in settlement discussions. However, you should be aware that your report will undoubtedly be scrutinized by the expert retained by one or more opposing parties.

After the lawyer reviews your report, he or she will decide whether the opinion provided is relevant to the intended case theory. It is important that there is open communication about the results of the report. The lawyer must communicate any unanswered questions, and the expert must be open to explaining how and why the report was written as it was. This requires professional courtesy and patience, as the lawyer may feel that not all the questions were answered, and the expert may feel as if his or her opinion is being questioned. As long as both parties communicate, an agreement and a plan for steps to follow can easily be reached.

Writing an Expert Opinion Report

There is a general format for writing an expert's report. The report must first include the expert's credentials in order to establish the expert as being able to provide the opinion evidence. The issues examined should then be isolated and clearly set out. A discussion of the procedure for forming the opinion evidence should follow. The expert should explain how the opinion evidence was gathered; for example, whether the information was exhibited through a paper review of the animal's history and/or a physical examination. Lastly, the expert provides an opinion or an answer to the questions posed in the section highlighting the issues to be examined. This section can provide recommendations and any additional comments, as long as a clear response to the questions identified is presented. See Tables 1 and 2.

Appearing in Court

After the report is completed, the last requirement of an expert is to provide testimony, should the action proceed to trial. The lawyer should prepare you for the upcoming trial. Given the fact that both you and the lawyer are very busy, be sure to coordinate your availability to prepare for and appear at the trial.

If you are inexperienced in the litigation process, be sure the lawyer educates you as to courtroom procedure and etiquette. Review carefully with the lawyer those areas of expected cross-examination. Be sure you have read any report(s) prepared to critique your own. If you are familiar with another expert's credentials, you should help the lawyer who has retained you by pointing out areas where that expert could be cross-examined.

On the day you testify, bring your entire file as well as any visual aids you will be using while giving evidence. If any visual aids require special technical arrangements, tell the lawyer well ahead of time so that your presentation will go smoothly.

Table 1
How to Write an Expert's Report

Four parts comprise an expert's report.

1. Expert's Qualifications
   - Credentials and experience are highlighted in this section
   - Attach curriculum vitae as appendix

2. Issues to be Examined
   - Set out clearly the issues on which the expert will give opinion

3. Investigation and Procedure
   - Establish what steps were taken to investigate the issues set out above

4. Expert's Opinion
   - Opinion as to reliability of facts, future outcomes, and hypothetical results for each issue as needed

Table 2
Tips on Writing a Good Report

- Opinion evidence is based on impartial and objective observation
- Be clear and concise
- Know the report's deadline
- Any documents in addition to the report that may be needed to explain an opinion should be attached as appendices
- Number all pages and paragraphs for easy referencing
- The more you write, the more ammunition for cross-examination
- Write chronologically
- Write in first person singular
- Double-space the text for easy note-taking
- Use visual aids to explain complexities

The first step in your testimony will be what is called "qualifying the expert witness." You should be sure to have your résumé in front of you, and the lawyer who has retained you will take you through your qualifications, asking about your "professional qualifications, actual experience, [your] participation or membership in professional associations, the nature and extent of [your] publications and [your] involvement in teaching." Further qualifications can be established by demonstrating "involvement in courses or conferences in the field, efforts to keep current with the literature in the field, [and] previous qualifications to testify as an expert in the area."[2] The opposing counsel will then have an opportunity to question you as to your qualifications. An expert in the process of being qualified must be prepared to prove and explain these tangible qualifications in a humble and appropriate manner. However, do not be shy about your accomplishments. The judge will then be asked to rule whether you are qualified to give opinion evidence.

If you are qualified as an expert, then your lawyer will ask you to go through your report. You will then be cross-examined. It is possible that your lawyer may have additional questions to ask you in reply.

It is important for lawyers and their experts to be aware of what is required by law for the admission of expert evidence. The definitive case on the use of expert evidence in Canada is *R. v. Mohan.*[3] This case sets out the legal requirements for a judge to allow expert evidence to be heard at trial. The requirements are as follows: relevance; necessity in assisting the trier of fact; the absence of any exclusionary rule; and a properly qualified expert. It is important for potential expert witnesses to understand these legal requirements, so that they can be discussed and met in advance in order to ensure that the opinion evidence will be admissible in court.

It will be for the lawyer presenting the argument to determine the relevance of the information being provided by the expert witness. However, it is important for you to be conscious of the issues being tried.

Always remember that you are giving evidence to assist the trier of fact. You are not an "advocate" for the party who has retained you.

Listen carefully to all questions. Take your time in answering them. Always ask for a question to be repeated or clarified if you do not hear it or understand it. The judge and/or jury will be taking very careful notes of what you say and how you express yourself.

Do not argue with anyone who asks you a question.

Even though you have been qualified to give expert opinion/evidence does not mean that all of your oral testimony and/or written report will become evidence for the trier of fact; some or all of your testimony may still be excluded (deemed not to be admissible). A recent decision in Ontario (*Dulong v. Merrill Lynch Canada Inc. et al.*[4]) emphasizes the need for impartiality and objectivity on the part of an expert. Expert evidence was found to be inadmissible because it "violate[d] the rule against oath-helping."[5] The expert's report was found to be "replete with comments about credibility [and] findings of fact relating to contentious issues."[5] The court found these comments "totally inappropriate."[6] Ensuring admissibility of your report requires knowledge of the law and will primarily be the responsibility of the lawyer; however, this example serves to show the importance of the expert's having some understanding of the legal framework by which their evidence will be bound.

Some cases are heard not just by a judge, but with a judge presiding with six members of the public in civil matters or 12 citizens in a criminal trial—what we know as the jury. Since members of a jury are likely to want to believe evidence given by an apparent experienced professional, a judge will guard against creating a biased jury through easy admission of expert evidence. In Canadian jurisprudence, judges will often be referred to in this context as the "gatekeeper." In their role as gatekeepers, judges may, from time to time, exclude the jury when an issue of admissibility of an expert's testimony arises. This prompts a *voir dire*, which may occur before you testify or during your testimony. The jury is out of the courtroom, and the judge and the lawyers are the only ones who hear the question(s) put to you. Depending on the judge's ruling, a certain question or questions may be allowed to be put to you in front of the jurors once they have re-entered the courtroom.

After the *Mohan* requirements are met, the testimony of the expert becomes a matter of substance. It is important that you as the expert be patient and state the scope of your report, your assumptions, your findings, and your conclusions in a clear fashion during your examination-in-chief. You and the lawyer should have designed a line of questioning that allows for the simplest explanation of the evidence. Foreign terms should be defined the first time they are used in your testimony. Most importantly, you must be able to state facts that support and defend both specific opinions about the case and opinions based on hypothetical questions.

Following the examination-in-chief, the opposing counsel will conduct a cross-examination of you that will be based on your written report and oral testimony at trial. The opposing counsel will attempt to cast doubt in the minds of the triers of fact on the evidence just given during the examination-in-chief. Cross-examination can be a stressful experience, and impartiality, objectivity, and humility are of the utmost importance at this time. Here you may be presented with various theories that traditionally or creatively oppose your professional opinion. It will be important to review such theories prior to trial.

Remember, counsel may examine your theories contained in prior articles or books you have written, in an attempt to highlight discrepancies with testimony presented in evidence at trial. Opposing counsel may indulge in any number of tactics so that their own expert evidence will be preferred. Again, the credibility of an expert witness is tested during cross-examination. Your credibility will be enhanced if you remain calm and give the impression of objectivity throughout your cross-examination. You will gain confidence if you have studied carefully the raw data upon which your report was based, all supporting documents, the other expert's report(s), and if you have previously considered how to answer the difficult questions.

Summary

In providing expert testimony, a specialized professional has the opportunity to participate actively in Canada's legal system, and the experience of concisely defending a theory can be very stimulating and invigorating for expert witnesses. In order to have the opportunity to participate in such an experience, the formation of a credible reputation is essential. Effective transfer of knowledge can occur only when individuals maintain the credibility of their profession through objective and informed action.

Your opinion, whether given outside of a lawsuit or in the crucible of the courtroom, may be one of the most important factors in resolving a question or dispute. Great reliance will be placed upon your comments by lawyers, their clients, and ultimately, the trier of fact. Your involvement in the Canadian legal system is critical for the proper adjudication of cases involving your area of expertise.

References

1.   Expert Evidence Checklist. Advocates' E-Brief, The Advocates' Society, Toronto, Ontario. 2005; Vol. 16, No. 2.
2.   *Ibid*
3.   (1994), 114 D.L.R. (4th) 419 (S.C.C.)
4.   *Durlong v. Merrill Lynch Canada Inc. et. al., Carswell Ont 1783, 2006, Ducharme, J.*
5.   *ibid* at para 16
6.   *ibid,* at para 14

Biographies

Ian Stauffer is an Ottawa lawyer. He received degrees in Political Science from Carleton University, Education from Queen's University, and Law from the

University of Ottawa. He restricts his practice to civil litigation, having been recognized by the Law Society of Upper Canada as a Specialist in this discipline. He has appeared at all levels of Court in Ontario. Since 1999 he has acted as a mediator in over 800 cases and was given the Chartered Mediator's designation by the Alternate Dispute Resolution Institute of Canada in 2002. Mr. Stauffer also sits as a Deputy Judge in Small Claims Court.

Catherine Maura Kehoe is a law student at the University of Ottawa in the Common Law Section. She is currently completing her second year and is working as a Teacher's Assistant for the Alternative Dispute Resolution Program for first-year students. In 2005, she completed her undergraduate studies in French Literature and Educational Studies at Colgate University in Hamilton, New York. In 2006, she was selected to participate in a summer internship program sponsored by the University of Ottawa where she gained experience in civil litigation. Prior to 2006, she interned for two criminal law firms in the Ottawa area. Maura hopes to complete her studies in law and pursue a career in civil litigation.

People, Pets, and Wills: Taking Care of Our Pets

Brian Ausman, BSc (Agr), DVM, MBA, LL.B
Real Estate & Business Broker, Lawyer,
and Practice Co-Owner,
Guelph, Ontario

> *Old age means realizing that you will never own all the dogs that you wanted to.*
>
> — Joe Gores

Introduction

The importance of the relationship between people and their pets has long been accepted in today's society. The amount of money that people are prepared to spend on their animals' happiness and health has grown in leaps and bounds over the years. It is no wonder, then, that there has been a marked increase in the number of people seeking the advice of their veterinarians and lawyers on how to best provide for their pet(s) if these pets survive them.

In the past, people who left fortunes to their pet(s) were mocked and ridiculed. However, providing for one's pet(s) is neither something to be ridiculed nor dismissed as unnecessary. Also, in most cases, the sums involved are hardly fortunes, and even modest bequests can ensure that a pet is cared for properly. For many people, pets are family, and in the same way that they would ensure other family members have been appropriately provided for upon their death, so should one consider providing for a cherished pet.

This article is a call to action for companion animal veterinarians. As part of the routine preventive medicine dialogue, I urge you to discuss with your clients the importance of making provisions for their pets in their wills. When confronted with questions from your clients regarding concerns they may have for their pet's well-being after their death, or in other situations where they are unable to personally take care of their pets, I encourage you to validate these concerns. It is important to stress that with proper estate planning, most pet owners can adequately address the future needs of their pets with a fraction of their overall estate. Many veterinarians have a close, personal relationship with their own pets. Consequently, by educating oneself on some of the options for taking care of pets that can be incorporated in a will, one can benefit both professionally and personally.

Preparing a Will

First, one should consider who will be the guardian of the pet. This often proves to be the most challenging aspect of caring for a pet, since what the future holds is unknown. It is much simpler to address this issue if one is 85 years old and in poor health than middle age with no expectation of premature death. The choice of guardian may need to be changed several times over the course of one's life, as circumstances change. In choosing the guardian, ensure that one is choosing someone who views the role of a pet in their family in the same way they do. For example, if the dog in question has always slept on the bed with its owner, placing that animal with a family that is equally fond of pets but does not permit them access to any furniture, including the bed, and prefers to cage their animals at night would likely create huge stress for the grieving pet. One must also consider the other pet(s) that any guardian may have and how well a new pet will integrate with them; animals, like people, are very territorial and do not always welcome new pets into their midst. Here the role of a veterinarian can be of great assistance in discussing with their clients the best ways to introduce new pets into existing settings and what steps they might take now to ensure that integration in the future.

The next step for pet owners to consider is how to financially provide for the care of their pet(s). As anyone who has ever had a pet knows, whether it is a guinea pig or a registered quarter horse, health care and maintenance of pets do incur some costs. One needs to determine whether the people chosen as guardians have the financial wherewithal to assume that burden. As part of a clients' financial planning for the future care of their pet, a veterinarian's input into the likely longevity of their pet, current costs for typical and special health care requirements, and pet insurance options is invaluable in helping them to make realistic estate plans.

If there is a decision to provide financially for a pet, it can be done in one of two ways. First, one can make an outright gift to the guardians for a specific amount of money or percentage of the estate and this money would be provided tax free. The downside is that if that individual then chooses not to care for the animal or have the animal destroyed, s/he would retain the monies. If this method is selected, one needs to be very sure that the person chosen will provide the appropriate care for the pet(s) notwithstanding that they have no legal obligation to do so.

The other option is to set up a trust with the stipulation that only the interest earned be used for the care of the animal or, as another alternative, a discretionary trust could be established where both the capital and interest could be used as needed. The disadvantage of setting up the trust is that there are costs involved in filing tax returns on an annual basis. The advantage of a trust is that it will provide long-term care that will move with the pet(s) in the event that they are placed in another environment for any reason. As well, one can stipulate that any monies that are left after the pet has passed away be given to an animal-related charity, such as a local animal shelter, veterinary school, or the humane society. In fact, one can stipulate any individual or any organization as a beneficiary of the monies that remain. As a lawyer, I caution pet owners against making the caregiver of their pet(s) the beneficiary, as it puts the caregiver in a difficult position when trying to decide whether to spend the designated money on the pet's care, as this will affect the amount of money left at the time of the pet's death. No matter how good intentions may be, money can have negative influences on some people.

As pet owners, one can also make recommendations in one's will about who should be providing the health care to their pet and many wills have specifically stated the primary care veterinarian to ensure consistency of a pet's care. Again, this only works if the guardians of the pet reside in geographic proximity to the veterinarian with whom the pet's health care is entrusted.

Other Issues to Consider

There are those who consider providing for pets in a will to be ludicrous. However, the alternative is to not make provisions for one's pet(s) in their will, and this can have devastating results on both the pet (undefined guardianship resulting in being passed from house to house at a time when consistency and stability are so important) and family (guilt associated in dealing with undeclared expectations, especially if circumstances make pet ownership difficult or impossible). Too often, loving, healthy pets are destroyed because no home can be found for them in a timely fashion, and their behaviour during the process can make them hard to place if there has-n't been a prior commitment from someone to take on the caregiving. One would never do that to any other family member, so why would any less care be taken for the other furry family members?

This is just as true when people find themselves having to go into hospitals or retirement homes, especially in unplanned circumstances. The advantage of having provisions in one's will for the care and placement of a pet is that today's Powers of Attorney for Financial Management require the appointed attorney to have regard to the contents of the will. That means if one is in a coma in a hospital, the person that has been appointed under the Power of Attorney can look at the individual's will and make provisions for their pet(s) from both the financial and caregiving perspective. This ensures that any pet(s) are not destroyed unnecessarily and will be there for the person if circumstances allow them to return home. I would urge you to encourage your clients (and yourself if you have not already done so) to think about the non-people members of their family and to provide for them appropriately in their wills.

Conclusions

This article is intended to make veterinarians aware of the increasing popularity and variety of strategies for making meaningful provisions for the care and maintenance of pets in one's will. Clients are asking for advice on how to ensure that their pets can live long and happy lives after their deaths. This trend can be seen as an increased awareness and celebration of the human-companion animal bond. This article is not intended to replace legal advice that, by necessity, is dependent on the specific facts of every case. However, veterinarians may find it useful to include information on this topic in newsletters that they send to their clients.

Biography

For Dr. Ausman's biography, please see Chapter 1-3, pages 25-26.

Section 6

MAKING SENSE
OF THE
UNEXPECTED

CVMA Insurance Program

As a graduate of veterinary medicine, it is essential that proper choices are made with respect to protecting yourself against the various risks inherent to the veterinary profession. As an educated professional, your ability to practice veterinary medicine is your greatest asset which deserves to be effectively insured. Further to this, throughout your career you may engage in practice ownership which will require a variety of specialized coverages relating to protection of property and liability. It is critical to understand that without effective risk transfer there is a great deal to be jeopardized.

The Canadian Veterinary Medical Association (CVMA), in partnership with Western Financial Group Insurance Solutions, has developed a specialized insurance program with risk management services for CVMA members across Canada. The Program is designed to help Veterinarians understand the risks faced in the veterinary industry and the various products available to most effectively provide protection at the lowest possible cost. The CVMA Insurance Program provides members with competitive insurance coverage for commercial property & casualty insurance, professional/malpractice insurance, employee group benefit plans, plus individual life and disability insurance. Further to this, discounted rating is provided on Home & Auto insurance through The Co-operators.

In addition to its uniquely customized coverages, the CVMA Insurance Program will offer Canadian veterinarians a degree of stability that cannot be attained through traditional insurance brokers. This is made possible through the development of a "Protected Self-Insurance" structure which avails scales of economy and a sense of ownership that Canadian veterinarians can be proud of.

For more information relating to the CVMA Insurance Program, visit www.cvmainsurance.com/home.aspx, the designated member Extranet. The site will provide an overview of various coverages and contact information to reach a veterinary insurance specialist.

CHAPTER **6-1**

"Here Comes 'da Judge":
Defending or Starting a Court Action—
A Primer on the Canadian Court System

Douglas C. Jack, BA, LL.B
Douglas C. Jack, Solicitors, Fergus, Ontario

> *And do as adversaries do in law — strive mightily,*
> *but eat and drink as friends.*
>
> — William Shakespeare

Introduction

The law is pervasive. It touches upon many aspects of the practice of veterinary medicine, including the use of the court system to either pursue or defend a lawsuit. Veterinarians may pursue the court system for the purpose of collecting outstanding accounts receivable. Clients may use the same system to assert their claims that their animal was injured or died as a result of veterinary incompetence. In either case, the successful practitioner will ensure that s/he has some general knowledge of the court system.

The Court System

It is important that you understand the court structure in your province. You also need to be familiar with some of the litigation process, so that you can make an informed decision prior to commencing an action against a client for the collection of a debt owed or in defending any claims brought of veterinary malpractice by the client.

Small Claims Court

The Small Claims Court, as it is commonly known in most provinces, is a simple but usually effective means of debt collection, and the forum in which the greatest number of claims are asserted for negligent treatment of an animal. The Small Claims Court is a relatively informal setting. Parties to a dispute appear before a judge in a trial to obtain judgment. The party asserting a legal right is referred to as the "Plaintiff" and the party against whom the claim is made is referred to as the "Defendant."

The Small Claims Court has limited monetary jurisdiction. In Ontario, your claim must be for less than $10,000. A claim for an amount in excess of $10,000 must either be brought in one of the other courts or waived in order to bring you within the jurisdiction of the Small Claims Court. Other provinces have different monetary thresholds; one should check with the courts of each province to determine the monetary jurisdiction.

As with any court, proceedings are commenced by way of the issuance of a Claim, which sets out the facts in narrative form (e.g., states that a debt is owing for the sale of goods or the provision of services provided by the clinic). In a malpractice context, the Claim brought by the client would set out facts upon which s/he relies to establish that the practitioner was negligent. The Claim forms may be obtained from the local Small Claims Court and deposited with the Small Claims Clerk to be served on the Defendant. Usually, the Clerk will arrange to have the Defendant personally served with your Claim and, having done so, the Defendant then is permitted a short period of time within which s/he must file a Dispute or Defence, if any. In some provinces, the Claim may be served properly by mailing it via registered mail to the address of the Defendant.

Once a Defence has been received by the Clerk or the time for delivering that Defence has expired, the Clerk will provide the Defendant with a Notice for a Trial or a Notice of Default Judgment. The latter is provided if the Defendant fails to defend the claim within the requisite time period. Unlike higher courts, no system is available by which the parties can obtain additional information regarding the Claim or the Defence through a discovery process. In most provinces, the only action prior to the actual trial is a pre-hearing conference, which is held before a Judge of the Small Claims Court. The pre-hearing conference attempts to narrow the issues for trial, to save time, and hopefully, to provide the parties with an objective understanding of the merits of their respective cases, with a view to settlement. The pre-hearing Judge is not the judge that will preside over the trial.

Notwithstanding the fact that the Small Claims Court is less formal than other courts in the legal system, the same principles of law apply. Therefore, it is necessary that you have adequate evidence of the amount owing to you and the reasons for the debt.

Higher Courts

The next higher level of court is called various names in different provinces: in Ontario—the Superior Court of Justice and in Alberta—the Court of Queen's Bench. These courts are presided over by a judge. Provincial legislation provides that these Courts have jurisdiction to hear any case, regardless of the value of the claim.

Like the Small Claims Court, the action is commenced by the issuance of a Statement of Claim, which is served upon the Defendant. The Defendant then has an opportunity to file a Statement of Defence.

You may appear personally in these higher courts; however, the process is much more formalized and a great number of rules must be followed in order to continue your proceeding. The rules often are complex and involve time limitations, which may seriously compromise your case, if not met.

PRACTICE POINT

The court process, at any level, can be both time-consuming and expensive; as well, litigation can be emotionally stressful. Effective practice management should be directed at avoiding the court process and, if unavoidable, streamlining the process and having effective evidence, so as to promote success for your case.

Court Proceedings

Proceedings in the higher courts usually are reserved for legal counsel acting on behalf of his or her clients. As such, clients often are inundated with various terms and jargon employed by their lawyers, which (for many reasons) they do not understand and do not seek clarification. The purpose of this section is to explain the court process, so that you better understand the actions of your lawyer. The collection of a debt owed is used as an example, based on Ontario law; however, similar provisions are found in the other provinces.

Pleadings

A court action is commenced by the issuance of a Statement of Claim. In the case of the clinic attempting to collect an outstanding account, the Statement of Claim sets out the facts upon which you, the creditor, rely in order to bring the matter to court. The drafting of pleadings is subject to many rules and usually is reserved for the experienced solicitor. The Statement of Claim then is "issued" by the court staff upon payment of an issuance fee. Unlike Small Claims Court, it is up to the Plaintiff to have the Statement of Claim served on the Defendant. Service, in most cases, must be done personally.

Once the Statement of Claim has been served on the Defendant, the Defendant has a period of time (usually 20 days) within which to file a Statement of Defence. Failure to do so will result in a default judgment being obtained by the Plaintiff. The Statement of Defence, if any, usually relates to an alleged breach of contract by the Plaintiff, such as a discrepancy in the agreed upon fee or the alleged failure to perform services in the manner the Defendant required. After the pleadings have been exchanged, each of the parties has a more defined understanding of the issues that eventually will be presented in court.

Default Judgment

Should the Defendant fail to deliver a Statement of Defence within the time limits, the Plaintiff may request the court registrar to enter a judgment against the Defendant immediately. However, it is important to understand that a default judgment only can be obtained in this summary fashion in the event that a clear, defined, liquidated debt outstanding has been set out in the Statement of Claim. Failure to fall within this particular rule for obtaining a default judgment limits your ability to use this summary procedure.

It is not unusual to obtain judgment in debt collection proceedings because, quite simply, no justification typically exists for failure to pay the account. Notwithstanding the lack of justification, the creditor veterinarian is put to aggravation and legal expense in order to obtain that judgment.

The Discovery Process

Once the action has been commenced and a Defence has been offered, the next stage of proceedings relates to obtaining detailed information from each of the parties to the action relating to the contents of the pleadings. The rules of court practiced in the higher courts provide for various means of "discovery" that effectively provide each of the parties with more information upon which to make a decision of whether or not to proceed to a trial, abandon the litigation or, alternatively, seek a negotiated settlement.

The discovery process is conducted by way of oral examination or deposition and presentation of written documentation that will be relied upon at any subsequent trial. All information collected in the discovery process becomes part of the court record.

Costs

One of the most misunderstood aspects of the debt-collection process relates to the payment of costs to the successful party in litigation. The Canadian legal system does not provide for the reimbursement of all expenses and costs incurred by the successful party, whether it is the Plaintiff or Defendant, in any court proceeding. Rather, partial reimbursement is provided.

The costs of litigation can be significant, especially if one proceeds with a trial. Accordingly, the cost factor becomes an important element in determining a strategy for any court proceedings. As will be discussed, obtaining a successful judgment does not necessarily mean that you will receive full payment. As such, lawsuits are not to be commenced and supported simply for reasons of principle. The astute veterinarian also will consider the relative cost of proceeding with the action, along with the risks associated with an unsuccessful lawsuit in light of the amount owed.

Enforcing the Judgment

> **PRACTICE POINT**
>
> The process after obtaining judgement in your favour is just as important as the legal steps taken to receive the judgement. You must be diligent in your collection proceedings so that effective post-judgement attempts are made to ensure payment of your account.

Obtaining a court judgment does not necessarily mean that the Plaintiff will recover full payment of any judgment. The next step in the litigation process relates to enforcing the judgment handed down by the court for payment of the debt. Several mechanisms are available to you.

Examination of the Defendant

The court rules provide that the unsuccessful Defendant, whether it is your client in an action to recover a debt or you in an action for veterinary malpractice, may be subjected to oral examination to determine the extent and whereabouts of his or her assets. Unless the Plaintiff is fully familiar with the assets of the judgment debtor, an examination of this nature should be held in order to assess the whereabouts and relative value of any assets to be seized and sold to satisfy the judgment, or the location of any bank accounts, which may be seized. Failure of the Defendant to attend such examination can result in imprisonment for contempt of court.

Writ of Seizure and Sale

The most popular method of enforcing a judgment is through filing of a Writ of Seizure and Sale, sometimes referred to as an "execution," against the judgment debtor. Provincial legislation provides that once judgment has been obtained, the successful party may, for a small fee, file an execution with the Sheriff in every court jurisdiction where the debtor may have assets. The effect of the execution is to charge or encumber all of the assets of the judgment debtor in that jurisdiction with the payment of the judgment and any interest, which thereon accrues. As well, the judgment creditor may give instructions to the Sheriff (an individual appointed by the province to enforce court judgements) to seize and sell assets of the judgment debtor in order to satisfy the debt, once the location and relative value of those assets has been determined through the judgment debtor examination.

Often, success in enforcing a judgment is not realized for some years after the judgment has been obtained, when the judgment debtor attempts to sell an asset (e.g., land) against which an execution is filed. It is important to remember that interest accrues on the judgment from the date it is obtained and also is recoverable through the execution.

Garnishment

Garnishment is another remedy available to a person who successfully has obtained a judgment against a debtor. Once a judgment has been obtained, the successful creditor may give notice to any person, most commonly employers, who owe money to the judgment debtor. A portion of the debt payable to the debtor then is paid directly to the judgment creditor in satisfaction of the judgment. Once again, failure to comply with a garnishment order by an employer may result in contempt of court proceedings.

It is important to note that under some provincial laws, a percentage of wages to be received by a debtor will be exempt from garnishment, under the principle that a certain minimum amount of money is required by the debtor to continue to exist.

Conclusion

The need to ensure that you receive fair payment for your professional expertise is as important as performing veterinary services competently. In some instances, it may be necessary to resort to the legal system to assist in that regard. Your familiarity with the justice system will lessen any anxiety you might have with the process and better prepare you for advising your legal counsel, if necessary.

Biography

For Douglas Jack's biography, please see Chapter 5-2 on page 362.

Why Me? Surviving a Client Lawsuit or a Professional Misconduct Complaint

Brian Ausman, BSc (Agr), DVM, MBA, LL.B
Real Estate & Business Broker, Lawyer,
and Practice Co-Owner,
Guelph, Ontario

> *There cannot be a crisis next week. My schedule is already full.*
>
> — Henry Kissinger

Why me? you ask. Imagine yourself hanging up the phone after a conversation with an angry client who has just threatened to sue you or report you to the veterinary association. Or worse, imagine you have just been served with a statement of claim in your front office, while your clients and staff look on in astonishment, or you have just received a call from your veterinary association registrar, informing you that a formal professional misconduct complaint has been filed against you.

You need a framework for surviving this type of crisis in your professional life and ensuring that you land on your feet. If you are like most veterinarians, a medical malpractice lawsuit or professional misconduct complaint

387

is your worst professional nightmare. As in any crisis, you have been caught off balance and can easily be knocked over.

What Should You Do?

1. *Lean on Your Support Network*
    Just as in a personal crisis, one of the best ways of dealing with a professional crisis is to have people around to support you. The role of your support network is to keep you from falling. The whole matter is emotionally stressful, whether or not you can acknowledge it at the time of the crisis. Remember that you are not two people. You cannot completely compartmentalise your personal and professional lives. It is important that your family and close friends understand that you are going through a stressful period, even if you cannot share the details.

2. *Call Your Mentors*
    Most of us have trusted colleagues to whom we can vent, without breaking client confidences or feeling judged. The mentors in our lives also serve to provide a reality check and help us decide when we need to get others involved to resolve our problems.

3. *Remember Your Provincial Veterinary Medical Association*
    Provincial Veterinary Associations strive to provide directly or indirectly through referrals members assistance in times of personal and professional crisis. These programs are constantly evolving and improving. Some provinces such as Ontario and Nova Scotia currently provide direct access to member's counseling services. For example, the Ontario Veterinary Medical Association (OVMA) provides a members' counseling service. A members' assistance line is also available if alcohol or substance abuse is involved. Members may use that hotline while maintaining complete anonymity and confidentiality. Other provinces such as New Brunswick and Saskatchewan while recognizing the importance of these programs currently can only offer contact information to other resources in the community

4. *Report the Matter to Your Insurance Broker*
    Even if the legal action or professional misconduct complaint is only being threatened at this point, report it to your insurance broker. Call your insurer and relay the name of the client and the allegation. Always confirm the report in writing. If you have actually been served with a

claim, forward a copy to the insurer along with a report of when and how it was served. The insurer will normally assign an adjuster to do an investigation.

5. *Tell Your Partners*

Many partnership agreements require this. Disclosing a lawsuit or potential legal action to your partners is almost always appropriate, even if not mandated by your partnership agreement. Remember, your partners know you well, so trying to hide an issue as critical as a lawsuit puts unnecessary stress on your relationship.

6. *Document Everything*

Pull the file in question and check it for completeness. If there are parts of the medical records such as radiographs, laboratory results, records of phone conversations with the client, audio-taped and computer records, or appointment book annotations in other locations, gather them together. Keep notes on everything pertinent to the case. Your lawyer may request the records in order to control access to the records in accordance with the legislation in effect (e.g., privileged information deemed by law and based on the client-lawyer relationship). Make notes of conversations your staff or colleagues may have had with the client or conversations you may have had with the laboratory (e.g., clinical pathologists), other colleagues (e.g., specialists), or others involved. If relevant, ask staff and other practitioners to write a letter recording their involvement with the case. When discussing the case with staff and others, always take notes. When your conversation is finished, ask the person with whom you were talking to read your notes, correct any mistakes, and sign the notes, thereby acknowledging their validity.

7. *Call Your Lawyer*

Anyone who has practiced veterinary medicine knows how frustrating it is when clients wait to bring in sick animals. Whether it is a blocked cat, a difficult calving, or an animal with a festering wound, it is usually best to call in the professionals at the onset. In law, as in veterinary medicine, early involvement by those with training and experience in a particular problem usually means a higher chance of success and, ultimately, less stress and less cost to you. Importantly, communication between you and your lawyer is confidential and cannot be used against you in court or in any other forum. Your lawyer can provide you with guidance on how best to secure and preserve potentially important evidence, as well as how to deal with the veterinary licensing/regulatory body and any potential criminal investigation or charges. When appropriate, your lawyer will recommend alternative methods of resolution, such as mediation or negotiation. In addition to these traditional roles, as a trained advocate, your lawyer is there to guide you to other professionals who may need to be involved in your support team, such as accountants or public relations people. Your lawyer can also provide advice on how to handle difficult situations and conversations with lay staff, associates, and others in the community.

The date you were served with a statement of claim is very important, because there are maximum time periods during which you are allowed to file your defense and any possible counterclaim. It is frequently helpful to write a letter or create a time line listing your involvement in the case in chronological order, to assist you in explaining the sequence of events at some later date. Remember that litigation can take months or even years to actually get to the courtroom, and refreshing your memory with notes made in the past is a legitimate and accepted practice. Always ensure whatever you or others write is dated with the date it was created.

What Should You Not Do?

1. *Do Not Panic*
   Remember, anyone can sue anyone or make any accusation at any time. With your support team in place, the damage to your pocketbook, reputation, and emotional health will be minimized.

2. *Do Not Be Confrontational*
   Your client is angry. As Sun Tzu writes in the Art of War, "The best way to defeat your enemy is to avoid battle."

3. *Do Not Admit Liability*
   Remember that when the registrar of your veterinary association contacts you regarding a possible complaint, s/he is usually wearing a "prosecutor's" hat. Listen politely to what the registrar has to say, take notes, offer no information, and call your insurance company/lawyer as soon as possible.

4. *Do Not Talk to the Radio or Press*
   Usually it is best to communicate through the radio and press with a well-thought-out press release rather than an off-the-cuff remark.

5.   *Do Not Talk to the Police Without Your Lawyer Present*
      In Canada, you can never be forced to speak without your lawyer present. It is human nature to make excuses or be defensive. Remember, this is not the time to "go it alone."

6.   *Do Not Fabricate, Modify, Backdate, or in Any Way Tamper With Existing Records*

      These do's and don'ts provide a framework for dealing with medical malpractice lawsuits and professional misconduct matters.

And Remember

This article is intended to prompt veterinarians to plan for dealing with crises in their professional lives and is not intended to replace legal advice that, by necessity, is dependent on the specific facts of every case.

Biography

For Dr. Ausman's biography, please see Chapter 1-3, pages 25-26.

6-3

Responding to a Complaint

Alec Martin, DVM, MBA
President, The Purple Grove Group Ltd.,
Ripley, Ontario

Anticipation is always worse than the actual event.

— Alec Martin

Introduction

Few things strike fear into the heart of a veterinarian like the words "Personal and Confidential" emblazoned on an envelope from his or her licensing body. Such an envelope frequently contains bad news and, in particular, may contain notification that someone has complained about the veterinarian's conduct. It would be almost unheard of for most veterinarians to avoid being the subject of a complaints investigation during their careers, particularly if that career includes time spent in clinical practice.

Most veterinarians respond to news they have become the subject of a complaints investigation with great indignity. They frequently are offended that any client has the audacity to have their professional conduct scrutinized or question their case management. These feelings are heightened to a state of outrage if the complainant owes them money. Typically these initial sentiments eventually pass and are replaced by a bizarre blend of invincibility and false bravado regarding the whole experience. Having read and re-read the letter of complaint, and the accompanying instructions regarding what is expected by way of a reply, the whole sordid mess often culminates in the veterinarian displaying a heightened resolve to fight the experience with every weapon at his or her disposal, leaving nothing behind but scorched earth in his/her wake.

Obeying their first impulse, most veterinarians first retrieve the medical record on the patient in question seeking to confirm their recollections of events, while hoping to refute those of the complainant. Where gaps appear in information or a risk exists that the documentation may be interpreted adversely, some veterinarians will add to the record, choosing their words and context carefully and, in such a way, as to cast themselves in the most favourable light. Many veterinarians will next grab a paper and pen or a keyboard (depending on their generation) to bang off some hastily constructed rebuttal, wherein they practice the three disciplines of interrogated prisoners: admit nothing, deny everything and if accused—counter-accuse.

Better approaches to responding to a complaint are available and it is hoped that every veterinarian in possession of this reference will review the advice contained herein before opening any apparently threatening correspondence from his or her regulator. From clarifying issues, to compiling materials for submission, to drafting the letter of response, what follows is meant to be a guide for veterinarians faced with this most unenviable of professional responsibilities.

The Complaints Process

Complaints investigations constitute a quasi-judicial process. As such, the format follows a set pattern not unlike a table-tennis match. The complainant makes the first serve and commences the process with his or her letter of complaint. The serve then switches to the veterinarian, who is provided an opportunity to reply. The final serve is given to the complainant, who is provided an opportunity to comment on the veterinarian's reply. Normally the match ends at this point and the Complaints Committee deliberates over the findings. Several important considerations arise from this process. First, the veterinarian is provided with an opportunity to salvage goodwill with the complainant, who may have been a loyal client up until the events giving rise to the complaint.

Second, it is important for the veterinarian responding to a complaint to cooperate with the investigating regulator. Attempts should be made to adhere to the timetable proposed by the regulator. Sometimes life gets in the way and it becomes necessary to request an extension. Most regulators will comply with such requests because it is never in the best interests of the investigation to base decisions on partial information. Every responding veterinarian needs to know his or her rights and those of the complainant, with respect to complaints. Typically the regulator is required to process the complaint within a given timeframe. While important to be patient with the process, it is not reasonable for a regulator to take an excessive period of time to process the complaint. The veterinarian needs to make timely responses and the regulator needs to process the complaint in a timely manner.

Third, consider issues of confidentiality before preparing any submission. The complainant is usually the client and, therefore, entitled to all information about his or her animal. However, this is not always the case. Third-party complaints (those arising from someone other than the client of record) are notoriously difficult in this regard. The most difficult being complaints related to animal-welfare agencies. In these situations, the veterinarian is hired by the agency to investigate allegations of animal abuse. The owner of the subject animals may be unhappy with the veterinarian's opinion and file a complaint. While the veterinarian can comment justifiably on the subject animals in his or her reply, s/he should not reveal details about the client (i.e., the animal-welfare agency), which invariably will be revealed to the complainant. Doing so constitutes a breach of confidentiality.

The regulator should avoid sharing personal and confidential information with the complainant, if the person would not otherwise be privy to this information. This responsibility should not be left to the regulator entirely. The responding veterinarian may have to take extra steps to ensure client confidentiality is not breached. Whenever doing so, it is important to offer an explanation.

Finally, the tone of the veterinarian's submission is important. While the response should give the impression of being helpful, it should not border on being conciliatory. Rather, the responding veterinarian should do his or her best to explain the situation, as s/he understands it. Sometimes it is necessary to introduce facts to the case that may not have been known to the complainant previously. By doing so, the veterinarian runs the risk of adding to the length of the "table-tennis game" in that newly introduced facts may give rise to additional issues or allegations, requiring further comment and reply. This risk is made greater if the veterinarian finds it difficult to resist heightening the rhetoric in the response. Investigators understand that considerable effort goes into formulating any response and efforts to cooperate in the investigation are appreciated.

Some veterinarians are tempted to deny any wrongdoing, even when the evidence is staring them in the face. While it would be wise to first discuss with a lawyer before admitting significant wrongdoing, it is quite fair to say that most complainants are seeking three things when they file a complaint. First, they are looking for acknowledgement. The veterinarian easily can acknowledge the professional relationship deteriorated, tragic consequences resulted for an animal, and communications failed. Second, the complainants are looking for an apology. Veterinarians can apologize for the fact that something transpired without admitting personal culpability (e.g., sorry for the loss of a pet without taking responsibility for the death). Third, complainants are seeking assurances that the same situation that happened to them or their animal will never be repeated. Veterinarians can share the steps they have taken to assure both the client and the Committee of their efforts to remedy the situation.

Many veterinarians want to know if the information they submit in a complaints investigation can be used against them in court, should the complainant file a lawsuit in addition to the complaint. The answer is that it could be possible for a complainant to rely on this information in court. Ordinarily, judges should not rely on the results of investigations conducted by complaints committees because they are not based on sworn evidence. However, judges may admit into evidence some or all of the documentation submitted in a complaints investigation. Veterinarians concerned about this prospect should seek the advice of legal counsel.

The Complaints Committee versus the Disciplines Committee

As a letter of complaint originates with the Complaints Committee, the veterinarian should have full appreciation of the limited powers of complaints committees. Most regulators (of all professions) rely on complaints committees and complaints investigations to screen complaints for the purposes of deciding whether or not the complaint is worthy of referral to the Discipline Committee. Complaints committees do not make findings, because they do not base their investigations on sworn evidence. Their purpose is not to hand out penalties. A complaints committee cannot revoke a veterinarian's license. These activities are the exclusive domain of the Discipline Committee. In order to justify a referral to the Discipline Committee, the Complaints Committee first must decide if the allegations are serious enough. Second, if the allegations are sufficiently serious, can they be proven? Third, does the complaint establish a pattern of unprofessional behaviour that, in an isolated occurrence, would not justify a referral, but because of a repeated pattern of uncorrected behaviour does justify referral? Finally, is an alternative disposition preferable to a referral, which would provide greater protection to the public interest? Complaints committees do not take these responsibilities lightly and most prefer to fulfill their public protection duties by furnishing advice or using some other rehabilitative measures to deal with members of the profession. This is not to suggest that complaints committees will avoid referrals to discipline committees at all costs, but rather that statistically such referrals comprise a very small fraction of the total number of investigations.

Responding to the Letter of Complaint

The veterinarian should do many things before responding to a letter of complaint. The first and most important is to set the letter aside for further reflection before replying. The worst thing a veterinarian can do is respond in the heat of the moment. The good news is that the complaints process frequently is designed to accommodate such behaviour. While each regulator no doubt conducts the complaint process somewhat differently, it is very important for the complainant to clarify, by some means, the exact focus of the complaint. Complainants can vary tremendously in their literary sophistication. Some may be attempting to express themselves using unfamiliar language. Ideally, the regulator compiles a list of issues arising from the letter of complaint that are confirmed eventually by the complainant as forming the basis of the complaint. If the regulator does not take this step, it is worthwhile for the veterinarian to do so. To avoid this step is to risk subjecting everyone involved to the "barking up the wrong tree" phenomenon.

The list of issues should be constructed in point form and approved or amended by the complainant before the veterinarian responds. A letter of complaint may contain the simple statement: "I couldn't believe that he had the nerve to charge me $1,500 for pulling all my dog's teeth." The veterinarian may interpret this statement to mean that the client was concerned about the fee of $1,500; however, the complainant may clarify that the concern was not about money at all, but rather that they had not consented to extracting all of the dog's teeth. Knowing this saves the responding veterinarian countless hours devoted to justifying their right to earn a living and helps them explain instead the steps they took to get the client's informed consent.

Medical Record Review

Once the list of issues is finally confirmed, the medical record should be reviewed, events relating to the complaint discussed with staff and colleagues, and the responding submission prepared. Complaints committees operate according to the adage, "If it wasn't written down, it didn't happen," and the documentation in the record is given a lot of weight by the Committee.

This is not a time to record events in the medical record retrospectively. Expectations are that medical records are completed contemporaneously with events as they unfold. Clinical findings, details of conversations, and labora-tory results can certainly be entered into the medical record at the end of a day, the following day and, in the case of laboratory results, upon receipt of the in-formation. However, adding pages to a medical record out of sequence or embellishing reflections of conversations that took place months earlier is not only considered unprofessional, it is harder to do without detection than one might think. While a veterinarian may believe that desperate times call for desperate measures, s/he should assume that any retrospective modifications made would be obvious to those investigating the complaint. Moreover, any veterinarian contemplating such measures should consider the detrimental impact such actions will have on relationships with staff and coworkers. Re-lationships built on trust and forged over a lifetime can be compromised se-riously and remain unlikely to ever fully recover. In short, the risks of altering medical records greatly outweigh any potential reward.

The Practice Team

With the medical record pulled, the responding veterinarian should review the case with other parties to the complaint, including co-workers. It is im-portant to note that in doing so, the veterinarian voluntarily may be relin-quishing his or her right to confidentiality. If this is a great concern, this step can be skipped. The veterinarian has no obligation to gather submissions from other parties to the complaint, but s/he should appreciate that the regulator will not conduct the investigation in a vacuum. Consider for a moment that the complainant has suggested the regulator consult with a particular techni-cian or receptionist for a submission in the belief the submissions will cor-roborate the complainant's version of events. It will not take long for that technician or receptionist to connect the dots as to which veterinarian has be-come the focus of the regulator's investigation. So, while the veterinarian has no obligation to reveal to co-workers that s/he is the subject of a complaints investigation, attempts to hide the investigation may be thwarted by the sim-ple reality that people have the ability to reason and may draw their own con-clusions. Arguably, more will be gained by being forthcoming with co-workers, and putting the issues on the table to better get at the truth and prepare the best response possible.

Formulating a Response

Which submissions the responding veterinarian should provide will depend on the issues being investigated. As a general rule, respondents should not provide more than what is required for the regulator to complete the investigation. For example, submitting radiographs to the Committee, even if they relate to the care of the complainant's animal, has no point if the complainant has alleged that the veterinarian was rude or used offensive language. In reality, the Committee is not mandated to consider the radiographs under such circumstances because it must restrict the scope of its investigation to the issues raised in the complaint. In the same example, if the responding veterinarian found themselves the recipient of advice from the Committee regarding radiographic technique, the veterinarian could choose to accept the advice in the spirit that it was extended or appeal the Committee's decision on the grounds it had exceeded its jurisdiction. In short, the veterinarian's response should stick to the issues approved by the complainant. Not doing so risks the dangerous prospect of the complainant raising new issues for investigation after having read the veterinarian's response.

Conversely, if the complainant has alleged that the veterinarian performed unnecessary surgery to remove an intestinal foreign body that could not be located at the time of the laparotomy, the pre-surgical radiographs upon which the decision to operate was based should be submitted to the Committee. Of course, a risk exists that the Committee may find the radiographs unconvincing, but it is more important that the responding veterinarian provide them in the spirit of cooperating with the investigation.

Regulators investigating complaints will consider any and all submissions provided. This is not to say they are all given equal weight. Many veterinarians, having consulted with their co-workers, ask that these same co-workers provide the regulator with submissions in respect of the events relating to the complaint or even simply to provide a good character reference for the veterinarian. Likewise, the complainant will often solicit submissions from friends, spouses, and other relatives in an effort to validate their version of events. Complaints committees are typically inundated with these "third-party" submissions. They frequently are unable to attach much weight to them; the notable exception being when all submissions are in agreement. If the complainant and their witnesses submitted that the dog fell off the table and the responding veterinarian and their witnesses submitted the same, the Committee can justifiably conclude that the dog fell off the table. It is far more typical for these submissions to be so varied as to wonder if the submitters were even in the same room when events transpired.

A responding veterinarian would be mistaken if s/he believed the regulator would attach a great deal of significance to the submissions of coworkers. However, it is extremely valuable to an investigating committee to get submissions from independent third parties, such as from people in the waiting room who may have overheard or visually witnessed events. Committees recognize that independent witnesses have no vested interest in submitting anything other than their recollections of events and do not run the risk of experiencing adverse consequences as a result of making their submissions. Information regarding others who may have witnessed important events should be provided to the regulator, along with a suggestion that the Committee solicit submissions from them. Responding veterinarians should not approach independent witnesses directly, as the investigating committee may consider such advances as potentially biasing of the witnesses; however, they can forward the names of independent witnesses for the regulatory body to contact.

It is always a good practice to recognize one's culpability when responding to a complaint. Complaints should be treated as learning opportunities. Responding with an open mind helps to facilitate such opportunities. Many veterinarians will survey their clients asking about their satisfaction with any services provided. Receiving a complaint is a wake-up call that unsatisfied clients have valuable information to share. While certainly people in the world make complaining a lifelong pursuit, most of us lead busy lives and will think twice before taking the time and devoting the effort to file a complaint. Consider for a moment the number of times customer satisfaction surveys are never completed. Understanding these situations will help put the complaint in perspective and provide some strength to resist the temptation to respond with self-righteous indignation. It is natural to want to blame the client, but this should be avoided. Responding veterinarians need to recognize their role in the complaint. It helps to know that the main instigator of any complaint is failed communication—communication that required effort on the part of both participants.

Veterinarians also should remember that we live in an electronic age and dissatisfied clients can communicate their opinion all over the world with a mouse click. Complainants have been known to post decisions of complaints committees on the World Wide Web, as well as launching door-to-door and media campaigns to discredit a veterinarian. Understanding this risk should stop most veterinarians from the temptation to add extra venom to their written submission.

Preventive Medicine—Avoiding Complaints

A recent article stresses that getting the informed consent of clients may be one approach to a complaint-free career.[1] It can be assumed that the veterinarian failed to obtain informed consent if the client was not prepared fully for what might arise. It does not hurt to acknowledge this lack of informed consent. Having a signed consent form may be of assistance and should be submitted if it is relevant to the case. However, you should recognize that writing the word "dentistry" on the list of consented to procedures does not, in and of it-self, give consent to extract 15 teeth.

Many veterinary procedures have recognized risks: performing a rectal examination on a mare carries with it the risk of rectal tears or perforation; ad-ministering a general anesthetic carries with it the risk of cardiac arrest; per-forming abdominal surgery carries with it the risk of hemorrhage. While it is true that these risks should have been discussed with clients in the process of obtaining their informed consent, occasionally the risks are not discussed specifically because they seem inherently obvious. If the focus of the com-plaint is the extent to which informed consent was sought, then it never hurts to remind investigators of these inherent truths. Frequently complaints com-mittees are comprised of both veterinarians and non-veterinarians alike. The veterinarian will benefit from providing information to those investigators on the Committee who, while they are undoubtedly blessed with traits of rea-sonableness, do not have any medical training.

Complaints often arise from disputes regarding fees. Fees constitute one aspect of informed consent. It would be virtually unheard of for a fee-based complaint to be referred for a disciplinary hearing. Therefore, always view fee-based complaints as learning opportunities. Complaints can be based on a failure to honour the fee estimate. If the client was quoted $1,500 for the pro-cedure and the bill for the procedure was $1,500, the complaint will not be over fees. However, if the quote was $750 and the client was not advised properly of the increase, the complaint is justifiably about fees. Many veteri-narians respond with the counter accusation that the client should have known added charges were accumulating, but realistically many of clients hope that the quoted fee will be honoured and can't rationalize any other outcome.

Under the same heading of fees is the issue of delivering value. Value is defined as "the price one is willing to pay for a perceived benefit." The key to understanding the concept of delivering value is that it is the *client's* and *not* the veterinarian's perception of what constitutes a benefit that matters. Many fee-based complaints arise when clients perceive they received next to no benefit for their money. Again, while not the stuff of discipline referrals, com-plaints such as these should serve as reminders that the veterinarian's value perception is out of touch with reality.

The final sin of money-related complaints is the unconscious signaling by the veterinarian or the clinic staff that money is more important than the patient's welfare. This can take many forms and again will never be the type of complaint that, on its own, results in a referral to a discipline hearing. Nev-ertheless, it is a bad message for any veterinarian to send.

Acknowledging any of these money-related sins of omission is never a bad plan when responding to a complaint. Truly no down side exists for so doing as failure on the part of many veterinarians to discuss monetary matters with their clients is one of the biggest concerns often expressed by members of the public regarding the veterinary care they purchase.

Another common cause of complaints made against veterinarians is the failure or perceived failure to provide continuity of care to a patient. Sometimes this takes the form of conducting improper case handoffs within a practice, or it may result from less than exemplary cooperation with another practitioner. It is rare for these to be blatant and if committed at all, will be the result of indiscriminate and subconscious actions. In the end, it is the client's perception of what happened that should become the focus of the response, and veterinarians should avoid any attempt to implicate other veterinarians. If the complainant wanted to name another veterinarian, s/he can file a separate complaint. The responding veterinarian should focus on his or her own involvement. Each veterinarian is responsible for his or her own conduct. It is perfectly acceptable to include in the response that the duty of care was shared with other practitioners; however, the veterinarian has no need to name them. Let the medical record speak for itself, as it should make proper reference to others involved in the case.

It has become increasingly popular for veterinarians to discharge clients who fail to fit their notion of an "ideal" client profile. However, most clients view being fired by their veterinarian as an assault to their dignity. Improperly performed, the termination of a professional relationship may result in a complaint. The risk for the veterinarian is that the amount of mud an irate client may choose to sling at their former professional advisor is unlimited. Suffice it to say that the veterinarian may end up responding to a plethora of allegations covering everything from the colour of his tie to the choice of automobiles. Avoiding these complaints in the first place is the best practice and some regulators are providing assistance with respect to this issue.[2] The responding veterinarian can take some comfort in the possibility that a complaints committee might determine some of the leveled allegations as frivolous and vexatious and an abuse of process. Beware, the complainant may dig up some past mistakes, which they had been willing to overlook previously and which many would consider serious.

Another significant cause of complaints filed against veterinarians is a perceived inability to empathize. While the veterinarian has no professional obligation to be empathic, it is an expectation of many members of the public. Occasionally, and in his or her zeal to provide optimum care for an animal, the veterinarian will impart feelings of guilt on the part of the animal's caregiver. Unconsciously they may have attempted to box the client in and not given him or her any choices. Once again, the only professional obligation the veterinarian must fulfill is to practice according to acceptable standards. Generally no consequences will be imposed for any veterinarian who acknowledges in hindsight that s/he could have tried better to relate (i.e., empathize) with the complainant's situation.

A final source of complaints against veterinarians is euthanasia. As with the previously cited examples, performing euthanasia carries with it the consequent risk of an adverse reaction or uncharacteristic response to the administered drugs. If the veterinarian failed to mention this potential risk to the animal's owner in advance of the procedure, they would do well to mention it in the response. Most complaints committees recognize that such adverse reactions are exceedingly rare, but when they do happen, represent one of the worst nightmares a veterinarian and client can experience. The Committee may wish to offer advice on how such tragic consequences can be avoided in the future— advice that would be heeded wisely and acknowledged by any veterinarian.

Additional Considerations

Veterinarians should be familiar with the regulatory environment in which they practice. Most regulators are happy to direct the respondent to appropriate resources for this purpose. In this way, it is possible to avoid costly bills for legal counsel to arrive at the same information. Regulators have a duty of fairness to fulfill in their investigation of all complaints. This includes a duty to the responding veterinarian, who should never consider the regulator the enemy in this process. If the veterinarian suspects s/he may have violated a regulation following research of the complaint, it would be worthwhile to seek a legal opinion. Many lawyers, having concluded their client may be guilty of such an infraction, will recommend seeking a resolution with the Complaints Committee, rather than risk referral to a disciplinary hearing.

It is important to recognize that while the complainant initiates the process, s/he does not drive it. Many complainants are quick to offer suggestions to the regulator as to what they believe would be a reasonable outcome to the complaints investigation. In reality, complaints committees are seriously restricted as to the types of decisions they can issue. It is worthwhile knowing in advance what these include, information that freely should be available from the regulator.

Some veterinarians may think it wise to approach the complainant directly after receiving notice of the complaint. This is rarely a good idea, and could be seen as an intimidation tactic by the complainant and look very suspicious to the regulator. Even if the complainant and veterinarian can agree on their own disposition (the veterinarian may offer and the client may accept remuneration for withdrawing the complaint), the veterinarian should know that the investigation might not necessarily be abandoned as a result.

Appeals Process

An opportunity to appeal the decision exists for most complaints investigations. Statistically complainants file most appeals because they did not agree with the decision of the Committee. Respondents should confirm with their regulator what appeal processes are available in the event they choose to appeal the decision of the Committee. Few veterinarians exercise this right of appeal, because they want to get on with their lives and stop this source of stress. Nevertheless, it may be important to appeal a decision, particularly if the committee exceeded its jurisdiction.

Summary

Responding to a complaint is stressful and most veterinarians do not appreciate criticism of their professional judgment. Many assume that responding to a complaint carries a possible consequence of losing their individual licence. Moreover, responding to a complaint can be expensive, particularly if the veterinarian seeks the advice of legal counsel. However, complaints are a part of professional life; the stress they cause and the negative consequences that arise from a complaint can be tempered by following these points:

1. Put the letter aside before replying.
2. Clarify the issues before replying.
3. Clarify what is required from the regulator by way of response.
4. Recognize your own culpability in the origins of the complaint.
5. Don't alter any records.
6. Discuss the case with staff members and get their stories.
7. Suggest neutral witnesses and get the regulator to approach them.
8. Protect client confidentiality where necessary (e.g., third-party complaints).
9. Provide only what is necessary to address the issues (e.g., records, radiographs, laboratory data).
10. Cooperate and avoid unnecessary delays in the investigation.
11. Don't approach the client.
12. "AAA" (Acknowledge what happened, Apologize for the fact that it happened and Assure the Complainant and the Committee of steps you have taken to remedy the situation).
13. Know the powers of the Committee and when it is exceeding its mandate.
14. Be patient, but insist on timely processing of the complaint.

References

1.   Martin, EA. Informed consent: One secret to a complaint-free career? College of Veterinarians of Ontario Update: Spring 2002;Vol 8. No. 2:7-9.
2.   Terminating the Veterinarian-Client-Patient Relationship. College of Veterinarians of Ontario: Draft Position Statement. http://www.cvo.org/uploadattachments/VCPR.pdf

Biography

Dr. Alec Martin graduated from the Ontario Veterinary College, University of Guelph as a Doctor of Veterinary Medicine in 1984. He practiced for 15 years in rural mixed practice, 8 years of which were in partnership. In 1991, Dr. Martin joined the Complaints Committee of the College of Veterinarians of Ontario (CVO). He was elected to the CVO Council in 1993, after which he chaired the Complaints Committee. In 1998, Dr. Martin was elected to the position of president of the College and in 1999 he joined the staff of the College as Deputy Registrar, where he served the Complaints, Accreditation, and Discipline Committees until November 2005. During his tenure at the CVO, Dr. Martin attended the University of Waterloo, where he obtained his Level I and Level II certification in mediation. He completed his Masters of Business Administration at Wilfrid Laurier University.

Dr. Martin is President of The Purple Grove Group Ltd., a consulting firm that manages the Veterinary Skills Training & Enhancement Program in Guelph, Ontario and provides consulting services to other professional regulators.

6-4

Family Law: Unravelling the Web We Weave

Poroshad Mahdi, BA (Hon), JD (LL.B), MA
Gelman and Associates, Toronto, Ontario

> *Love is blind, but divorce is an eye-opener.*
>
> — Anonymous

Introduction

An interviewer once asked the renowned social anthropologist Margaret Mead how she felt about her failed marriages. To this question, Mead responded that she had been married three times, and not one of her marriages was a failure. Perspective is everything.

Although it may seem facile to say, there are always two sides to every matter, including a divorce proceeding; and although it is easy to view the whole separation and divorce proceeding as an anarchical war of each against all, this is not the inevitable end result. Family law is governed by rules of practice. Although these rules are often broken and manners are set aside, it is important to at least be cognisant of the rules that govern addressing the breakdown of our most intimate relationships. The following is a brief overview of the rules governing family law in Canada; the information provided does not apply to the United States (US), where family law may vary from state to state.

Divorce

The first sign of a soured marriage is talk of divorce. In order to obtain a divorce, parties have to be separated for 12 months, one party has to have committed adultery, or there must have been cruelty. It is noteworthy that the adulterer or cruel spouse cannot use the grounds of adultery or cruelty in supporting their claim. Only the "innocent" spouse may raise the aforementioned grounds for divorce in the divorce papers. It is always recommended that, barring some exceptional circumstances, the grounds for divorce be listed as separation. The reason for this is practical: a person who is slandered in court documents by being labelled as cruel or an adulterer will likely respond with his/her own court documents providing equally unkind descriptions of the other spouse. In short, the whole process soon descends into a mud-slinging match.

Regardless of which ground is used for divorce, a person can apply for divorce as soon as s/he is separated from the spouse. Many people apply for divorce shortly after their separation; however, the divorce is not granted until the parties have been separated for 12 months (unless the ground for divorce is cruelty or adultery). There is nothing barring the parties from applying to the court sooner and obtaining the court's assistance in more urgent matters such as child custody, access, and support.

A common misconception is that there is a distinction between a "legal separation" and an "ordinary separation." Any time parties are living separate and apart, they are considered as separated, and their separation is "legal." The test for living "separate and apart" is less than exact. The following are some of the factors that will be taken into account in determining whether or not a couple is truly living separate and apart under the same roof: sharing the same bedroom, the absence of sexual relations, whether or not the couple do one another's chores or eat together, whether or not the couple interacts with the outside world together and presents itself as a couple, etc. Keep in mind that people can live separate and apart even under the same roof—in such an instance, they will still be considered separated for family law purposes.

During the 12-month separation period (assuming one is using separation as the grounds for divorce), parties can attempt to reconcile without necessarily interrupting their separation period. If spouses reconcile for a period of less than 90 days but break up again before the 90-day reconciliation period is up, their date of separation will still be considered as the date when they first chose to live separate and apart.

So how does one apply for divorce? The document by which the formal process of divorce is commenced is called an "Application for Divorce." The party who applies for divorce is referred to as the Applicant. The party who is served with the Application for Divorce is referred to as the Respondent. The Applicant sets out all of his/her claims in the Application for Divorce. The Applicant can ask for a simple divorce, or requests can be made for custody of the children, access to the children, child support, spousal support, division of net family property, exclusive possession of the matrimonial home, restraining order, costs, etc. As a rule of thumb, the more the Applicant asks for, the more expensive, bitter, and lengthy the divorce proceedings are likely to be.

The Applicant must serve the Respondent with the Application for Divorce (either personally or through the use of a process server). Once the Respondent is served with the Application for Divorce, 30 days are allowed for a response (assuming the Application is served in Canada). The Respondent responds to the Application for Divorce by filing and serving a document called an "Answer," wherein the Respondent sets out his/her own claims.

Once the paperwork has been prepared, the parties can look forward to repeated court appearances and various interim (meaning temporary) and final court orders. The last step in a matrimonial proceeding is trial (except for a limited number of cases, where the trial decision is appealed). The vast majority of cases never reach trial. Trials provide parties the opportunity to air their grievances openly in court, explain respective sides of the story, and cross-examine one another on various inconsistencies. Although cathartic, trials are to be avoided, if at all possible, because they are extremely expensive and often result in a zero-sum game where one party feels likes a complete loser and the other gloats with victory. Such a result may further antagonize relations.

It is usually recommended for parties to attempt to settle their matrimonial dispute by means of negotiation or mediation. There are various types of mediation, ranging from open (where matters that are discussed in mediation can be discussed in future court papers and at trial) to closed (where absolutely nothing discussed at mediation can leave the four walls of the mediation room). Mediation can take place with only the spouses and a mediator present, or it can take place with both spouses represented by their lawyers before the mediator.

The Children—Custody, Access, and Primary Residence

One of the most bitter battlegrounds in a divorce proceeding pertains to the children. Unfortunately, the children themselves are often the first casualties in the battles over custody, access, and child support.

There are many misconceptions with respect to what constitutes "custody." If one parent has custody of the child, that does not mean that the non-custodial parent cannot be involved in the child's life. Custody only refers to which parent will make significant decisions concerning the child. If a parent has sole custody, then that parent will make all important decisions concerning the child (i.e., health, religion, and education) on his or her own. If parents have joint custody of their child, then they will together make major decisions concerning the child. Custody and primary residence are two separate concepts. "Primary residence" refers to "with whom the child will ordinarily reside." Parties can have joint custody of a child, while the child only primarily resides with one of the parents. Similarly, parties can have shared parenting of their child (this is where the child lives with both parents), while only one parent has the right to make important decisions concerning the child (sole custody).

In general, if the parents cannot cooperate effectively with one another and do not have a history of coming to joint decisions concerning the children, a court will likely order sole custody. In relationships marked by abuse, sole custody is usually the rule.

Access is considered to be the right of the child. The norm with respect to access tends to be that the access parent has the child on alternate weekends and for one dinner visit during the week.

The Children—Child Support

Child support is also considered to be the right of the child. Child support is perhaps the only definite area in family law. An access parent has to pay child support to the parent with whom the child resides in accordance with the Child Support Guidelines (CSGs). The CSGs were introduced in 1997 to popular applause and include a handy chart that states how much an access parent has to pay in child support for his or her child(ren). As per common sense, the higher the access parent's income, the higher the child support obligation; as well, the more children one has, the more child support one has to pay. The CSGs are slightly different in each province. To access the CSG, visit the web site for the Department of Justice Canada at http://canada. justice.gc.ca/en/ps/sup/grl/pdftab.htm. Keep in mind that courts are loathe to deviate from the CSGs.

On top of regular monthly child support, the access parent may also have to contribute to a portion of the child's extraordinary or special expenses, such as daycare, summer camp, and university tuition. Once the activity has been deemed to be a legitimate extraordinary or special expense in which the child should be partaking, how much of the additional expense the access parent will be ordered to pay will depend on the parties' incomes.

In determining child support, much confusion is caused by the case of the self-employed parent. When a parent is an employee and s/he has no other source of income (e.g., rental income, dividend income, etc.), determining his/her child support obligation is simple; one need only look at their T4 slip (federally mandated notification regarding taxable income, assuming that all taxable benefits are included in the T4) and the CSG. When the parent is self-employed, one needs to examine the payer's income tax return and corporate tax return in considerable detail. Many items that are legitimate business expenses for tax purposes are not legitimate for the purpose of determining a parent's child support obligation. For example, a doctor may write off part of his/her car, entertainment, and "home office" expenses in determining income for tax purposes; however, a family court may add back much of the written-off expenses in determining the doctor's "true" income for support purposes.

Child support is not taxed in the hands of the recipient. This means that the payer spouse cannot deduct his/her child support payments, and the payee spouse need not include the child support received as taxable income.

A common misconception with child support is that it will automatically end when the child turns 18 years of age. It is true that if an able-bodied, mentally alert, self-sufficient child turns 18 and is no longer enrolled in an educational institution on a full-time basis, the access parent may be successful in terminating the child support obligation. However, if the child has a disability, child support may be continued. Also, if the child attends university or college full-time, the access parent will likely be paying child support (that may include the child's tuition and residency costs) until that child completes an undergraduate degree or even longer. However, keep in mind that just because the child lives away from home does not mean that the access parent has to only contribute to the child's education and residency costs. If, for example, the adult child returns home to the mother's home during school holidays, the access parent may be ordered to pay the mother child support in addition to the payments already made for the child's educational expenses. Often, access parents will be paying child support well into the child's 20s.

An access parent may successfully stop paying child support for the adult child if the adult child has unilaterally severed the parent-child bond. The test for this is difficult to meet and is based on the model of the loving parent and the ingrate child. This is a really tricky area, with no set test. An example would be a parent who has never abused the child or been accused of abuse, and who can show that s/he has endeavoured to be involved in the child's life as much as possible. Meanwhile, the child has to be completely difficult; for example, despite having grown up with a good family, s/he joins a gang and decides not to give the parent the time of day (i.e. does not return phone calls, or see the parent).

Another common misconception is that the income of the recipient spouse is significant in determining the child support that they receive. Unless the payer spouse can make a successful claim for undue hardship, s/he will be required to pay child support in accordance with the CSG—it will not matter if the recipient spouse earns a higher income than the payer or that the recipient spouse may now be residing with a wealthy individual. Except in cases of undue hardship, the recipient spouse's income is only relevant in determining what share of the children's extraordinary or special expenses (e.g., daycare, summer camp, university tuition, etc.) each parent will have to pay. Also, keep in mind that starting a second family will usually not decrease the amount of child support a parent is required to pay for his/her first family.

Spousal Support

Although most payers claim not to mind paying child support (after all, this money is meant for the children), almost all payers complain bitterly about their spousal support obligations.

Spousal support is perhaps the murkiest area of family law. It is fraught with emotion, and case law is generally inconsistent with respect to the quantum (how much support is ordered) and duration (how long support must be paid) of spousal support. Aside from the lack of certainty, another key distinction between child and spousal support is that spousal support is tax deductible to the payer and taxable to the recipient as income (child support has no tax consequences). As a general rule, the longer one has been married, the longer the spousal support obligation; and the greater the discrepancy between the respective incomes, the more onerous the spousal support obligation. Those who have lived in a long-term, traditional relationship (where one has been the primary income earner) are in for a rude awakening when met with a demand for spousal support.

Two computer calculations are used by lawyers and judges alike to provide some framework in the calculation of spousal support; usually both are performed and taken into account by the judge when determining spousal support. The first means of calculation is referred to as "Supportmate." Supportmate is based on a division of net disposable income. In a nutshell, net disposable income refers to the money in each spouse's hands at the end of the month after taxes (some other deductions are taken into consideration, but taxes are the most significant deduction). In general, courts assume that the spouse with whom the children reside is entitled to at least half of the family's net disposable income (this means that the payer spouse has to pay the recipient enough support so that after taxes and other deductions, the recipient spouse has the same amount of money in his/her hands as does the payer). It is not at all unusual for the payer spouse to give more than half of his/her aftertax income to the recipient.

Another calculation used in determining the appropriate quantum and duration of spousal support is referred to as "Checkmate." Checkmate is a program that offers a range of the appropriate quantum and duration of support. In using Checkmate, such factors as the age of the recipient, the number of children, the ages of the children, and the length of cohabitation are used in the calculation for the range provided.

One misconception with respect to spousal support is that a party is not entitled to spousal support unless the children are living with them. In reality, although courts generally believe that the parent who has the children requires the greater disposable income, courts may order the parent who has the children to pay spousal support to the parent with the lower income. The recipient in this scenario would receive less support than if s/he were the primary residence.

Another common misconception with respect to spousal support is that the payer's spousal support obligation always ends as soon as the recipient finds a new mate. This is not the case. It is possible for a recipient to be cohabiting for some time with another individual and still be entitled to collect spousal support from the ex-spouse. Remarriage does not mean an end to spousal support. Although the payer spouse may have the right to demand financial disclosure regarding the ex-spouse's new partner, such disclosure (if received) may not assist if the new partner's income is low.

Another misconception is that the support recipient will only be entitled to a limited duration of support because courts always want to encourage economic independence. Today, courts greatly value the role of caring for the home and the children. Courts also look at the pattern that was established in the relationship. Consider the example of one spouse who worked outside of the home and earned a high income while the other spouse stayed home with the children and then later chose to work part-time. After these parties separate, especially after a long-term marriage, the court may be loath to force the dependant spouse to work full-time immediately following separation. This may be very frustrating to the payer who complains that while working long hours, most of his/her money ends up going to the ex-spouse who "chooses" to stay at home and/or engage in social activities throughout the day. Naturally, the recipient has an entirely different perspective on this situation—namely, a career and aspirations that were sacrificed for the family, resulting in being disadvantaged in the current-day employment market, precluding the ability to become financially independent.

Regardless of which perspective one chooses to adopt in the above dispute, it is important to keep in mind that, where family law is concerned, habits are important. If you have established a certain pattern of parenting and financial obligations throughout your marriage, you should not expect these patterns to be drastically deviated from immediately following separation.

Marriage Contracts—(Prenuptial Agreements)

No one enters a marriage in the hopes of divorcing. Marriage Contracts are akin to disability insurance. People do not purchase disability insurance in the hopes of becoming disabled; rather, people purchase such insurance as a precautionary measure to assist them if and when the unmentionable happens.

Marriage contracts can be crucial in protecting one's assets in case of divorce. Marriage contracts can also deal with spousal support; however, marriage contracts cannot deal with matters involving one's future children. If a marriage contract addresses the issues of child custody, primary residence, or access, the court can and will on application ignore the agreement set out in the Marriage Contract in favour of an analysis of what is in the children's best interest.

It is important to keep in mind that Marriage Contracts are binding contracts. Do not enter into a marriage contract without independent legal advice. For additional information, read the following chapter on marriage contracts for professionals.

Division of Property

The challenge of extricating oneself "neatly" from the web of marriage is to know one's limits and, more importantly, to know when to compromise and when to stand one's ground." —Poroshad Mahdi

This chapter does not deal with the issue of division of property or, to use legalese, "equalization of net family properties." The reason for this omission is that division of property is governed by provincial rather than federal law. As such, the rules with respect to division of property differ between provinces and cannot be generalized in this pan-Canadian chapter.

Conclusion

Divorce, like marriage, is an unpredictable roller coaster with many ups and downs. One can view divorce as a death of sorts, symbolizing the end of a loving relationship and the breakdown of the family unit. Alternatively, one can view divorce as a fresh beginning, with the potential of improved relations, if the spousal relationship is hostile. The challenge in extricating oneself "neatly" from the web of marriage is to know one's limits and, more importantly, to know when to compromise and when to stand one's ground. A key ally in a divorce proceeding will be one's family law attorney. Although not as significant as choosing one's spouse, choosing one's divorce lawyer will have dramatic ripple effects on all aspects of one's life. Choose carefully.

Ideally, the divorce lawyer and the client will share the same philosophy with respect to conflict management. That said, the divorce lawyer is paid to be more than just a spokesperson for the client. The divorce lawyer should have the knowledge and expertise to assess which of the client's concerns are pressing and must be resolved by immediate court actions, and which concerns are better addressed through negotiation. There is a time to fight and a time to compromise in every battle. A good lawyer will advise as to which course of action is necessary at each step of the proceeding.

Your divorce lawyer will not and should not become your best friend. However, s/he will get to know more about you than perhaps your closest confidants. Choose a lawyer that has a style and perspective you are comfortable with, and one with whom you can converse easily and who is open to your questions and suggestions.

Biography

Poroshad Mahdi practices exclusively in the areas of family law and wrongful dismissal. Ms. Mahdi joined Gelman & Associates in 2004. Prior to that, she was an associate at one of Canada's largest and leading downtown Toronto law firms.

Ms. Mahdi received her law degree from the University of Toronto concurrently with an MA in International Relations. She completed her undergraduate degree at the University of Toronto, where she received a Bachelor of Arts (with High Distinction) in Political Science and Psychology.

Aside from professional activities, Ms. Mahdi has been extensively involved with numerous international non-governmental organizations, where she has gained experience in the impact of law from diverse perspectives. Ms. Mahdi has appeared before various courts and has led workshops and discussion groups regarding family law and conflict management. As a family law lawyer, Ms. Mahdi's practice ranges from preparing separation agreements where the parties are amicably separated, to arguing matters before the courts in more acrimonious disputes.

6-5

Affairs of the Heart: Marriage Contracts for Professionals

Brian Ausman, BSc (Agr), DVM, MBA, LL.B
Real Estate & Business Broker, Lawyer,
and Practice Co-Owner,
Guelph, Ontario

> *There is only one basic human right, the right to do as you damn well please. And with it comes the only basic human duty, the duty to take the consequences.*
>
> — P. J. O'Rourke

Introduction

This article is intended to make veterinarians aware of the issues that marriage contracts are designed to address. Clearly, the decision to enter into such a contract is highly personal and influenced by your specific situation and values. Marriage contracts are just one of several legal tools that can be used to address your specific needs. This article is not intended to replace legal advice which, by necessity, is dependent on the specific facts of every case.

Cohabitation Versus Marriage Agreements – One and the Same?

Let us start at the beginning. You and your soul mate are deeply in love and are contemplating marriage or cohabiting. Perhaps the most compelling argument for a marriage contract is simply that at this point in your relationship, when your hearts are most open, you should agree on how you will treat each other should you ever decide to go your separate ways.

A cohabitation agreement is ideal for couples choosing to simply live together rather than marry. Yet the breakup of so-called "common-law" relationships can be as devastating as a divorce in a traditional marriage, thus making any such agreement equally important. The common perception that after three years of cohabitation a common-law relationship bestows both the rights and responsibilities of marriage is wrong. Statutory rights to claims in division of property are given to married persons only. Claims to ownership of assets in common-law relationships are based in law on trust principles rather than property rights. Consequently, if a common-law partner challenges your ownership rights, you have the burden of establishing the framework for your rights before the courts; they are not protected by statute as they are for married couples.

With respect to marriage contracts, many people approach a lawyer a few weeks before the marriage, wanting a simple marriage contract; but, after all the options are explained, they find that a few weeks does not allow sufficient time to complete the agreement. Unfortunately, marriage contracts tend to be more complicated and take more time to work out than most people expect.

What a Marriage Contract Can Accomplish

There is no such thing as a "standard marriage contract;" it is best tailored to the needs and wishes of the parties involved. Marriage contracts can deal with very discreet matters, such as the disposition of a professional practice only, or they can be all-encompassing and deal with all aspects of property and support. The most common form of agreement is the "what's mine and what's yours agreement." If the couple separates, ownership of property will govern division of property. If the parties want to share the value of any property on separation, they would simply put it in joint names.

Section 52 of Ontario's *Family Law Act* sets out what can be included in a marriage contract.

A man and a woman who are married to each other or intend to marry may enter into an agreement with respect to the rights and obligations under the marriage, or on separation, annul ment, or dissolution of the marriage on death including:

(a) ownership in or division of property (aside from the matrimonial home discussed below);
(b) support obligations for spouses only (not children);
(c) right to direct education and moral training of the children to some extent;
(d) any other matter in the settlement of their affairs.

Marriage contracts are a special form of contract, whereby a duty of good faith is placed on both parties during negotiations. Thus, a key necessity of marriage contracts is financial disclosure. Your partner must be told about all your income, assets, debts, and liabilities as of the time of the agreement. People often do not like discussing their financial affairs, because in doing so, it "feels" too much like a commercial transaction and not a marriage. However, failure to disclose can make the agreement voidable at the option of the other partner.

What a Marriage Contract Cannot Accomplish

Dealing with issues surrounding young children can be the most emotionally difficult and painful aspect of divorce. The right to direct education and moral training of the children can be agreed upon in a marriage contract; however, it is important to remember you cannot deal with the issues of custody of, support for, and access to children in a marriage contract.

Where the family resides is the "matrimonial home" and occupies a special position in family law. It is usually the single item of greatest value owned by either or both spouses during their relationship. Typically, couples tend to view it as an asset belonging to both spouses, at least while the relationship is an ongoing one. But the matrimonial home is more than a valuable asset; it is the focal point of family life, and family members often develop deep emotional attachments to it. Furthermore, the right to occupy the matrimonial home satisfies one of the basic human needs—namely, the need for accommodation. If young children are involved, they have schooling within the neighbourhood and ties to friends. These ties are particularly important during family breakup, for this is a time in the child's life when they need continuity and stability. In order to reflect the importance of the matrimonial home, current laws are not governed by reference to ownership alone. Thus, one of the most important exceptions to a marriage contract is that it cannot be used to limit certain rights in the matrimonial home. You cannot, for example, waive your rights to possession of the matrimonial home. However, this exception does not mean that a party cannot waive the right to equalization of the value of a matrimonial home that one of you owns on the date of marriage. Furthermore, people often deal with sale and possession of the matrimonial home in marriage contracts and ask the court to follow their expression of intent.

For professionals, it is worthwhile to note that the courts have ruled that contracts of employment, degrees, and licenses should not be considered proprietary items capable of division for the purpose of equalizing family assets.

Where Marriage Contracts Are Especially Important

In reality, parties usually enter into a marriage contract when they are concerned about protecting the interests of third parties, such as practice partners or children from former marriages. A party who owns a house on the date of marriage may want a marriage contract, since without one the other party would get one-half of the value of the house if they both occupied it as the matrimonial home on separation.

Often people who own a number of assets on the date of marriage want a marriage contract simply to confirm what each party owns at the date of marriage and the value of such assets. This eliminates a lot of problems years down the road if the couple separates. Each partner will know the value of the property they brought into the marriage and that it will be taken into consideration should they split.

Typically people with significant assets (such as a professional practice) or who are entering a second marriage want a marriage contract to clearly set out their property rights on death that will prevent their children from starting a court action to get more from the other spouse than is provided in the parent's will. Since every marriage (even the successful ones) will come to an end in one of two ways (either by separation or death), and since family law issues arise in both scenarios, couples with significant assets have good reason to worry about the family law implications of their remarriage.

Strategies for Exploring These Issues

Lawyers are not experts in affairs of the heart, so it is not unheard of for marriage counselors and other professionals to be involved in helping a couple decide if a marriage contract is right for them. For some, a marriage contract may not be right in their current situation, but it may be useful to them sometime in the future.

Symbols express ideas and feelings. A marriage contract for some symbolizes the rational ability of a couple to have a business partnership. For others, marriage contracts symbolize betrayal, lack of trust, or insecurity. Symbols represent the emotional meaning and interpretation with which we see the world. To be meaningful, any framework for discussing marriage contracts must acknowledge the importance of symbols and incorporate them as an integral component of those discussions.

One suggested framework for discussing marriage contracts is to first know you and your future spouse's personal values. Second, decide what outcome you both can be comfortable with before attempting to work out these issues with your partner. For example, if you value relationships first and property second, then you may decide not to have a marriage contract. Also, if you discover that your future spouse would be terribly offended if you discuss property issues surrounding a hypothetical marriage breakdown, you may also decide not to have a marriage contract. On the other hand, you may decide that the reasons you as a professional should consider a marriage contract (such as concerns over protecting your practice assets or partnership issues) outweigh the reasons not to have a contract.

While a marriage contract may not be right for your situation, exploring the ideas outlined might suggest legal or business issues you should clear up before you get married. For example, if you are getting married and choose not to enter into a marriage contract, it is a good idea to keep an ownership file as proof of any valuable assets you own on the date of marriage. While this information is readily available today, years down the road this information is often impossible to obtain.

Perhaps the simplest advice for broaching this topic is to hand to your significant other a copy of this article, asking him or her to read it and share afterward with you any thoughts or opinions.

Biography

For Dr. Ausman's biography, please see Chapter 1-3, pages 25-26.

CHAPTER 6-6

Pet Health Insurance
- Evaluation, Caveats and Benefits

Peter R. Beaumont B.V.M.& S., M.B.A, M.R.C.V.S.

A Little History........

Pet Health Insurance has been available for at least 30 years in the US, from a multitude of different companies, for some of which it has proved to be an expensive exercise in failure, with bankruptcies of even large players, e. g. Fireman's Fund, through the years. While one company has survived during this whole period, it is instructive to consider why there has been such a problem with pet insurance offerings gaining traction with the consumer. For this entire time, despite the survival of the company referenced, the penetration level of insured pet dogs and cats was less than 0.5% in the US—this compares to rates of approximately 40% in the UK and even higher rates in the Scandinavian countries (see graph on next page).

This is all somewhat counter-intuitive, since in a country such as the US, with high disposable income, and private health insurance coverage for its humans, it would be anticipated that we would also, by extension, purchase health insurance for our pets. In contradistinction, in countries with socialized medicine for humans, as in the UK and Sweden, we would have expected more resistance to buying pet insurance. What are the causes of this topsy-turvy situation?

This author would argue that there are multiple reasons:

- Bargain veterinary fees, historically, making it easy for owners to pay for most procedures with credit.

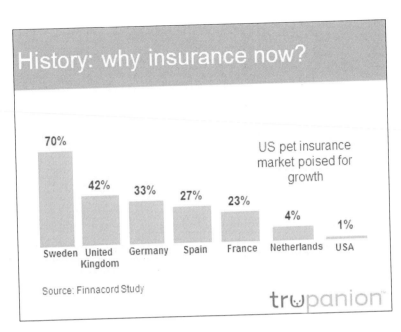

- High levels of disposable income.
- Insurance products which fail to have salience either for owners or (particularly) veterinarians resulting in no backing from pet-care providers.
- Wide availability of credit (credit cards and Care Credit).

So.....for a long period veterinarians and their staffs have been trying to decide whether their practices should be endorsing and/or actively proselytizing the role of insurance, and have consequently ended up sitting on the fence. Such early experiences with the available products as existed were unfavorable, particularly, in the author's opinion, because of the "usual and customary" caveat in most policies (see Definition of Terms). The part that the company paid of the cost of a procedure was often unacceptable to both owner and veterinarian, and such reimbursements as were received took an unacceptably long period of time to arrive. Additionally, the policy wording was very complex, voluminous and intimidating. Multiple plans with multiple confusing options, loads of 'fine print' and too many policy restrictions and exclusions caused further detriment.

Undoubtedly this type of history is one reason why penetration rates remained so low over three decades. So, clearly, the mix of insurance product/marketplace/consumer need/timing did not, and has not, inspired purchase, until perhaps now. Is now the time?

What do we want to achieve with insurance?

The over-arching goals of any pet insurance program should be the following:

- Enable the reduction (or, idealistically, elimination of) the need for "economic euthanasia" by which I mean euthanasia based upon expense grounds, not upon prognostic or humane grounds.
- Allow the veterinarian to discuss treatment plan A (versus B or C) and have the owner, since this is in the best interest of the pet, accept plan A, because it has become affordable by virtue of insurance.
- Improve practice financial stability by encouraging more patient visits.
- Free up more cash flow for re-investment in the practice, its staff and equipment by having an increased spend per pet.
- Make processing insurance claims simple and time-effective for veterinarians using technological advances as the accelerator.
- Reduce the number of acrimonious discussion about money and hence improve the 'customer experience' of pet owners.

Is it likely that we can accomplish these things? There is good data to suggest that in practices with a modest level of insured clients, all these goals can ultimately be achieved.

Market trends

Escalations in spending on animal health have exceeded growth in GDP over several years. Part of this is because of increasing pet ownership, which continues to grow and is expected to go up again by 3% in 2012. Insofar as the pet industry is concerned, annual spend has increased from $35 billion in 2004 to over $50 billion in 2011. Additionally the animal health industry as a whole has grown 13.1% compared to GDP for Q2 2011 of 0.4% (Source: US Bureau of Economic Analysis)

Even "Business Week" had a front page spread on the relative-resistance that animal health spending has had to the recent recession. However, it is probably safe to say that most veterinarians have not particularly experienced this increased spending being translated into take-home pay!

Some of the spending increases have come about because of increased incidence of disease; for example between 2006-2010 canine diabetes increased in prevalence by 32%; similarly there was a 12.3% increase in dental disease. Cats have fared no better, since, among other diseases, they have suffered a 34% increase in otitis externa. (Source: Banfield Pet Hospital's State of Pet Health Report 2011). Illness is therefore one of the drivers of increased animal health expenditure.

Alongside these trends has been a general increase in the costs of delivering veterinary services to clients (see sidebar). As well as vastly increased capabilities, a growing use of specialists has occurred with the increasing urbanization of society, again resulting in higher fees. Clients' perceptions of why costs are increasing correctly blame inflation and medical advances as major causes, but erroneously also find lawsuits and pet insurance companies as culpable! (Source: AVMA data)

Why is 'now' the time for insurance?

So what, then, has changed, in order for now to be the time for increasing penetration of insured pets? In the author's view the main driver to an owner purchasing pet health insurance is the "disposable income vs. cost of veterinary medicine" equation. Good quality veterinary medicine has been such a bargain for many years, but, as just discussed, the cost has risen. In the past decade, arguably, US disposable income has in general gone down, making the need for insurance greater. The major competitor to insurance has always been credit cards, as a mechanism to allow consumers to pay for a large bill over time. As pressure has been placed on the availability of credit, pet owners are less able to rely on this mechanism. It is also worth mentioning that the pets-as-children concept has become much more mainstream—88% of owners now consider their pet as one of the family (Source: Harris Interactive Poll 2007) and consequently expect to provide them with the same quality and extent of care that they themselves receive.

Newer companies with different, more relevant, insurance products have come to market and these products appear to be of increasing salience to pet-owners such that approximately 1% of dogs and cats are currently insured (up from approximately 0.4% five or six years ago, a level which had persisted for the prior 25 years!).

Should practices be promoting health insurance? I believe the answer is yes, for a number of reasons, but the main reason why veterinarians are still reluctant concerns the previous history of insurance products in the human marketplace. Veterinarians have watched with dismay as their human-medical counterparts have been subjected to the disadvantages of HMOs, PPOs and "capitation" whereby human health care has become somewhat commoditized.

Factors affecting veterinary fee increases

Most, if not all, of the factors influencing veterinary fees, which are generally increasing faster than the cost-of-living, are difficult to control, especially in those practices which strive to remain at the cutting edge of medicine:

- Explosion of new diagnostic tests, and procedures, some of which have made the leap from human medicine and are now available to veterinarians, and demanded by clients.
- These necessitate equipment expenditures, and upgrades, which have to be paid for, plus sometimes more real estate.
- Qualified staff, who have long been underpaid in our profession need to properly remunerated; health insurance and other benefits are becoming more costly.
- Continuing education is nowadays mandated and all staff need to keep up-to-date; all ancillary costs associated with this—travel, hotels etc.—continue to rise.

All the above must be paid for by ever increasing fees, hence driving the need for high-quality insurance.

We do know, however, that the 'stop treatment cost' (the cost of treatment at which an owner says: "No, I can't afford that, you'll have to put Fluffy to sleep") goes up by approximately 400% for an insured vs. non-insured pet (assuming an 80% payout)—from $1407 to $5600. This is enormously beneficial to everyone involved, of course including the pet that escapes euthanasia and is satisfactorily treated.

It's hard to argue that this would not be beneficial. In fact everyone wins—the pet gets better more complete healthcare, the owner is relieved of financial stress and the practice gets to do what it does best, namely to practice high quality medicine to save lives.

The vast majority of pets will eventually be treated for one or more chronic health conditions, the average age of onset being approximately four years of age; one in three dogs will experience a major emergency in any given year (Purina Life Study of Labrador Retrievers). These types of statistics add weight to the idea that being prepared for large veterinary bills is merely prudent.

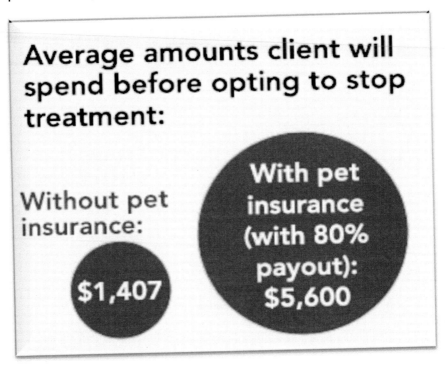

Clearly, then, the choice of insurer, and type of insurance product, becomes highly relevant to the degree of satisfaction obtained by the consumer. If your practice has made the decision to support or promote the idea of health insurance, how does it decide which company(ies) to endorse?

Should owners insure against routine well-care costs (i.e. "Wellness" coverage)?

This query also begs the question as to whether insurance companies should offer this option. Your author feels strongly that this is a very poor value-proposition for several reasons:

- Owners should budget for well-care when they take on the responsibility of a pet; these costs are well-known. (Insuring for these expenses is rather like insuring for gasoline usage and oil changes for your car!)

Why insurance now?

Consumer Benefits

➤ Peace of mind
➤ Enables (large) extra-budget pet illness expense w/o consideration of euthanasia
➤ Small monthly outgoing vs. (say) cell phone
➤ Decreases potentially adverse relationship with veterinarian
➤ Increases client compliance w treatment
➤ Better customer experience

trupanion

- "Well-care" is a very squirrelly issue. Does it include annual blood-testing (as well as vaccines, parasite screens etc.)? Are chest X-rays, urinalysis included? How often? How does an insurance company price this concept to make a good value proposition?
- Along with these caveats consider regional differences— for example, dogs do not need Lyme vaccine, flea, tick, or heartworm control if they live in Nevada
- Any owner motivated enough to buy wellness cover will surely take advantage of every last exam and test; this then results only in "dollar-swapping" though the company would always have to charge more than the service is worth, in order to stay in business. In other words, owner pays insurance company, which takes an anount to cover
- Surely insurance is for that catastrophic, unexpected event. Like home insurance, it is insurance that you would prefer never to have to use, but which covers you in the event that your house burns down—"coverage for the unthinkable".
- Be sure however, to buy accident AND illness cover, since "illness" is by far the largest claims category, and with the availability of radiation therapy, hip replacements and even bone marrow transplants, can now be very expensive.

This author believes that wellness programs can and should be customized to individual practices/communities/regions. Plans run by a practice avoid the insurance company being a profit-taking middle-man, and more importantly discourage the development of commoditization of well care, which would be quite detrimental to the profession.

How do we evaluate different insurance companies and their offerings?

This is at best a complicated issue but this author has found it easier to divide the considerations into "Macro" and "Micro" categories. As Jeffrey Feinberg states in "The Definitive Guide to Pet Insurance", pet insurance companies come in all shapes and sizes; some offer wellness coverage, others just 'accident' or 'accident and illness'. We should consider whether wellness coverage is important but in this author's opinion it is rather like insuring one's car for gasoline and oil changes—namely theses are predictable, budgetable and inevitable (presuming you are a conscientious pet-owner) expenses, not truly a subject for insurance coverage

On the "Macro" end of the scale we should start with reliability, consumer satisfaction, and ease of the owner and/or veterinarian

Why veterinarians should not be afraid of "HMO-ification"

Veterinarians are understandably nervous about the prospect of pet health insurers having the power to perhaps force their clients into an HMO-like situation whereby shoals of clients may be diverted to amore compliant/less costly service provider. This author is certain this will not happen within a 30 year window, and probably not at all:

- Look at individual company philosophy—if a company is veterinary-centric, and is successful, it, or any successor company/ subsequent owner would never abandon its effective business model; moreover, now is the time for the profession to support a company which has the 'correct' attitude.

- There are huge regulatory burdens to changing an insurance business model, particularly since it has to be accomplished in all 50 states.

- Such maneuvering requires a far greater degree of penetration of insurance, hence leverage, than will occur for years to come (even in the UK (42% vs. <1% here, remember?) this has not happened.

- Veterinarians are fiercely independent! If you believe this you know that no efforts will convince them to do something they do not wish to do.

dealing with the company (www.petinsurancereview.com). Some companies strive to find reasons to decline coverage when a claim occurs, for example, due to non-coverage clauses for congenital or hereditary clauses—see if these are present. The simpler and easier the policy is to understand, the better.

How 'veterinary-centric' is the company? This is not necessarily a critical feature but if we, as veterinarians, want to see pet insurance develop in ways that we find to be conducive for utilizing the products on offer, it is helpful to know that at least the company understands our point-of-view. Does the company have solid protocols in place for the adjudication of disputed claims, and some mechanism for helping practices/practitioners troubleshoot problems?

Does the company own its own insurance company or is it just an MGA (Managing General Agency) which markets, prices and services policies, though does not underwrite them? This is important for two reasons: first, for most MGAs there are two profit subtractions from the gross revenue of the company—the first is for the MGA itself, while the second is for the underwriting company (e.g. ING, AIG, Prudential and the like). This necessarily means fewer dollars to give back to policy-holders. For non-MGAs there is just one profit component—a better value-proposition by far. Second, the absence of a controlling underwriter means that a non-MGA company can often be more flexible, responsive and innovative.

Regardless, all insurance entities are highly regulated (they file policy details and various reports for state approval), need substantial reserves of capital and produce actuarial data for setting premiums. They are very complex businesses to run and manage, but consumers can be assured that all companies will be there to pay claims as the need arises because of this strict regulatory environment. Nevertheless check the credit score of companies at www.ambest.com.

Most due diligence that needs to be done on a macro-level can be done on-line, or by soliciting input from colleagues and/or pet-owners with experience of the company. Go to each company's proprietary web site and try to do side-by-side comparisons of the various policies offered.

Things get much more complicated on a "Micro" level; the very first need is to understand some of the terms which are involved.

Definition of Terms

"Usual and customary" means, for example, that if I perhaps perform a splenectomy on a dog, and give my client a bill for, say, $1200, that the insurance company might only refund to the owner $213.15 (these figures are fictitious, but to make a point). While saving the company money, this is a disaster on all sides; the owner is upset with the veterinarian (for presumed overcharging) and the insurance company for returning such a small percentage of the actual bill. Undoubtedly, this type of history is one reason why penetration rates remained so low over three decades. So clearly the mix of insurance product/marketplace/consumer need/timing did not inspire purchase.

Deductible—The portion of the veterinary bill the pet owner is responsible for before the pet insurance provider will start payment. This differs from coinsurance in that the full deductible amount must be paid before the coinsurance begins.

Lifetime deductibles per condition—Offered by some insurance companies, nice for pet owners, once a deductible is met for a condition, e.g . Diabetes, there is no annual reset.

Coinsurance—The percentage of the veterinary bill the pet owner is responsible for versus the percentage the pet insurance provider will pay. A set amount of co-insurance is typically a much better value proposition than 'usual and customary'.

Payout Limits—Often pet insurance providers place a limit to how much will be paid out per claim, per year, or over the lifetime of the pet. Plans with no limits are also offered.

Coverage Limits—Some pet insurance providers place limits on the type of treatments covered. Treatments for certain illnesses, such as hereditary or congenital conditions, could be excluded.

Pre-Existing Condition—Signs or diagnoses present prior to enrollment and waiting periods. E.g. left leg lameness related to a ruptured cruciate ligament or hip dysplasia.

Waiting Periods—There are always waiting periods between the time a pet is enrolled in a plan and the time coverage officially begins. These waiting periods are in place to ensure detection of pre-existing conditions, i.e. ones which arose immediately before insurance was purchased, and to discourage fraudulent claims,

It is better for both owner and veterinarian if your company pays a set percent of the veterinary fee—i.e. it does not distinguish between an expensive practice and a practice that maybe does less complicated procedures. Critically too, it should be a company which allows you to use the veterinarian of your choice (not all do). What limits are placed on a per illness, per annum or per lifetime claim?

Look for the amount of deductible, co-insurance clauses, exclusions. Can the owner elect a customized deductible? Does the policy pay for seeing a specialist or treatment at an emergency clinic or tertiary care center? While this would not necessarily affect your own practice, these are important criteria in the overall satisfaction with the policy. Is the owner penalized for having an 'unhealthy pet'? I.e. do the premiums change with increased claims? What about as the pet gets older, do the premiums become punitive? Are other things covered—cancer treatments, renal transplants, hospitalization costs etc.?

How does the company deal with congenital or hereditary conditions, preventable conditions and procedures regarded as being experimental (and therefore not covered)? Does it have a mechanism for deciding why something is regarded as being experimental and when it is considered mainstream or "current state of care"?

Is the policy regarded as one continuous policy (provided premiums are paid) or does it renew every year? This is important because of how the company may view both deductibles and pre-existing conditions in the event that the policy becomes a "new" policy on January 1st.

Do chronic illnesses result in reduced coverage, or do claims for illness cause premiums to be increased? Does the premium increase at certain birthdays of the pet or policy anniversaries (some companies automatically increase premiums at, say, 4, 6 and 10 year birthdays)?

Every company precludes coverage for pre-existing conditions and most impose a waiting period before coverage can commence (these are designed to protect the company from fraudulent claims). This has a rational basis in that if owners were allowed to insure their pets after they became sick, the actuarial basis of coverage (whereby a bunch of healthy pets pay for the few sick ones) would become invalid. However, it's worth knowing how the company defines 'pre-existing'.

How are premium charges established? For example it may be more logical to expect higher premiums for a French bulldog whose owners live in Manhattan, than a domestic short hair cat living indoors in Boise, Idaho. Some companies actually have premiums broken down by zip code and breed—this seems eminently sensible to me. What about alternative therapies (e.g. chiropractic, acupuncture etc.)?

And all importantly: *What about the fine print?*

Once your practice has decided to endorse insurance coverage, how do you proceed? It is very helpful to have the company's representatives come to make a presentation to the veterinarians and staff of the hospital. One person in the practice might become the 'expert' to whom all questions flow, and from whom records would be sent to the company when a claims question arises. Some companies have reduced premium rates for veterinary staff, and even programs whereby practices can pay for their staff pets' insurance cover—once your own pet is covered and the benefits are apparent, you will become an avid evangelist for coverage.

Insurance Trends

Awareness of pet insurance among pet-owners is 87%, and 50% want and expect information from their veterinarian and his/her staff about insurance. In all likelihood, this desire is not consummated very often despite the fact that veterinarians are generally positive about insurance and are slowly getting on-board after years of questionable experiences.

Current premiums range anywhere from less than $20 per month to over $85, the averages being $30-40 for dogs and $20-30 for cats. Approximately 75-80% of all claims whether for dogs or cats are below $250, although for those companies with 'no limit' insurance some extraordinary claims have been paid out (e.g. a $44,000 claim paid by Trupanion in 2012). Almost 25% of policyholders filed claims within 6 months of the inception of their insurance, while electing deductibles of approximately $220 in the US and $180 in Canada (Trupanion data).

How does insurance penetration affect practices?

There is overwhelming evidence that insured clients utilize veterinary services more. Actual data indicates that, on average, insured clients visit their veterinarian 165% more than uninsured and have a 200% increase in lifetime 'spend' for their pet (Trupanion data, 2012).

These factors enable subtle changes in practice-life. For example, practices which have a high penetration of insured clients begin to practice a 'pet-care delivery orientation' versus what might be considered to be a cost-effectiveness orientation. Utilizing a pet insurance product which delivers simplified service and understandable value helps practices eradicate potentially adversarial relationships with pet owners.

Happier clients mean fewer stressful financial conversations, increased compliance with suggested treatments, and end-of-life discussions that center on quality of life and prognostic considerations instead of money.

This also translates into a healthier financial picture for practices, with a more predictable revenue stream, and greater profitability. Obviously, the beneficial effects, which are even documentable at levels of insured clients in single digits, increase dramatically as the percentage of insured clients increases.

How can the veterinary team market pet insurance?

Once the practice owner(s) have decided to promote insurance, the best people by far to bring the message to clients are the staff (besides veterinarians hate to sell things!):

- Office manager should formulate a cohesive message and written guidelines, perhaps appoint a staff person as an insurance 'guru'.
- The best question a receptionist can ask a client coming to the front desk is "Did your insurance change since the last visit?" Slightly disingenuous perhaps, but a very good and gentle way to introduce clients to the availability of insurance.
- Everyone should be completely familiar with the main features of the policy you recommend (if it does not include wellness, make sure that clients don't claim for maintenance care). Try to acquaint owners with realistic expectations of the policy they have chosen.
- The Vet Tech returning the sick pet after a surgery can inquire if the owner had purchased insurance—too late for this, but not for the next, illness.
- Maybe a professional sign at the front desk—"Please give all insurance forms to us before your appointment'?
- Ask the company you have chosen to provide in-practice educational seminars for staff and doctors in order to make this process seamless.

What does the future hold?

Veterinarians hate paperwork! Therefore axiomatically, one of the keys to increased utilization and acceptability by the profession will be the increased integration of insurance claims mechanisms into practice information management systems (PIMS). This author has great confidence that this will happen since these system-integration software programs are already being developed. Increased ease of implementation by veterinary staff will also open the door to express modes of payment, either to pet-owners or directly to practices themselves. Technology will certainly be the key to enhanced customer experience, as well as ease at the veterinary practice interface.

There is no doubt that most practices' bottom-line profitability will not accommodate the addition of extra personnel to fill in insurance papers, as happens in human medical practice, so it is incumbent on pet insurance companies to obviate that potential need via more sophisticated technology development.

Wellness plans will continue to be developed both as commercially available add-ons to PIMS as well as by individual practices. Imagine a future where clients' pets are covered by a practice-wellness plan and a complete insurance program for accident and illness! Immediate savings of 3-5% credit-processing charges will be available to practices which embrace this direction, as insurance companies remit payment directly to practice bank accounts.

As such cloud-based systems become available, both veterinarian and customer experience will be enhanced; customer service and Plan 'A' veterinary care will become standard. Conversations with clients should then center around optimization of health instead of budgets. Time will be spent focused upon screening and early diagnosis of disease, and following health trends of individual patients with data developed by better wellness care.

Finally........

So, to recap, what are the features that make pet health insurance such a persuasive addition to a practice?

- Increases client's ability to manage a financial burden. If a pet-owner has a pet with a costly illness, or a young animal in need of long-term care, insurance gives much-needed financial support

- Ability to provide the best care possible. Often the cost of quality care exceeds the owners ability to pay and so, as veterinarians, we start talking about Treatment Plans 'A', 'B' and 'C'. Insured clients are much more likely to adopt Plan 'A' happily, resulting in enhanced medical care. Less effective therapies and acrimonious conversations with clients about money and fees become a thing of the past.
- Peace of mind because of protection against the (almost) inevitability of significant expense; pet owners are especially vulnerable in a poor economy.
- Ability of each practice to become more financially stable by virtue of having a large portion of insured clients who are asking for and receiving the best quality medicine.

Marketing insurance to your clients, in most cases, should be a very low-key affair. Certainly both puppy and kitten owners, as well as owners who have just paid a large veterinary bill (!) are willing listeners, and the value can be explained easily when comparing the monthly cost of premium with the potential benefits. No one wants to be put in the position of deciding if they can afford the treatments being suggested for their beloved family member. Compassionate doctors and staff don't want to be put into that situation either—the author's belief is that with increasing penetration of insurance cover, euthanasia performed for solely economic reasons could hopefully become a thing of the past.

Biography

Peter R. Beaumont is a board member of Trupanion Inc. and American Pet Insurance Company Inc. and the chairman of its Veterinary Advisory Board. He is also past or present director of other entities including th NJ Association of Biomedical Research, Pet Angel Inc., Veterinary Business Development Ltd., and Broadband Maritime Inc.. As a serial entrepreneur, Peter has been involved as principal, owner or operator in many veterinay businesses; he was a founder of one group of corporate practices in the UK and is Managing Partner of Yorkshire Realty LLC. He has been a consultant to Novartis and The Seeing Eye Inc. as well as for many years a practicing small-animal veterinarian and practice-owner.

Peter received his veterinary degree from the Royal School of Veterinary Studies of Edinburgh University, Scotland, and completed his internship and soft-tissue surgery residency at the University of Pennsylvania, Philadelphia. He also completed the Certificate of Veterinary Practice Management at Purdue University, Indiana, and his MBA at New York University Stern Business School.

Section 7

LIFE OUTSIDE
THE HERD:

Other Career Options

Introduction

In 1964, I left Whitby, Ontario, to attend the Ontario Agricultural College with hopes of entering the Ontario Veterinary College (OVC) to follow my father's footsteps (Dr. Cam MacKay, OVC 1950) into the veterinary profession. That dream came true, and I graduated in 1970 from OVC and began to work as a practicing companion animal veterinarian in our family practice. Forty years later, I have had the privilege of being able to participate in a virtual smorgasbord of experiences in veterinary medicine. Beginning as a one-doctor, one-employee practice, it grew to a six-doctor general and specialty practice before the end of the 1980s. It became an American Animal Hospital accredited practice in 1974, and the one employee became 30 employees. I have been privileged to serve as President of many veterinary organizations, among them the Ontario Veterinary Medical Association, the College of Veterinarians of Ontario, and the American Animal Hospital Association.

The experiences gained through involvement in organized veterinary medicine led to consulting positions in the biological, pharmaceutical, pet insurance, and microchip industries. The ability to speak and travel throughout Canada, the United States, and (eventually) globally, allowed me to seek positions in the administration of a veterinary school (OVC) and then to my current employment in the pet food industry.

The reason I mention the above is to give you some insight into the vast horizons that your degree in veterinary medicine will open for you. If starting your career as a practitioner, please take the time to continually look around, follow trends, and make sure you are always happiest in the role you have chosen. Your veterinary degree can help you open the door into many other employment areas, but you often need to have additional pieces of the puzzle to acquire your dream job. This chapter, written by experts in their job areas, gives you a brief glance at other options available to you.

Clayton MacKay, DVM
Director of Veterinary Affairs,
Hills Pet Nutrition Canada, Inc., Mississauga, Ontario

Dr. Clayton MacKay is currently the Director of Veterinary Affairs at Hill's Pet Nutrition Canada Inc. He is an accomplished international speaker who has served in many capacities including: past-president of the Ontario Veterinary Association (OVA 1980; now College of Veterinarians of Ontario or CVO); past president of the of the Society of Ontario Veterinarians (SOV 1986, now the Ontario Veterinary Medical Association or OVMA); and past president of the American Animal Hospital Association (AAHA 1995-1996), being the first Canadian to hold this honour. In addition, Dr. MacKay was the director of the veterinary teaching hospital (OVC) from 1992-1996 and is a past practice owner.

Career Paths in Veterinary Medicine: Pharmaceutical Industry

Walt Ingwersen, DVM, DVSc, Diplomate ACVIM
(Internal Medicine),
Boehringer Ingelheim Canada Ltd., Vetmedica Division

> *Do not go where the path may lead; go instead where there is no path and leave a trail.*
>
> — Anonymous

Introduction

If someone had told me upon my graduation from the Ontario Veterinary College in 1982 that I would eventually embark on a career in industry, I would have given no credence to the prediction. My place was in the operating room, not the board room. And my attire was to be scrubs "accessorized" with a stethoscope—not a suit and briefcase! However, here I am very happily employed in industry, approaching my 25th anniversary of being a veterinarian and having explored career paths in academia, private practice, editorship of a scientific veterinary journal, and as a consultant to a number of different corporate endeavors. Perhaps some will view my career to date as the wanderings of someone who lacks focus (I have always said that I still am trying to figure out what I want to be when I grow up!); however, I look at it as a testament to what a degree in veterinary medicine has allowed me to do—namely, to change my career paths without changing my profession. Never underestimate the value of what you have already achieved. A degree in veterinary medicine is the broadest and most comprehensive degree that science has to offer, and it will remain one of your most valuable assets throughout your career—regardless of how you choose to apply it.

Despite the breadth and depth of a veterinary degree, veterinary school is focused on clinical applications of the knowledge gained, and we are taught in an environment that stresses the individual unit of health—individual companion animals or the herd for food-producing animals. Rarely are we provided with the larger perspective of the animal health industry as a whole. Additionally, we are rarely, if ever, exposed to alternate career paths (ACPs; loosely defined as anything other than a career in private clinical practice), and this not only applies to veterinary school, but to our postgraduate life as well. Even today, with the explosion of the information age, there is a relative paucity of information on ACPs in veterinary medicine. Based on this "indoctrination" into traditional career paths, it is no wonder that virtually no newly minted veterinarians enter industry upon graduation. Figures from a 2005 study of veterinary career choices for United States (US)-based school graduates demonstrated that of 1,747 survey respondents, 0% of female graduates and 0.8% of male graduates chose to begin their veterinary profession in industry. (Compare this with 55% of female graduates choosing private practice and 32% choosing academia, whereas similar figures for male graduates were 67% and 27%, respectively.) However, statistics from the Canadian Veterinary Medical Association (CVMA) indicate that fully 6% of the approximately 6,000 licensed veterinarians in Canada are employed in industry. This mirrors figures released by the Canadian Animal Health Institute (CAHI), an industry self-interest group that includes pharmaceutical and pet food companies, which estimates between 85 to 100 veterinarians are employed within CAHI member companies. So why? What causes a veterinarian to migrate toward a career in veterinary industry at some later stage in a veterinary career? To answer this, we must first understand just what an ACP in veterinary industry entails.

What Is Veterinary Industry?

"Alternate career paths" is a term that essentially covers anything outside of private clinical practice, and its breadth is reflected in the other chapter titles covered in this section of the textbook. In terms of employment market size, an ACP in veterinary industry falls behind veterinary opportunities in government, but it is similar to careers in academia. Traditionally, most view an ACP in industry as being composed of pharmaceutical and pet food companies; while these do represent the largest employment sectors, there are other industry participants providing products or services to the animal health industry that include but are not limited to:

*   Clinical pathology laboratories, who employ veterinarians generally as diagnosticians based on their expertise in the various diagnostic modalities (e.g., hematology, cytology, histopathology, microbiology, etc.)
*   For-profit continuing education ventures, including publication of scientific literature, internet resource sites, some conferences, etc.
*   Practice management, including software development and application
*   Financial services, such as practice evaluation, practice management consultation, pet insurance, etc.
*   Legal services; multiple degrees are becoming more common, with a number of DVM branching out into niche markets, such as legal firms specializing in veterinary law
*   Technology provision, including advanced diagnostic equipment (e.g., ultrasonography, magnetic resonance imaging, etc.)

Why Choose Veterinary Industry?

While exploring a career in industry is prompted by different things for different people, it should be interesting to note that this decision comes with time and is rarely a choice for the fresh graduate. Therefore, the reasons can generally be slotted into three main categories: interest generated by exposure to industry; dissatisfaction with the current career path; or a combination of both. In a 2001 Ontario Veterinary Medical Association (OVMA) survey that explored reasons for veterinarians entering ACPs, 25% of respondents cited a desire to pursue academic interests; 25% expressed a desire to reduce working hours; 15% indicated a desire to explore "new" interests; and remaining respondents cited reasons such as disillusionment, financial pressures, stress, and health concerns. Similar reasons were identified in another 2001 study done through the North Carolina Veterinary Medical Association, and also included benefits and proximity to family. Interestingly, the predominant driving force for exploring an ACP, aside perhaps from academia, is a search for something better and not so much an interest in industry per se. While industry does offer some differential benefits to private practice, it is not always the panacea people desire.

Pros and Cons of Industry—A Reality Check

There is no question that when it comes to financial reward and stability, benefits, and overall working conditions, industry does present some major advantages. While there are exceptions to every rule, veterinary employment surveys (whether Canadian or US based) have consistently reported a higher mean and median remuneration for veterinarians in industry compared to those employed in private practice. Also, industry/pharmaceutical careers consistently top the income-earning potential of the ACPs sector, especially for those in managerial or administrative roles. Generally, benefits are also far more comprehensive and often encompass generous insurance coverage (disability, dental, extended health, malpractice, life, and travel), continuing education stipends (including time to attend), employee pension plans (including Registered Retirement Savings Plan contributions), professional association dues and membership, and a vehicle allowance or provision of a company car. Working conditions, as a general rule, are safer and less physically demanding as direct hands-on care of animals is virtually non-existent.

A reduction in the hours worked, however, is not always realized—a finding that was revealed in the 2001 OVMA Alternate Career Path survey where, on average, ACP veterinarians logged more hours than veterinarians in private practice. It is of interest to note is that the group of respondents who had actually cited a desire for reduced work hours as a reason for leaving private practice, actually did end up working, on average, fewer hours than their other ACP veterinary counterparts.

Other advantages to an ACP in industry include the ability to have an impact on multiple rather than single animal lives through the development of new cures or preventative medicines, being on the forefront of science, the greater opportunity to publish, more likelihood of management and advanced training opportunities, exposure to/ability to learn more about business practices, and the opportunity to travel, to name but a few.

Potential disadvantages include time away from home (dependent upon one's area of responsibility and need to travel), a well-defined corporate culture that may dictate behavior, the realities of being an employee rather than the employer, employment and/or advancement potentially predicated on an advanced degree, a reduced ability to use technical training/expertise (e.g., surgical skills), and the (at times) reduced status in the eyes of peers.

While there are distinct advantages and disadvantages to a career in industry, it is not for everyone, and any career choice should not be a knee-jerk reaction, fuelled by job dissatisfaction and the belief that it represents a panacea solution to one's professional concerns. Many challenges, principally the balance of work-life, are no different than the challenges in private practices and may, depending on the scenario, be even worse due to the stressors of a corporate environment ruled in large part by quarterly performance expectations.

What Does Someone In Industry Do?

While the job responsibilities will vary from company to company, using the pharmaceutical sector as a template, the following are the general entry-level categories:

Regulatory Affairs

Individuals working in regulatory affairs are the liaison between the company and the governmental regulatory authorities. Their principal responsibilities are to:

- Satisfy the regulatory authorities as to the safety and efficacy of a new drug or biological (i.e., vaccine) submission via supportive, generally company-sponsored but independently run research studies
- Assist in designing and monitoring the studies required for the above, which are often carried out in the country where drug approval is being sought
- Oversee government-mandated pharmacovigilance protocols—in essence, the collection and reporting of any suspect adverse drug and biologics reactions
- Facilitate acceptance of/compliance with packaging and label claim revisions and/or other post-licensing product alterations (e.g., changes in manufacturing protocols or government-mandated Good Manufacturing Practices [GMPs])

Animal Care

Many larger human pharmaceutical companies have their own research facilities, which house a variety of animal species required for various aspects of product safety and efficacy testing. Unique species care requirements and more comprehensive animal welfare legislation generally require specialty veterinary expertise (e.g., Diplomate status with the American College of Laboratory Animal Medicine). Industry careers in laboratory animal medicine are available predominantly in US-based and human pharmaceutical companies; however, similar specialty career opportunities do exist in Canada within academia.

Research and Development (R&D)

New drugs or biologics arise from a need spawning a conceptual solution that requires proof of concept validation. The identification of new molecules and biologics through to and including Phase I (safety study in healthy members of the target species) and II (safety and dose determination in a small number of affected target species animals) clinical trials is under the realm of R&D.

Technical Services

Technical services encompass a whole gamut of responsibilities, which include but are not limited to post-product licensing studies (often for claim validation and/or extension), product sales force training, veterinary user support (product specific and overall case care assistance), development of technical materials supporting the product and/or disease entity, provision of continuing education, and company liaison with academics and/or other opinion leaders. This can be done in-house, as a dedicated field veterinarian, or—more commonly—as a combination of the two. Based on the rapid expansion of medical knowledge, most technical services veterinarians would be species focused (i.e., small animals, equine, or food-producing animals) and discipline specialized as well (e.g., Diplomate board certification).

Marketing and Sales

As the title implies, this area of responsibility generally involves deriving the marketing and branding platform, as well as the product life-cycle management including sales programs and sales force supervision. Market forecasting and strategizing are key components.

Looking at generalized statements as to additional unique job requirements and expectations, consider the following:

R&D and regulatory affairs:
- Ideal background is in research (a must for a career in R&D)
- Advanced research degree (e.g., PhD) an advantage for regulatory affairs and a must for R&D
- Minimal travel commitment

Technical services:
- Clinical background is essential
- Advanced veterinary degree an advantage (e.g., Diplomate specialty) and becoming more the norm
- Peer recognition (see next section)
- Moderate amount of travel expected

Marketing and sales:
* Ideally a background is in practice management and/or marketing
* Advanced business degree an advantage (e.g., MBA)
* Often a heavy travel expectation

Given time within the industry, more and more administrative opportunities will become available (depending on one's aptitudes), and these generally come with a remuneration premium. Also, it should be noted that while the focus has been on the veterinary industry, similar opportunities exist for veterinarians in the human health care industry as well, although they are generally restricted to animal care, regulatory affairs, and R&D.

What Is Industry Looking For?

While veterinarians play a vital and active role within veterinary industry, a veterinary degree will be looked on as an asset that provides technical aptitude assurance but not a guarantee for employment. For a number of the non-technical positions, such as marketing-sales and R&D, the reality is that veterinarians will be competing with non-veterinarians having similarly relevant work experience and advanced degrees (e.g., MBA, PhD, etc.). So, what are some other key attributes that industry would be looking for—attributes that are likely to tip the scale in favor of someone with a DVM behind their name? Consider the following:

* Overall industry knowledge and background. As with any job, experience is always an asset, as employers tend to give preference to a proven or known commodity. Specific knowledge—especially hand-on experience—regarding the individual company's products would also be viewed as an asset.
* Overall knowledge of both veterinary clinical practice and business. Considering that this is the industry's customer base, an intimate knowledge of the profession's needs, issues, and challenges is critical when bringing a product to market—right from R&D to life-cycle management.
* Additional veterinary training. See previous discussions regarding advanced degrees.
* Peer recognition and/or networking capability. The veterinary-clientpatient relationship (VCPR) is a business affiliation that is relationship-based, built on foundations such as trust, respect, and service. This is also true of the industry-veterinary relationship; having a well-known and professional reputation will be invaluable, regardless of which ca-

reer path you follow!

- Communication skills. Many of the roles a veterinarian may assume in industry require the ability to communicate ideas and findings, and impart knowledge within the veterinary community.
- The ability to problem-solve and a keen analytical/decision-making ability. Fortunately, the DVM curriculum is founded on problem-solving strategies, and the practice of medicine dictates decisiveness.
- Self-motivation and organizational skills. A number of the job categories have a significant autonomy component; therefore, the ability to manage time, prioritize needs, and maintain focus while working independently is critical to success.
- Team leadership and people management skills. As in private practice, the team is also the functional unit in industry, and it is often composed of varying personalities with differing but relevant backgrounds to the project at hand. The ability to facilitate solutions that represent win-win-wins for individual team members, the team as a whole, and the company is a valuable human resources skill set.

How Do I Pursue This Career Path Further?

As with any employment opportunity or desired career path, there will be competition, and competition is tight. This stems from the relatively low number of positions, compounded by the steady but sure industry amalgamation that has occurred (both in Canada and globally) over the last 2 decades—translating into position attrition—and the fact that industry tends to hire from within. So, how can one stand out during the recruitment phase? Consider the following suggestions that will not only provide a differential advantage as a candidate, but will also provide hands-on experience to help you better determine whether this career direction is right for you:

- Invest at least 2 to 5 years in private clinical practice. This will provide a good grounding of veterinary practice knowledge, which is a valuable asset to any company keen on better understanding its customer base.
- Work toward an advanced degree
- Volunteer within veterinary medical associations. This will help from a variety of perspectives, including:
  - An enhanced view of the bigger industry perspective
  - An investment in expanding your network of colleagues and peer recognition
  - Working with industry representatives (often regarding sponsorship or

the provision of continuing education) who will provide you with a better understanding of the industry as a whole, as well as the corporate philosophies of individual companies

- Consider participating in a clinical field trial. Many companies use private veterinary practices to do post-licensing expanded claim and/or marketing studies. This would be an ideal opportunity to get hands-on R&D experience.
- Hone your public speaking abilities. There are a variety of programs and associations that focus on developing this skill set.

Conclusions

While far from complete, this chapter provides a general overview of the animal health industry and hopefully provides some insights as to how to further explore this ACP. The critical issue when considering industry as a career is not to leave it too late. Don't let yourself fall into a situation where the driving force for change is simply to escape one's current poor working conditions; instead, plan ahead and take the steps necessary to ascertain whether an ACP would suit you. Then begin to work to develop and apply the skills that will ensure success.

Additional Recommended Reading

Canadian Veterinary Medical Association (CVMA); website accessed May 16, 2006: http://canadianveterinarians.net/index.aspx

Canadian Animal Health Institute (CAHI); website accessed May 16, 2006: http://www.cahi-icsa.ca/

Osborne D. Ontario Veterinary Medical Association (OVMA) Report on Veterinarians Employed in Alternate Career Paths; 2001.

Brown JP, Silverman JD. The current and future market for veterinarians and veterinary medical services in the Unites States (executive summary). J Am Vet Med Assoc 1999;215: 161-183.

Huml RA. Transitioning from private practice to industry. Veterinary forum; October, 2004.

Biography

Dr. Ingwersen is a 1982 graduate of the Ontario Veterinary College (OVC), where he returned to complete an internship and residency in small animal internal medicine, resulting in his post-graduate Doctor of Veterinary Science degree and certification by the American College of Veterinary Internal Medicine as a specialist in the area of veterinary internal medicine. From 1987 to 1998, he was chief of veterinary internal medicine at a multi-person, general/specialty veterinary clinic on the east side of Toronto; he became its hospital director in 1993. Beginning in September of 1998, he changed career directions by becoming the first Canadian to act as editor of the *Journal of the American Animal Hospital Association*. Dr. Ingwersen also provides consulting services to the pet health industry, including the areas of microchipping, pet health insurance, and clinical pathology laboratory medicine. Since June 2002, he has been a consultant to the Boehringer Ingelheim Canada Ltd., Vetmedica Companion Animal team, joining them in a full-time capacity as of January 2004. He is currently Honorary Secretary of the World Small Animal Veterinary Association and continues to provide internal medicine consultative advice, assisting veterinarians across Canada in making health care decisions and recommendations for the patients they treat.

7-2

Career Paths in Veterinary Medicine: Pet Food Industry

Nicole Judge, DVM
Formerly Veterinary Customer Marketing Manager,
Hill's Pet Nutrition Canada Inc., Mississauga, Ontario
Currently Operations Manager, Ontario Veterinary Group,
Toronto, Ontario

> *Twenty years from now you will be more disappointed by the things you didn't do than by the ones you did do. So throw off the bowlines. Sail away from the safe harbor. Catch the trade winds in your sails. Explore, Dream, Discover.*
>
> — Mark Twain

Careers in Industry—Why Should I Consider One?

When you ask someone to think of a veterinarian, they will usually envision someone working in private practice, looking after dogs and cats, or a large animal veterinarian working with livestock or horses. The general public (and even veterinarians themselves) typically wouldn't envision someone working in industry as a first thought. Of veterinarians in Canada, 75% are involved in private practice, 10% work for the government at some level, 5% are in teaching and research, and the remaining 5% are in industry.

Consideration of taking the leap from private practice to industry is a big decision; many people are torn between staying in the typical job that people expect them to be in and searching for something new. Society assumes that most veterinarians are involved in practice, and many people face a lot of questions from colleagues, family, and friends when they decide to change their career path. The most common comments and questions faced by those new to industry are: "So you couldn't hack private practice?", "What a waste of an education," and "That's too bad that you're not a veterinarian anymore." These remarks can be very difficult to deal with, especially at first, when facing a steep learning curve and wondering if you've made the right decision. However, the long-term benefits of this type of career path are more than worth dealing with the initial questions you may face.

How Did I End Up in Industry?

When I graduated from veterinary school, little did I know that I would end up as a veterinarian in industry. I had envisioned owning my own practice and being very involved with my clients and the community. Industry was the farthest thought from my mind. So, how did I end up here? After being in small animal practice for five years, I was ready for a new challenge, so I started to explore the possibility of buying a practice. I pursued two options: buying into the clinic where I was currently working or buying into the practice where I had worked during high school. On a personal level, my husband and I owned and operated a fruit farm and seasonal market/bakery, so the decision to open "another business" was a big one—both personally and financially. A friend and classmate of mine was working for Hill's Pet Nutrition and mentioned to me that they were looking for a Veterinary Account Manager. I was intrigued but unsure as to whether this was the direction that I wanted my career to take; however, I decided to go for the interview. After much lengthy discussion with my husband and other classmates who had taken the same leap, I made the decision to try industry on for size, feeling that for me and my personal situation at the time, the Veterinary Account Manager position was a good fit. It allowed me flexibility in hours, a good salary, health and dental benefits, and the new challenge for which I was looking. I figured that if I didn't like industry, I could go back into private practice and reevaluate practice ownership at that time. For the first few years after I started at Hill's, I continued to work one Saturday a month at the practice that I had left. This allowed me to maintain my skills and relationships with clients and made the transition a little less dramatic.

Someone had told me that once you start in industry, it is difficult to leave, and I have certainly found that to be true. I stayed in the position as Veterinary Account Manager for four years, and then I accepted a promotion to move into the head office at Hill's, where I have worked for the past two years as Customer Marketing Manager for the Veterinary Business. In this position, I work as a liaison between the sales force and marketing. I love this role, as it allows me to have influence on the brochures and programs that are produced for clinics and keeps me in touch with what is happening in practice.

Do I miss private practice? The quick answer is yes and no. I miss the interaction with clients, the excitement of a challenging medical or surgical case, and the day-to-day "hands on" work with pets. We all get into the veterinary field because of an innate love of animals. Being on the road was very difficult for me at first. I missed the everyday conversations with good clients and the support of my colleagues. It was lonely driving around by myself, and I faced a steep learning curve. I was lucky in that I had three classmates who also worked for Hill's, doing the same job, and that made the initial transition a lot easier than it would have been otherwise. As time went on, I developed relationships with the practices that I called on, rebuilt my personal support system within Hill's, and learned the skills that I needed to succeed.

What don't I miss about practice? I don't miss the stress of wondering whether I made the right decision for the patient or worrying about the dog or cat whose owner couldn't afford the best in care. There is certainly stress in industry, but it's a different type of stress. Emotionally, I find industry a lot easier than practice. I found it very difficult in practice to distance myself, so euthanasia and breaking bad news to clients was very draining. I am now able to help pets on a much different level than in practice—not through one-on-one care, but more by enhancing the overall health of pets through improved nutrition. I enjoy playing a role in educating veterinarians and healthcare teams, as well as pet owners, on the importance of nutrition to overall health. I also receive satisfaction from knowing that I am helping to enhance client compliance, the well-being of pets, individual practices, and the profession as a whole.

I have found my career in industry to be extremely rewarding. As veterinarians, we are naturally information seekers or gatherers. Life is a never-ending learning experience, and in this field, you are constantly learning. Veterinary school teaches us how to research, learn, diagnose, and treat. In practice, these skills are refined and additional skills are learned, such as how to foster interpersonal relationships with clients and colleagues, how to deal with emotional clients, creating quotes and billing, and the importance of communication and follow-up. Embarking upon a career in industry opens up another world of learning opportunities. I have been constantly challenged to grow, and the skills that I have picked up have been ones that I can use in my personal life as well. I have improved my public speaking, learned how to negotiate, and couldn't survive without Excel! I have expanded my horizons beyond the walls of private practice and become much more aware of what is happening in the world of veterinary medicine and business.

There are approximately 200 veterinarians who work for Hill's Pet Nutrition globally, so my new network of colleagues is tremendous. What an amazing opportunity to be able to email or call one of the researchers at the Hill's Pet Nutrition Centre and ask a technical question or find out how practice is different in Japan or Brazil. I find it very exciting to be a part of groundbreaking advances in pet nutrition, such as the use of antioxidants or the unfolding field of nutrigenomics. Hill's is also a leader in practice support, so I have the opportunity to work on projects like Client Compliance and Veterinary Standards of Care. I find the combination of medicine, the importance of great patient care, and business to be very fulfilling. Hill's holds an annual Veterinary Renewal Conference where all of the veterinarians who work for the company around the world meet to network, brainstorm, socialize, learn, discuss career opportunities, and welcome new veterinarians to our company. It is an event that is highly anticipated each year and reflects the company's commitment to its veterinarians.

What Skills are Needed for a Job in Industry?

When looking for a career in industry, it is important to consider the skills and competencies that companies are seeking. Some skills are learned, and others are inherent. Educational requirements are typically a veterinary degree with at least three to five years of experience in private practice. What makes veterinarians valuable to a company is not only the background veterinary knowledge and education they bring to the table, but also the insights gained from experience in private practice. Who better to understand the needs of the pet, pet owner, and the practicing veterinarian? The insights that veterinarians can bring to industry are tremendous. If you are considering a career in industry, experience in private practice should be considered as a strong foundation to build upon, rather than jumping into industry immediately following graduation from veterinary school. Proficiency in computer applications is vital to success in industry. It is impossible to function without being skilled in email, Internet use, Microsoft Word, Excel, and PowerPoint. Additional skills such as knowledge in using SAP (a commonly used brand of business software) and call reporting systems are also helpful. Strong interpersonal, communication, and presentation skills are necessary, as are organizational, planning, and implementation skills. Being bilingual in French and English is often preferred but not mandatory for most jobs. Strong analytical ability is needed in order to understand and analyze research data and communicate it to those in practice. Additional education of benefit could include a degree in sales or marketing, law, business, computer science, or an MBA. For technical positions, advanced education such as an internship or residency may be required. Many industry jobs require travel, so a willingness to be on the road is also important.

The change from a practice environment to corporate culture may be a difficult adjustment for some people. In practice, veterinarians are often individuals left to make their own decisions in regard to product choice and patient care. In industry, there are well-defined reporting structures, protocols, and processes in place. This makes for a more structured workplace, but it is necessary to ensure corporate responsibility.

What are the Benefits of a Career in Industry?

The first question most people ask is, "What is the pay like in industry?" Starting salaries in industry are typically comparable to those in private practice, with added benefits such as bonuses for meeting targets. Benefit packages usually include medical and dental plans, pension plans, and matched savings plans. Three weeks of vacation plus statutory holidays and extra floater days are standard, with an increase in the number of weeks of vacation based on years of service. Generally, veterinary fees and membership dues to voluntary organizations are paid, along with paid yearly continuing education (CE) opportunities. Industry veterinarians often attend more veterinary conferences than the average veterinarian in practice and are, therefore, more up-to-date on the latest veterinary advancements in treatments, drugs, and diets. Subscriptions to veterinary journals are often part of the overall package. Shared payment for gym memberships, lunch allowances, cell phone, Internet access, and a company vehicle are also common perks of an industry job. There may be awards for years in service or for projects well done. For those considering having a family, some companies provide "top ups" to maternity leave, based on the number of years of service.

Additional training on top of traditional veterinary CE is commonly found in most companies. Although veterinarians have great technical training, quite often formal business training has been minimal. The majority of corporations will provide yearly training either internally or through an outside source. This can include courses in computer skills, sales, coaching and feedback, marketing, presentation skills, negotiating, key account management, people management, statistics, data analysis, or regulatory affairs. Some companies may allow for time to pursue specialty training or an MBA, depending on your function within the organization and the potential benefits to your role and the company.

If you decide to leave industry to return to private practice, the skills learned while in industry can be very valuable. Sales and marketing, negotiating, inventory management, public speaking, teaching, practice management, adherence to evidence-based medicine, and standards of care are all key to being successful as an associate or practice owner. The network of support gained while in industry is a tremendous thing to draw upon when back in private practice.

Feedback and personal development are a more formal process in industry than in private practice. There are typically a few components to this, although in each company the process may be somewhat varied. The first step involves setting individual goals and objectives for the year, and establishing a plan to achieve those objectives. The second step is in the form of an individual development plan—basically, a road map of where you want to go with your career and what skills you'll need to develop in the short- and long-term future in order to get there. The third step is the semiannual review process, where you rate yourself against your objectives and how you feel you've done. Your manager also evaluates you. This is a very positive experience that lets you know exactly where you stand. If improvement is needed, the skills you'll need to learn are identified, as well as the tools you'll need to use to get there. Salary increases and promotions are usually based on how well you rate on your annual review. Many opportunities exist for career advancement within industry. Most companies have veterinarians involved at all levels of the organization, from account managers to directors and general managers. If you are willing to relocate, there may be opportunities to live around the world while advancing your career.

Jobs in industry tend to be fairly social, so if you enjoy interacting with people as well as pets, this could be the job for you! Most jobs involve working with other veterinarians—either on the phone or in person—so the network of contacts you develop is large and diverse. It is fascinating to meet veterinarians involved in all types of practice (from single-practitioner to large, multiple-veterinarian referral practices) and learn how they approach medicine, practice ownership, and management. I have learned a lot more about business skills and practice management while in industry than I ever did in private practice.

Work/life balance is a hot topic these days and one that comes up in the discussion regarding industry jobs. There is a fair amount of flexibility in industry job schedules, depending on your position. As an account manager, you typically set your own weekly schedule (however, you have a set number of expected calls per day); therefore, it can be easier in industry than in private practice to have defined hours of work in order to be home for children, appointments, etc. Staying late because of an emergency walk-in is rare! Travel is involved, and, depending on the territory that you are assigned, there may be overnight stays required. Expect to spend a lot more time in your car! Most account managers work out of a home office and, while you may be home earlier than you were in practice, there is often a lot of work to be done at night. Some weekend work is usual in order to prepare for the following week or to attend veterinary conferences and trade shows. Many people enjoy the change in location each day; for those that prefer a set work location, a head office job may be the better choice.

Where Do I Look for an Industry Job?

Any industry that deals with animals has a need for veterinarians. These companies may range from research companies and biotechology companies to feed companies and pharmaceutical companies. On the pharmaceutical side, veterinarians are involved with the development and testing of new drugs for humans and animals through conducting research, developing new products, acting as technical advisors and problem solvers, and ensuring the health and welfare of research animals. The pet food and feed industry employs veterinarians at many levels. There are opportunities in research and development, providing technical advice to those in clinical practice, sales, marketing, and senior management.

Where do you look if considering a change to a career in industry? Quite often, the best route is through talking to your veterinary account manager from companies that interest you. There may be openings due to maternity leaves, new territories opening or expanding, new departments being created within the company, and employee turnover. Account managers will often know of a position before it is advertised and may even know of opportunities within other companies. Veterinary journals and web sites from your provincial associations will usually list classified ads, as does the Canadian Veterinary Medical Association (CVMA). Many companies will advertise in national newspapers (e.g., *National Post* or *The Globe and Mail*) or in large, local newspapers. Headhunters are another avenue to explore; many will specialize in pharmaceutical or medical careers and can be found through the phone book or online. Company web sites typically have a careers section where current job openings are listed, or you can submit a resume to be considered for future positions. There are a number of search engines available for job hunters, such as workopolis.ca and monster.ca.

If I'm Seriously Considering This Change, What Should I Do Next?

For those contemplating an industry career, the first step is usually talking to others who have made the change. The majority of veterinary account managers are more than happy to talk about why they decided to switch to industry and what they like about their current position. You can make an appointment to meet with them over lunch, or perhaps even spend a day on the road with them to see what the job entails. There is a lot of information available on company web sites regarding their products, what opportunities exist for veterinarians, and the names of people that you can contact to find out more. Other great places to explore career opportunities are national or provincial veterinary conferences, where the majority of companies will be represented in the trade show or exhibit hall. This can be an easy way to talk to a large number of people from a variety of companies in a short period of time.

A veterinary degree opens up a world of opportunities. The hardest and most exciting part is deciding which road you'd like to take.

Additional Recommended Reading

Career Choices for Veterinarians: Beyond Private Practice. Smith CA. Smith Veterinary Consulting, Peshastin, WA; 1998.

Biography

Dr. Nicole Judge received her DVM from the Ontario Veterinary College in 1995. She worked as a small animal practitioner for 5 years before joining Hill's Pet Nutrition as a Veterinary Account Manager. As an account manager, she was responsible for working with clinics to provide nutritional training and advice to both veterinarians and the rest of the veterinary health care team. In April of 2004, she assumed the position of Veterinary Customer Marketing Manager where she acted as a liaison between the sales force and the marketing department. In early 2008, she combined her marketing, human resources, and administrative skills to become the Operations Manager for the Ontario Veterinary Group, which owns multiple practices in Southern Ontario. Her current interests include evidence based medicine and the evolution of veterinary standards of care.

Dr. Judge is the current chair of the Northern College Veterinary Sciences Advisory Committee and is a past president of the Brampton Veterinary Association. She lives with her husband, Tom, in Caledon where they also own and operate an orchard and country market/bakery. Her pets include Wylie, a 12-year-old German Shepherd Husky cross and two cats: Roxie who is 2 years old and L.B. who is 7 years old.

In her spare time, Dr. Judge enjoys the outdoors, reading, cooking, and exploring new places, even more so if these passions can be combined. Recent trips include attending Le Cordon Bleu cooking school in Paris for a week and traveling to Thailand and Cambodia where she spent time at the Thai Elephant Conservation Centre and Veterinary Hospital.

Career Paths in Veterinary Medicine: Teaching and Academia

Brigitte Brisson, DMV, DVSc, Diplomate ACVS
Associate Professor, Ontario Veterinary College,
Guelph, Ontario

> *Find something you love to do and you'll never have
> to work a day in your life.*
>
> — Harvey Mackay

I was asked to write a short chapter describing my career path and my current professional activities, challenges and opportunities. I am a clinician and academic at one of Canada's four veterinary colleges. Here's my story.

I am a French Canadian woman who attended veterinary school at the Faculté de Médecine Vétérinaire at the University of Montreal. During the second year of my veterinary program, I realized I had an interest in small-animal surgery and thought I might want to pursue further training in this specialty area after graduation.

I had the option of pursuing an internship at the University of Montreal or to apply to the Matching Program, in order to spend my internship year at an English-speaking institution elsewhere in Canada or in the United States. Given the level of competition that exists for surgical residency programs, the fact that all but one program are offered outside of Quebec, and my training until then had been in French only, I opted to move elsewhere as my next step. I applied to various veterinary institutions and was matched with the Ontario Veterinary College (OVC) for a small-animal rotating internship. This year of general training was excellent, although the transition to English was a bit of a shock. In the first few weeks, I sat in rounds wondering for what various acronyms, such as "GDV," "HBC," and "BDLD," stood. It must have taken me six months to forget all I had learned in veterinary school and learn it again, this time in English. My internship year prompted me to pull my knowledge together and develop a thought process that allowed me to work my way through cases, no matter the final diagnosis.

Only a few months after beginning my internship, I applied to various surgical residency programs through the Matching Program, and was lucky to match into the small-animal surgery Doctor of Veterinary Science (DVSc) program at the OVC. This intense, three-year program involved 24 months of clinical duty in the small-animal surgery section. In addition, one year was dedicated to course work, performing an original research project and writing and defending a thesis. The busy residency program allowed me to develop excellent surgical knowledge and skills. I was exposed to challenging cases and was taught by extremely talented surgeons.

The exposure to research through the DVSc program was very enlightening. I had not thought of myself as a researcher, but soon realized that I enjoyed asking a question and trying to answer it through research. I also had the opportunity to present the results of my research at the University of Guelph, at the American College of Veterinary Surgeons (ACVS) Annual Symposium, and at two Japanese Universities. These opportunities made me realize I enjoy public speaking, and certainly would wish to continue to present research results at such venues in the future. This, along with the fact that I enjoyed teaching and being part of the stimulating environment of academia, pushed me into an academic career, rather than a career as a specialty surgeon in private practice.

After completing my residency program, I was hired as an assistant professor in the Department of Clinical Studies at the OVC. The next hurdle was to study and pass the ACVS-board examinations. After studying intensively for a few months, I passed the three-day exam in February 2001. Since then, I have been progressing in an academic career as a faculty surgeon.

Where Am I Now?

I am an ACVS-boarded, small-animal veterinary surgeon, currently working as a tenured associate professor in the Department of Clinical Studies at the OVC,

University of Guelph. Most academics are hired at a level of assistant professor. When in a tenure-track position at the University of Guelph, you have six years to demonstrate capability in teaching, research, and clinical service in order to obtain a permanent job contract, or tenure. Tenure is intended to provide some degree of academic freedom and job security; this ultimately is meant to lead to increased productivity for faculty members. Associate professor and full professor status are earned, based on academic achievements assessed periodically throughout your career.

As an academic, approximately half of my time is spent working as a referral surgeon in the small-animal clinic. During this time, I perform surgery on client-owned patients, and I train undergraduate and graduate students, as well as interns and residents. A typical day begins with case rounds or teaching rounds and is filled with a combination of appointments, advice calls for practicing veterinarians, internal consultations for colleagues on other services, and performing surgery. The weeks spent "off clinics" are used to prepare and give undergraduate, graduate, or continuing education (CE) lectures; teach surgery laboratories; work on various research projects; write research grants and research papers; prepare CE materials; and assist graduate students with their research projects. As an academic, I am a member of various departmental committees, the work of which can be time consuming.

Life at the Ontario Veterinary College

Unlike other institutions, OVC offers the unique opportunity to perform general surgery (i.e., soft-tissue surgery, orthopaedic surgery and neurosurgery) all in one service, rather than separating surgery into various specialties. This has been great because it has allowed me to train and practice as a general surgeon, without being forced to choose a specific area of interest. After being a surgeon for six years, I now know that if I had to choose, I would become a soft-tissue surgeon and a neurosurgeon, although I would miss orthopaedics for sure.

OVC's clients come from a radius of 10 hours by car, with most of the clients being local or from the greater Toronto area. Most patients are dogs, with a lesser number of feline patients. My veterinary colleagues are specialists in various areas, such as internal medicine, emergency critical care, neurology, radiology, and obviously surgery. Daily, I also work with undergraduate and graduate students, interns, residents, technicians, and kennel staff. As an academic, I continually am exposed to new people and new techniques and procedures. I constantly am challenged by difficult cases, residents, interns, and senior undergraduate students, forcing me to keep up-to-date with new developments in my field.

A Career as an Academic

My academic career path has allowed me several opportunities that may not have been available otherwise. I have travelled to various European and Asian countries as an invited lecturer or speaker and have given multiple CE lectures in Canada and the United States. Part of my work also involves doing research and presenting the results at international conferences. Since I enjoy traveling, I take advantage of any opportunity to travel and visit new countries and other veterinary institutions.

As a teacher, I have been faced with having to teach increasingly large amounts of material in less time. In addition, the materials (i.e., basic and advanced small-animal surgery) I teach are difficult topics to teach in the classroom. Finding innovative ways of teaching, in a context where time and financial resources are scant, is a challenge. My attempts at dealing with these challenges have involved the development of interactive web-based materials that provide complete visual (i.e., text, images, and video) references for students to use. This online, highly visual and interactive "textbook" also includes quiz modules that can be used for formative or summative evaluation.

The biggest challenge I face in my career is that as a clinician you know when your day begins, but you never know what time it will end. You always have patients that are very sick and require intense monitoring and treatment, and emergencies that get you out of bed in the middle of the night. You can't leave the building until each patient is taken care of and is stable for the night. This, along with the various other demands of my academic appointment, has led to my biggest challenge until now—trying to balance work and personal life. Something always needs to be done: a patient needs some attention; a student, intern or resident needs help. One must learn to prioritize, delegate, and sometimes leave the building! An additional factor increasing demands on veterinary surgeons in academia is more and more surgeons are leaving the academic environment, in order to work in a private referral practice setting. In private practice, they more easily can find work-life balance by working three-to-four days a week, without all the additional demands of academia. This situation has made it difficult to maintain a full staff of surgeons and has led to additional demands on those of us who have chosen to remain in academia. Although private practice has significant financial benefits over academia, and may be more conducive to developing a healthy work-life balance, I have not felt that this path would suit me, given my interest in research and teaching.

Summary

A career as an academic surgeon is highly demanding, but also extremely rewarding. I have not once regretted choosing the path I took. I knew surgery was for me and I knew that teaching had to be part of what I do. I encourage anyone who has a genuine interest in surgery to pursue his or her dream. The path from veterinary school to board certification is not easy and, in some cases, can be quite convoluted. However, it is worth every effort in the long run.

Biography

Dr. Brisson graduated from the University of Montreal's Faculté de Médecine Vétérinaire, St-Hyacinthe in 1996. She then completed a small animal rotating internship at the Ontario Veterinary College (OVC) followed by a combined residency and graduate degree (DVSc) in small animal surgery; her research focused on free radicals and reperfusion injury. Dr. Brisson was certified by the American College of Veterinary Surgeons in 2001. She is currently an Associate Professor in the Department of Clinical Studies at the University of Guelph's OVC. Her current research focuses on the effect of disc fenestration for prevention of recurrent intervertebral disc disease in chondrodystrophic dogs, comparing myelography and magnetic resonance imaging as diagnostic modalities as well as the development and evaluation of various minimally invasive surgical procedures. Dr. Brisson has published the results of her research in several peer-reviewed journals and presented these results in America, Europe, and Asia. Her clinical interest lies in the field of neurosurgery, soft-tissue surgery, and minimally invasive surgery. The focus of her teaching has been the development of web-based teaching tools to facilitate instruction in the field of basic and advanced surgery.

CHAPTER 7-4

Career Paths in Veterinary Medicine: Part-Time and Locum Work

Hélène Bouchard, MA, MHA, DVM
Locum/Self-Employed, Vaughan, Ontario

> *Find something you love to do and you'll never have to work a day in your life.*
>
> — Harvey Mackay

Introduction

Working as a locum can be both an exhilarating and challenging experience. It is hoped that this career path "tour" will outline the skills required to be an effective locum, the range of activities a locum is expected to perform, and the key elements of what to do and pitfalls to avoid. After reading this chapter, the new graduate or current associate contemplating a career change to independent contractor should have a better understanding of what is involved in becoming a locum and be provided with some tools to facilitate the transition.

Getting Started

Over the past few years, a greater proportion of new graduates have immediately entered the workforce as independent contractors.[1] Veterinarians, whether they are associates or former practice owners, are also contracting out their services as self-employed professionals (locums) in greater numbers. Part of the reason for this change in status is that being a locum offers you more freedom to choose your hours of work and place to practice your chosen profession. Therefore, you are in the driver's seat as to how much or how little you wish to work, and that decision directly affects your income.

It is not very difficult to become a locum once the final decision has been made. However, before embarking on this new career path, it is first necessary to register with Revenue Canada for a GST (Goods and Services Tax) number if you are planning on earning more than $30,000 per year. The next step is to have your name listed in the locum bank of your provincial association. Information packages providing details on being a locum can be obtained from some provincial veterinary medical associations (VMAs) such as the Ontario VMA (OVMA).[2] Marketing strategies to facilitate your transition to a locum can be anything from distributing your business card and/or résumé to local hospitals/clinics, to setting up a Web site, to networking with friends and acquaintances so as to let them know of your availability. Knowing the average locum remuneration in your region will help you in coming to a decision about setting your hourly and travel time rates, if applicable.

Avoiding Pitfalls

Legally, a locum is defined as an independent contractor, because there is no set employer. Each position that you take is a separate employment arrangement and has to be negotiated. Because there is no set employer, there are certain pitfalls to avoid.

According to the Canada Revenue Agency, the definition of an independent contractor includes the following three points: owning your own equipment, control over the workplace, and ability to hire staff at one's own expense. In reality, the owner of the practice sets the hours of work, and the locum primarily uses both the staff and the equipment provided by the hospital. Despite the discrepancy between the definition and reality, the Canada Revenue Agency still grants locums the benefit of using the tax deductions available to other independent contractors.

Independent contractors are not always covered under the hospital's malpractice insurance. Therefore, it is recommended that locums purchase their own coverage. Even where the clinic provides malpractice insurance for locums, it is advisable to have your own coverage, since in some cases you might be at odds with the clinic management.

It is also vital that, as a locum, you protect yourself legally before starting employment situations. Before commencing as a locum in a practice, both you and the practice owner should discuss all possible employment terms. Every locum should request that a written contract be drawn up, reflecting the relationship with the practice owner. Ideally, both you and the practice owner should decide on mutually agreed upon terms that define the contract. This is especially important when the position is permanent part-time or meant to cover an extended period, such as when you are replacing someone on maternity leave. In cases where the practice owner neglects to take this step, it is advisable that you render the employment terms in writing yourself. It is recommended that the agreement contain formal arrangements that clearly outline how the relationship may be terminated. This is crucial where the parties anticipate that the employment relationship will continue for a considerable period of time. In light of a recent court case in which it was found that a locum had not given reasonable notice of termination, it is now essential that any locum contract include a definition as to what constitutes reasonable notice.[3] The contract should also clearly spell out how you are to be paid and how often, the hourly rate, travel benefits if any, and other terms specific to the employment relationship.

Is Locum Work Right For You?

Most veterinarians have at least one to two years of experience as an associate or have done an internship before electing to become a locum. When a practice owner decides to hire a locum, there is an expectation that the locum can work independently with the confidence and experience necessary to deal with any emergency. The range of activities you would be expected to perform as a locum include internal medicine, surgery, and anesthesia. Knowing how to treat exotics such as birds and small mammals is always an asset. You have to be versatile and prepared to handle anything that unexpectedly walks through the door. If you need a structured environment and have to plan your day in advance, then locum work is not for you.

In order to be successful as a locum, you must cultivate a number of skills outside the bounds of medical knowledge. Crucial to your success are effective communication skills. You must be able to communicate with the clinic staff, other veterinarians, and their clients. Due to the intrinsic nature of being a locum, it is imperative that ongoing cases be discussed with the owner of the practice or their associates. Being able to develop a quick rapport with their clients is vital, because you do not have an opportunity to develop a long-term relationship with them as you would if you were a permanent employee. In order to instill confidence in the clients, you must be able to quickly develop their trust and clearly communicate to them what needs to be done for their pet.

A locum is usually catapulted into a practice. Every practice has a different culture, atmosphere, and style. A locum must be able to adapt to each new practice. Getting a sense of the culture of the hospital and the dynamics among the staff is one of the first things you need to do when entering any new clinic. Every clinic has its own idiosyncrasies that are unique to that practice. The best source of information about any clinic is from the staff. Using the staff members as your guides will prove to be an instrumental asset in helping you to understand the protocols of any clinic, which, in turn, will facilitate your blending into the workings of the hospital. Appraising the skills of the staff and respecting the knowledge they have acquired about their clients and the everyday functioning of their hospital are critical. You must make a conscious effort not to have unrealistic expectations about the staff and rely on your leadership skills to instill cooperation from the practice team. You can also enhance your locum experience by exercising effective staff management, minimizing unnecessary stress, and promoting a team approach.

It is best to follow the practice approaches that each hospital provides to its patients. Although as a locum you are not a regular member of the clinic staff, having a team approach to case management is important in providing a continuum of care. Contradicting another associate or practice owners' advice constitutes poor professionalism. Therefore, you need to be aware of the style particular to that practice. This does not mean you should compromise your standards, however. Working in concert with the owner is imperative for effective case management. If you do disagree with the treatment, you have to communicate alternative diagnoses and treatments in such a way that you don't sound like you are contradicting the veterinarian's previous assessment. You must be flexible in your approach to medicine, keeping an open mind to new suggestions and/or different techniques. This approach will enhance your skills as a clinician and make your locum shifts more enjoyable.

Working in a variety of clinics allows you to become familiar with a wide range of management styles and to observe new practice approaches and/or medical techniques. Since you are exposed to a variety of cases, staff, and clinics, working as a locum is both exciting and rewarding. However, the lack of follow-up to cases, the possibility of not developing a long-term relationship with clients, a lack of benefits provided by the employers, and the uncertainty of work schedules are drawbacks to being an independent contractor.

Financial planning before becoming a locum is prudent and should take into account potential dry spells and known slow periods.

Recommendations Based on Personal Experience

Over the years, I have learned a number of lessons. First, it is essential to set boundaries of what you are prepared to do and not do. Keep true to your values, philosophy, and medical standards; never sell yourself short. Second, as a locum, it is incumbent on you to write above-average medical records and initial all medical notes. Medical records should be written in the SOAP format and include the history, data, assessment, and plan for each patient. Details of telephone conversations with clients and practitioners should be recorded in the files. Finally, a written contract between the independent contractor and the practice owner should be formulated, which outlines the hours of work, hourly rate, and notice of termination.

Summary

Locum work is exciting, challenging, and rewarding. If you can be flexible in dealing with a variety of work environments, are prepared to set your boundaries both financially and medically, can adapt to any practice setting, and, above all, are capable of promoting good communication with all the relevant stakeholders (client, staff, associate, and practice owner), you will have developed essential tools to becoming successful as a locum.

References

1. Tait, J. Associate compensation: Self-employment or salaried? Can Vet J 2005;46:79-82.
2. OVMA Locum Kit. www.ovma.org
3. Jack DC. Locums on Notice. Focus 2006;25:11.

Biography

Dr. Hélène Bouchard practices small animal medicine in the Greater Toronto area. In addition to her locum work, she has also had extensive experience in emergency medicine and has taught a course as a part-time instructor at the out-of-hours emergency service, small animal clinic, Ontario Veterinary

College. Dr. Bouchard earned her Doctor of Veterinary Medicine degree in 1999 from the Ontario Veterinary College. In addition to her DVM degree, she also has a Master of Psychology degree from MacMaster University and a Masters of Health Administration degree from the University of Ottawa. She has worked in a number of clinics as an employee in the Greater Toronto area before deciding to become an independent contactor.

Dr. Bouchard has published a number of articles in the areas of both veterinary medicine and health administration. She is currently devoting her energies to setting up her own clinic in Vaughan, Ontario.

Career Paths in Veterinary Medicine: Government

Gwen Zellen, DVM, MSc, Dip Path, MBA
Director, Policy Development Branch,
Ontario Ministry of Agriculture, Food, and Rural Affairs
(OMAFRA), Guelph, Ontario

Tom Baker, DVM, MSc
Director, Food Inspection Branch, OMAFRA,
Guelph, Ontario

> *Opportunity is missed by most people because
> it is dressed in overalls and looks like work.*
>
> — Thomas Edison

Introduction

There's no place like it—but how were we to know? We are two publicly employed provincial government veterinarians working in policy and operations at the senior management level and providing leadership in the field of food safety. So, how did we end up where we are? Did being a government

475

veterinarian appeal to us in veterinary college? Absolutely NOT! Then how did we and 5% to 10% of veterinarians in North America end up in public service?[1,2] Globally in 2000, approximately 28% of veterinarians were working as government officials.[3]

Public veterinarians are integral to the protection of animal health, veterinary public health, food security, and food safety; however, "the future of food safety veterinary medicine (FSVM) professionals is at an uncertain juncture," a published study warns.[4] By 2016, while demand for FSVM practitioners is expected to rise between 12% to 13%, the shortage in the United States federal government is expected to be in the 7% range. With the public more focused than ever on food safety and security, the role of the food safety veterinarian has never been more important.[5] A spokesperson for the American Veterinary Medical Association (AVMA) states that such a shortage "would be catastrophic for the industry and society."[6] Exposure of veterinary students to career paths in veterinary public service would provide them exposure to this potential career option and also raise awareness of the projected shortfall.

The paths leading to veterinary public service are infinite. Here are the stories of two public veterinarians, illustrating a few variations in entry points and paths within the government.

Dr. Thomas Baker's Story

In veterinary school, Tom participated in a program for students aimed to increase exposure to the various aspects of federal government veterinary careers (e.g., border security, animal health, and meat inspection). There was an annual grant program that covered tuition with the student's promise to work in large-animal practice for a specified period of time; this financial assistance and exposure favourably predisposed Tom to later consider a career with the federal government.

After fulfilling his commitment in large-animal practice, Tom was looking for a new experience and moved to Edmonton to work at one of Canada's first small-animal emergency clinics. Despite the excitement of emergency work, the stress of the job and extraordinary hours resulted in the aggravation of Tom's allergies and development of severe asthma. Tom was advised to cease contact with animals. After being out of practice for several months, a colleague in the federal government suggested he apply to the federal government.

Tom prepared a list of "positives" to help make his decision:

- Attractive salary   √
- Possible animal health role   √

- Regular hours √
- Good working conditions √
- Limited exposure to allergens √

This list corresponds closely with attributes identified by other public-sector veterinarians as outlined in the Food Supply Veterinary Medicine Coalition Report.[7]

A role in animal health wasn't immediately available. While working in the field of meat hygiene was not considered the preferred option, Tom decided to give it a try. Tom was immediately impressed by being able to work with a large group of veterinarians, many of which had post-graduate degrees. Working with scientists, pathologists, and epidemiologists provided a rich environment. The exposure to continuous learning was something he hadn't anticipated, but it was a welcome bonus. Tom was given the opportunity to return to post-graduate school with full support, and he obtained a Master's degree in epidemiology.

In addition to these benefits, his responsibilities and decisions made an impact on public health, export markets, people's jobs—in other words, the greater public good! So Tom added to his list other advantages to being a public veterinarian:

- Intellectually stimulating environment √
- Post-graduate opportunities √
- Improving the public good √

Armed with a post-graduate degree and a desire to seek greater responsibilities, Tom became a Regional Veterinarian for the province of Ontario. Only six months later, the infamous Hagersville tire fire catapulted Tom into a dynamic environment of working with people in laboratory diagnostics, emergency response, environmental risk assessment, and, of course, the briefing of senior management, elected officials, and the community. A veterinarian's training provides diverse knowledge and skills, including communications, analysis, and problem solving. All of these facilitate career mobility, and Tom was experiencing this firsthand.

Within a year of starting with the provincial government, Tom became a manager in meat inspection and focused on policy and audit. Since then, he has become the director of food safety inspection programs, contributing as well to policy development directed at continually improving Ontario's food safety and animal health programs. Tom's job has afforded him the privilege of having broad exposure to various issues and projects, including a multi-ministry enforcement integration effort. Add to Tom's growing list of benefits of public-sector employment:

- Ability to work in multidisciplinary teams   √
- Exposure to a broad range of complex issues   √
- Multiple careers with one employer   √
- Respect and pride in the job   √

All of these √ reasons AND the opportunities to make a real difference provide Tom with ongoing job satisfaction! Tom is able to make an impact on public health and safety while supporting strong communities and industry competitiveness, working on significant long-term projects, interfacing with elected officials and the public, and fulfilling government's mandate while strategically advancing the public good.

Dr. Gwen Zellen's Story

While in veterinary school, Gwen was impressed with forward-thinking industries, such as swine and poultry, and thus was attracted to preventive medicine. She wanted to work in the food supply field rather than small-animal practice, but large-animal practice and developing allergies gave her pause to think. This led to taking a summer externship (between her third and final year of college) with a local poultry practitioner. Exposure to this enthusiastic, forward-thinking veterinary leader served to secure her interest in poultry. What a superb role model!

As a new graduate, Gwen didn't feel equipped to enter this specialized area. She fortuitously was offered the opportunity to study for a Master's degree (MSc) in poultry virology, funded by the Ontario Egg Producers Marketing Board. This provided a perfect solution.

A year into her MSc, the opportunity arose to compete for an Ontario government position as an avian pathologist. Gwen was well positioned, having completed several related courses, and she was successful in becoming an avian and fur-bearing animal pathologist for the provincial veterinary diagnostic laboratory. After completing her MSc, now supported by the provincial government, she continued on to obtain a Diploma in Pathology.

Gwen's allergies were unexpectedly aggravated as a pathologist, and she was also looking for a different challenge. Subsequently, she was successful in becoming head of the main government veterinary diagnostic laboratory. After some time, she did a special project involving the development of strategies for all of the provincial agriculture and food laboratories. Wanting additional change, Gwen received support from her employer to pursue, on a part-time basis, a Master's degree in Business Administration.

This opened more doors. Gwen's work as a pathologist had provided her with experience in client education and public speaking, which qualified her for her first director role in field extension services, coupled with program responsibilities in the areas of leadership and organizational development. Talk about continuous learning! Seeking change and challenge, Gwen has been a director in other areas, including business development, education and laboratories research, food inspection, food safety policy, and now broader policy development (although food safety is closest to her heart).

Besides the obvious advantage of being able to continually alter her career and satisfy her desire for continuous learning, Gwen finds it especially rewarding to influence public good. She enjoys coordinating analyses and making recommendations to elected officials on changes the government could make to improve food safety, and then securing the appropriate resources to protect the public.

Summary

Employment with government, whether it is with municipal, provincial, or the federal government, offers a broad range of areas in which to focus.[8] Tom and Gwen's careers have illustrated the many potential roles in public veterinary medicine, including:

- Food hygiene
- Animal health and welfare
- Policy development (food safety, animal health and welfare, etc.)
- Laboratory diagnostics
- Biosecurity
- Emergency response
- Disease control and eradication
- Public health
- Epidemiology

Although Tom and Gwen's career origins and rationales for change are different, the motivations and the rewards are similar. Those pursuing veterinary careers would be well advised to keep their options open to various opportunities, especially those serving the public interest.

How, then, can the veterinary profession attract veterinarians to consider careers in government? How can we attract more veterinary students to public service careers and meet the projected shortfall? We believe this can happen through:

- Exposure to role models and veterinary careers in the public sector
- Provide scholarship opportunities for students entering FSVM careers
- Allergies help too!

References

1. American Veterinary Medical Association. (2006) Veterinary market statistics: US veterinarians. <http://www.avma.org/membshp/marketstats/usvets.asp> Accessed 24 Jul 2006.
2. Canadian Veterinary Medical Association. Veterinarian statistics 2005. <http://canadianveterinarians.com/news-media-veterinarian.aspx> Accessed 24 Jul 2006.
3. Kouba V. Quantitative analysis of global veterinary human resources. Rev Sci Tech Off Int Epiz 2003;22:889-908.
4. Gwinner KP, Prince JB, Andrus DM. Attracting students into careers in food supply veterinary medicine. J Am Vet Med Assoc 2006;228:1693-1704.
5. American Veterinary Medical Association. (2006 June 2) Press release: Projected serious food supply veterinarian shortage poses threat to industry, society. <http://www.avma.org/press/releases/060602_food_supply_veterinarians.asp> Accessed 25 July 2006.
6. Richardson, Z. Study: Vet shortages could impact safety of food supply. Food Chemical News, 2006 June 12; Volu. 48, No. 18: 1 & 11.
7. Andrus DM, Gwinner KP, Prince JB. (2006) Food Supply Veterinary Medicine Coalition Report: Estimating FSVM demand and maintaining the availability of veterinarians for careers in food supply related disciplines in the United States and Canada.<http://www.avma.org/public_health/fsvmc/fsvmc_toc.asp> Accessed 24 July 2006.
8. USDA. FSIS. (2000 August) The future of FSIS veterinarians: Public health professionals for the 21st century. <http://www.fsis.usda.gov/oa/pubs/vetsfinal.htm> Accessed 24 July 2006.

Additional Recommended Reading

Andrus DM, Gwinner KP, Prince JB. Job satisfaction, changes in occupational area, and commitment to a career in food supply veterinary medicine. J Am Vet Med Assoc 2006;228:1884-1893.

Prince JB, Andrus DM, Gwinner KP. Future demand, probable shortages, and strategies for creating a better future in food supply veterinary medicine. J Am Vet Med Assoc 2006;229:57-69.

Biographies

Gwen Zellen graduated from Ontario Veterinary College and subsequently did a Masters of Science and a Diploma in pathology to further develop expertise in the poultry virology and pathology fields, respetively. She began work with OMAFRA as a Poultry and Fur-Bearing Animal Pathologist in 1984 and since that time, has held a variety of director-level positions within OMAFRA, including Laboratory Head of the Guelph Veterinary Diagnostic Laboratory. She has continued to pursue her education, obtaining a Masters of Business Administration from Wilfrid Laurier University in 1995. As a director of the Food Safety Policy Branch, she has been instrumental in the implementation of a multi-ministry process to improve Ontario's food safety system and is concurrently involved with various national federal/provincial/territorial committees with a link to food safety. She is currently Director of Policy Development covering food safety policy as well as broader agri-food policy issues.

Dr. Tom Baker is the Director of the Food Inspection Branch for the Ontario Ministry of Agriculture, Food, and Rural Affairs. He leads an executive team, which manages over 210 inspectors and support staff in Ontario's dairy, livestock, meat, and foods of plant origin industries. Dr. Baker graduated as a veterinarian from the Ontario Veterinary College in 1973, working in private practice for 10 years before joining Agriculture Canada as a veterinary meat hygienist. In 1987 he completed a Masters degree at Guelph in epidemiology. Dr. Baker has over 22 years of leadership experience in meat regulatory programs with both the federal and provincial governments. His perspective on food safety is often sought by the media, industry, elected officials, and his professional colleagues.

Career Paths in Veterinary Medicine: Shelter Medicine

Miranda Spindel, DVM, MS
Director, American Society for the Prevention of Cruelty to
Animals (ASPCA) Veterinary Outreach,
New York, New York USA

Lila Miller, DVM,
Vice President ASPCA Veterinary Outreach,
New York, New York USA

> *The future belongs to those who believe in
> the beauty of their dreams.*
>
> — Eleanor Roosevelt

Introduction

Shelter medicine is a rapidly developing discipline within the field of veterinary medicine.[1] Animal welfare and pet overpopulation are tremendous global concerns, and veterinarians are integral to managing these issues successfully. Veterinarians who work in shelters must be capable of practicing a different type of medicine than private practitioners. Shelter medicine is just beginning to be recognized as a specialty for the unique skills it requires. The objective of this chapter is to provide an overview of shelter medicine and the exciting professional opportunities available in this evolving discipline.

Changing Field of Sheltering

Until recently, veterinarians worked in a limited capacity with animal shelters. Shelters focused on animal control rather than animal welfare. Providing for public safety, protectionng against dog bites and disease, and handling nuisance complaints were the primary functions of most programs. Shelters were constructed mainly as short-term animal-holding facilities.[2] Euthanasia was the primary means for minimizing animal numbers, and it was used as a method for maintaining population health in these facilities. Veterinary involvement in shelters did not extend much beyond surgical sterilization, disease outbreak control, orand euthanasia services. Over the last 20 years, animal sheltering has changed. In many communities, multimillion-dollar facilities with budgets to match are being built as focal community centers. This expanded interest in animal welfare, and recognition of the power of the human-animal bond, has resulted in the desire for in-house and outreach shelter programs that provide hope and rehabilitation for animals rather than just housing. This has led to an unprecedented demand for skilled veterinarians to design comprehensive programs to both maintain wellness and prevent spread of disease in shelters. Regular and sustained veterinary intervention has become more urgent:because the health of animal populations being housed for longer periods of time,time under stressful situations, is at high risk. As public awareness rises regarding animal welfare issues, and the full spectrum of veterinary medicine's expertise continues to increase, science-based recommendations are now required to protect the health and welfare of homeless animals. Many veterinary colleges are incorporating shelter medicine into their primary and elective curriculum, and externship, internship, post-graduate, and residency programs are being developed.[3] The Association of Shelter Veterinarians, formed in 2001, has grown into a professional organization of over 600 members and 14 student charters, and it has taken the initial steps to establish a shelter medicine board specialty.[4] It is anticipated that the need for skilled shelter veterinarians who can guide communities effectively, scientifically, and humanely toward reducing the suffering of homeless animals can only increase. The role of shelter veterinarians is expanding rapidly into exciting new realms!

Defining Shelter Medicine

In general, shelter medicine is very different from private practice. Veterinarians in a practice setting focus on the individual patient. Owners provide detailed histories and authorize diagnostic tests that help determine the levels of care that ensue. Treatment decisions in shelters are often made based primarily upon the results of a physical examination and without the benefit of a history or diagnostic tests. In the shelter, most animals present with uncertain medical backgrounds, and difficult decisions must be made about how much to invest—in terms of time and resources—toin every patient. Most shelters cannot function as veterinary hospitals. Instead of individualized treatment, shelter veterinarians aim for wide-scale preventative health plans that allow rapid placement of healthy animals into lifelong homes. Veterinarians are often working in situations where resources are limited. Making challenging, ethical decisions that protect the health and welfare of animals is an everyday part of a shelter veterinarian's job, for which there is no simple guidebook. The veterinary profession is beginning to recognize that unique challenges are encountered in shelters, and that special knowledge is required to prevent disease- spread and increase or maintain health of a small animal population. However, many of the topics that are key to animal shelter medicine are not yet taught in veterinary colleges. Sufficient studies and research regarding disease and the maintenance of wellness in shelter animals have not been conducted or published in the peer-reviewed literature. Although veterinarians have been working with shelters for many years, a great deal of pioneering work still needs to be done in the field.

The Veterinary Role in Shelter Medicine

Shelter medicine is a multidisciplinary field that encompasses specialties from many different areas—not all of which are strictly veterinary in nature. Many types of shelters require differing types of veterinary guidance. Shelters vary widely—from small sanctuaries that provide lifetime care, to large facilities that intake thousands of animals annually. In addition to the design and oversight of basic preventative health care protocols, veterinarians play a role in almost every community service that shelters provide, including: spay/neuter programs, cruelty investigations, public health protection, stray animal capture and control, behavior, foster care, volunteer and animal placement programs, and the provision of humane animal euthanasia, when necessary. The skilled shelter veterinarian must be able to pull from the various disciplines in order to design an effective program that meets the needs of the individual shelter.

Skills Required for Success

In order for veterinarians working with shelters to succeed and excel excel, they must be adept in medicine and surgery, as well as be flexible and creative practitioners. Without histories, and with limited diagnostic capabilities, shelter patients can be among the most challenging to diagnose and treat. Few shelters offer the same work experience day after day, and it is helpful to enjoy variety and to be adaptable when, for example, the shelter suddenly takes in a large number of animals from a hoarding case or diagnoses an outbreak of ringworm. In many cases, when working with a group of animals versus a single patient, the veterinarian focuses less on treatment and more on the design and implementation of effective strategies for preventative health care. From creating vaccine protocols, to implementing nutrition plans, to enriching the environment, veterinarians who successfully work with shelters must possess a wide skill set. They must be innovative in creating new solutions for unanticipated problems, possess stamina and resiliency, and be prepared to withstand criticism when trying out new strategies. In addition to a conventional veterinary education, a strong background is necessary in areas likesuch as epidemiology, immunology, infectious disease, behavior, public health, general management, facility design, statistics, and veterinary forensics. Familiarity with the care of the different animal species that are surrendered to shelters is important. While surgical ability, infectious disease knowledge, and individual patient care are part of the work, some of the most applicable skills and knowledge are decidedly non-medical. Shelter veterinarians are often responsible for staff training and must be ever mindful of the overall goals of the shelter while performing their job. Developing favorable relationships with community veterinarians can be beneficial. Many shelters employ only one veterinarian. In other situations, veterinarians must report to and interact closely with boards of directors, management, staff, and volunteers who have little veterinary knowledge. Conflict (or dissension) is inherent in many of the everyday decisions that shelter veterinarians must make. Strong ethics, decision-making capabilities, and interpersonal skills can help veterinarians manage workplace stress. Shelter veterinary medicine is a career in which burnout is not uncommon unless balance between one's personal and professional life is consciously sought, and self-preservation is not always natural to veterinarians.[5] It is easy in shelter medicine to work excessively, because it's easy to convince oneself that this is necessary, as the lives of so many animals may ultimately be at stake. However, it is important to establish healthy personal habits that balance what can be a very demanding and emotionally challenging career.

Opportunities in Shelter Medicine

Career opportunities in small animal populations are expanding greatly. Once thought of as a second-rate professional choice, shelter medicine is now a rewarding primary career. Jobs are few where the decisions one person makes can positively affect the lives of thousands of animals. Veterinarians work with shelters in a number of ways. Because the field of shelter medicine remains relatively new, veterinarians with shelter interest and experience are highly sought after to fill full-time staff veterinary positions. As with any employment situation, but especially in shelter medicine (because of its wide range of interface with all shelter activities), it is important to have a complete understanding of the veterinarian's role and responsibilities within the shelter management structure. Many part-time opportunities also exist. Some shelters contract veterinary services with local clinics, allowing area veterinarians opportunities for shelter practice. Veterinarians who are skilled surgeons are also highly sought after to work in high- quality, high- volume spay and neuter practices. They also serve in administrative capacities, act as board members, and work internationally. Opportunities are growing for consultants, humane researchers, public educators, and public health workers. Finally, it shouldn't be overlooked that there are many ways community practitioners can work voluntarily or in concert with local shelters and thereby make a tremendous impact without making shelter medicine a primary career.

Compensation

Shelter veterinary compensation is generally comparable to that of private practitioners, and salaries are no longer a deterrent for entering this field. The potential for veterinary work includes: full-time work at shelters; part-time, contractual, per diem, or consultant work; and voluntary service. Salaries may be paid on an annual, daily, or hourly basis. Some veterinarians have contractual agreements, and some are paid base salaries with percentage-based pay for numbers of surgeries performed. Regardless of the arrangement, it is important to negotiate a salary that reflects the skills, professionalism, education, and services a veterinarian will provide.

Future of Shelter Medicine

Interest in shelter medicine is growing exponentially. Continuing education courses are offered at most regional and national conferences and via Internet resources such as the Veterinary Information Network. The first shelter medicine textbook was published in 2004; texts on the veterinary forensic investigation of animal cruelty exist; and a text focusing on infectious disease management in shelters is forthcoming.[6-8] Because it is so new, there is great potential for growth and development over the next few years, and this promises to be an exciting time for those entering the field. With anything new, challenges and growing pains are anticipated. Increasing concerns about zoonosis, public health, legal issues that involve animals, emerging infectious diseases, and the advent of non-surgical contraceptives may shape and change shelter practices. Animal shelters are only just beginning to establish minimum welfare standards. It falls increasingly to shelter veterinarians to advocate on behalf of the animals, because no national system exists to oversee or regulate facilities. Growing emphasis on decreasing euthanasia statistics has generated concerning situations, because some communities with insufficient or mismanaged resources unintentionally end up with high disease rates and other welfare issues. Shelter veterinarians will need to create and stay abreast of innovative solutions to emerging issues in animal welfare.

Recommendations and Resources

For anyone considering a career path in shelter medicine, just as in private practice, they must realize that much of the work involves dealing successfully with people as well as with animals. It is important to develop communication, management, and interpersonal skills. Seek out opportunities to interact with those already active in the field, and find mentorship. Attend a shelter medicine track at a national conference, or join an Internet chat group for shelter professionals. Ask people about the best and worst aspects of their jobs. Acquire practical experience. Externship, internship, or volunteer experiences at several different types of shelters are great ways to test whether shelter work will be enjoyable. When pursuing job opportunities, look for a first position where mentoring and professional support are available. Realize it may take time to find a shelter situation that matches your skills and temperament. Consider exploring a one-year internship or post-graduate shelter medicine opportunity for further specialized training.

Summary

Animal shelters have evolved considerably since their inception. Shelter veterinary medicine is a relatively new and emerging specialty that has boundless, rewarding opportunities for veterinarians to greatly impact the welfare of millions of human and animal lives.

References

1.   Burns K. The eevolution of sshelter mmedicine. JAVMA News. J Am Vet Med Assoc 2006;10:1541-1562.
2.   Zawistowski S, Morris J. The eevolving aanimal sshelter. In: Zawistowski S, Miller L, eds. Shelter Medicine for Veterinarians and Staff. Ames, IA: Blackwell Publishing, 2004:3-9.
3.   Shelter Medicine Educational Opportunities. The Association of Shelter Veterinarians, 2008 <http://www.sheltervet.org/documents/Miscellaneous/Externships%20-%202007.pdf> (accessed1/29/08)
4.   About the Association of Shelter Veterinarians. The Association of Shelter Veterinarians, 2008 < http://www.sheltervet.org/about_us.asp> (accessed1/29/08)
5.   Figley C, Roop R. Compassion Fatigue in the Animal-Care Community. Washington DC: Humane Society Press, 2006.
6.   Zawistowski S, Miller L, eds. Shelter Medicine for Veterinarians and Staff. Ames, IA: Blackwell Publishing, 2004.
7.   Merck M. Veterinary Forensics Animal Cruelty Investigations. Ames, IA: Blackwell Publishing, 2007.
8.   Sinclair L, Merck M, Lockwood R. Forensic Investigation of Animal Cruelty. Washington, DC: Humane Society Press, 2006.

Biographies

Dr. Lila Miller is a graduate of the Cornell University College of Veterinary Medicine. She has over 25 years of experience working in the field of shelter medicine for the American Society for the Prevention of Cruelty to Animals (ASPCA) in New York City. She is the co-editor of the first veterinary textbook on shelter medicine, entitled *Shelter Medicine for Veterinarians and Staff*. She teaches at Cornell University, the University of Pennsylvania, on the Veterinary Information Network (VIN), and at various veterinary and animal welfare conferences. She received the 2005 Hill's Animal Welfare and Humane Ethics award from the American Animal Hospital Association (AAHA), in addition to awards from the American Humane Association and the Veterinary Medical Association of New York City. She is Cco-founder and past-president of the Association of Shelter Veterinarians (ASV), former member of the New York State Veterinary Board, current member of the National Board of Veterinary Medical Examiners and Human-Animal Bond Veterinarians, and she is a member of numerous professional associations.

Dr. Miranda Spindel first began volunteering at a humane society veterinary clinic when she was 12- years old. She graduated in 1999 from Colorado State University's Professional Veterinary Medical program, completed a rotating small animal internship, and spent several years in small animal practice before returning to work in her true passion, shelter medicine. Dr. Spindel has a strong interest in merging shelter medicine with the veterinary curriculum, believing that the world within an animal shelter is rich in opportunity for veterinary education to be integrated with improving the lives of animals. Dr. Spindel developed and taught a junior shelter medicine course for five years at Colorado State University. She initiated and completed the first residency in shelter medicine offered though Colorado State University, and she serves as a founder and advisor to the CSU Student Chapter of the Association of Shelter Veterinarians. She has been a board member of the Association of Shelter Veterinarians since 2005, and she is currently acting president of this international organization. Additionally, Dr. Spindel is an active volunteer with Rural Area Veterinary Services, and she continues to work on a local and regional level with area shelters. Her current position is Director of Veterinary Outreach with the American Society for the Prevention of Cruelty to Animals.

Career Paths in Veterinary Medicine: Laboratory Animal Medicine

Michele M. (Smith) Bailey, DVM, MRCVS, Diplomate ACLAM
Associate Vice Provost Research, Animal Resources
Director, Cornell Center for Animal Resources and Education
Director, Laboratory Animal Services
Cornell University, Ithaca, New York USA

> *The best scientist is open to experience and begins with romance – the idea that anything is possible.*
>
> — Ray Bradbury

Introduction

Laboratory animal medicine is a very exciting special area of veterinary medicine. Although laboratory animal medicine is truly a "specialty" area within the broad field of veterinary medicine, the word "special" has been deliberately used to describe it. Becoming a laboratory animal veterinarian actually broadens the range of species of animals that one has the opportunity to work with, from companion and agricultural animals studied in veterinary college to amphibians, reptiles, birds, rodents, rabbits, and non-human primates. It also expands the career opportunities available. A laboratory animal veterinarian can work in academia, government, or industry—enjoying potential roles as a researcher, clinical veterinarian, administrator, or a combination of the above. Work can be carried out in a large facility with many other veterinarians or a small facility where one person does it all and, in addition to their veterinary skills, a laboratory animal veterinarian must call on accounting, business, architectural design, and human resources skills.

What Is the Practice of Laboratory Animal Medicine?

Laboratory animal veterinarians ensure the welfare of animals used in research, teaching, and testing. The American Society of Laboratory Animal Practitioners (ASLAP) defines animal welfare as "all aspects of animal well-being, including proper housing, clinical and behavioral management, nutrition, disease management and treatment, responsible care and use, humane handling, and, when necessary, humane euthanasia."[1] Of course, it is ethically important to ensure the clinical and behavioral well-being of animals, but it is also important to make sure the animals experience optimal well-being, because animals that are healthy and content assure that research and testing data are reliable, accurate, and reproducible.

Laboratory animal veterinarians provide veterinary medical care and management for a wide variety of research animals, and they ensure optimal animal welfare through consultation, policy development, teaching, medicine, and rounds.

Why Would I Want to be a Laboratory Animal Medicine Veterinarian?

The laboratory animal veterinarian facilitates the animal-based research, teaching, and testing process from the preliminary stages through to project completion based on a team approach. The members of the research team may include the principal investigator (who could also be a laboratory animal veterinarian), post-doctoral fellows, graduate and undergraduate students, research technicians, the animal care staff, the Institutional Animal Care and Use Committee (IACUC), and the veterinary staff (laboratory animal veterinarians, veterinary technicians, and support staff). So, if you have interest in being an essential member of a research team that works together to ensure the conduct of high-quality, humane research (which will ultimately benefit human and/or animal health and contribute to the understanding of biological principles), then a career as a laboratory animal veterinarian may be ideal for you.

It is also a high-demand career, as there is a national shortage of veterinarians in laboratory animal medicine. In 2004, the National Academies' Committee on Increasing Veterinary Involvement in Biomedical Research (National Research Council or NRC) published its findings in a document called "National Need and Priorities for Veterinarians in Biomedical Research."[2] This study found that from 1995 to 2002, the number of National Institute of Health (NIH)-funded grants utilizing animals increased by 31.7%. It was predicted that mouse use alone would continue to increase by 10% to 20% annually from 2000 to 2010. In contrast, the number of individuals who completed residency training in laboratory animal medicine was 25% lower in 2002 than in 1996.[2]

As an added bonus, because there is a high demand for veterinarians to enter this diverse and interesting field, the salary and benefits packages are attractive!

What Does a Laboratory Animal Medicine Veterinarian Do?

Lots of things, and different things on different days – it is definitely NOT a boring specialty! Laboratory animal veterinarians assist in regulatory compliance of animal care and use programs. For instance, they serve the IACUC in many capacities. The IACUC is the institutional group with responsibility for the oversight of the institution's animal care and use program. The committee is usually comprised of scientists, non-scientists, community members (who represent the interests of the general public), the chair, and of course, a laboratory animal veterinarian. In fact, it is mandatory for a veterinarian trained or experienced in laboratory animal medicine to serve on the IACUC. The IACUC monitors compliance of the animal care and use program with the appropriate federal, state, and local regulations, standards, and guidelines. The committee conducts bi-annual inspections of all areas where animals are housed or used, and it reviews and approves the detailed animal care and use protocols that cover all facets of the animal work (why animal use is necessary, why the particular species was chosen, justification for the number of animals requested, acquisition and disposition of the animals, hazards involved, animal housing, and details of all aspects of animal care and use).

Although the principal investigator is responsible for the overall design and implementation of specific research projects, the laboratory animal veterinarian provides advice on the design and conduct of the proposed research, teaching, and testing involving animals. They provide advice on the following matters: such as appropriate health care and housing of animals; safety involving animals; animal models; research design; sources of animals; animal handling and restraint; anesthesia; analgesia; and surgical and other manipulative procedures.

They provide clinical veterinary care, including the following: on-call emergency services; diagnosis,, treatment, and progress monitoring of sick animals; preventative medicine programs; post-mortem examinations; routine rounds of animal housing and procedure areas; and overall health monitoring and surveillance. Laboratory animal veterinarians perform routine rounds of animals used in research, teaching, and testing to ensure animal health and well-being; they provide guidance to research and animal care staff; they assure that appropriate methods of handling and restraint are being used; and they ensure the proper use of anesthetics, analgesics, tranquilizers, and methods of euthanasia.

Laboratory animal veterinarians are also involved in animal resources management. They direct institutional animal care and use programs; they direct the day-to-day operation of animal facilities; and they develop and implement policies. They are responsible for financial management, personnel management, animal facility design, construction, renovation and maintenance, and animal user health and safety programs.

Laboratory animal veterinarians develop and implement training programs for anyone using or caring for animals in research, teaching, and testing, to assure that those working with the live animals are appropriately qualified and experienced in the humane and proper care of animals. They often participate in the training of veterinary students, medical students, medical doctors, and post-graduate veterinary residency programs in laboratory animal medicine. They are often involved in community educational programs about why animals are used in research and how research animals are treated.

Laboratory veterinarians usually act as the institutional liaison with regulatory and accrediting agencies, as well as with the media and general public.

The key to a successful animal care and use program is for the laboratory animal veterinarian to have a positive rapport with the investigators, research staff, animal care staff, IACUC members, and external agencies. The laboratory animal veterinarian must be, and must be seen to be, a valuable member of the research team.

How Do I Pursue a Career in Laboratory Animal Medicine?

Rigorous training, experience, and publication requirements must be met, as well as successful passing of a comprehensive examination in order to become certified as a laboratory animal medicine specialist. The American College of Laboratory Animal Medicine (ACLAM) is the organization recognized by the American Veterinary Medical Association (AVMA) as the certifying organization for laboratory animal veterinarians.[3]

ACLAM establishes the standards of education, training, experience, and expertise necessary to become qualified as a laboratory animal medicine specialist, and it recognizes that achievement through board certification.

Examination candidates must successfully pass a certifying examination to ensure their qualifications to become specialized as a laboratory animal medicine specialist.

Each candidate must meet two specific requirements before taking the certifying examination. The first requirement is to have completed a post-DVM residency program in laboratory animal medicine and science that meets the ACLAM training program minimal standards, or to have completed a minimum of six years, post-DVM, relevant full-time experience in laboratory animal medicine and science. The second requirement for candidates is to have published a first-author, original article that demonstrates application of the scientific method. It is extremely important for laboratory animal veterinarians to understand the entire process of hypothesis-driven research, and the best way to understand the research process is to fully participate in all aspects of it!

Conclusions

The practice of laboratory animal medicine is one of the most interesting and rewarding careers possible. Every day is different. Laboratory animal veterinarians work with a wide variety of interesting people and an extensive array of animal species. They are instrumental to the success of cutting- edge research, and they are enriched through opportunities to teach, mentor, and provide outreach to the community.

Laboratory animal veterinarians are first and foremost veterinarians, but they also are human resource professionals, accountants, architects, teachers, advisors, and most importantly advocates for animals used in research, teaching, or testing!

References

1. http://www.aslap.org/ASLAP_Welfare_Definition2007.pdf (accessed 30/05/08)
2. National Need and Priorities for Veterinarians in Biomedical Research; Committee on Increasing Veterinary Involvement in Biomedical Research, Institute

for Laboratory Animal Research, Division of Earth and Life Studies, National Research Council of the National Academies, The National Academies Press, Washington, DC (2004) Institute for Laboratory Animal Research (ILAR)

3. American College of Laboratory Animal Medicine (ACLAM) website http://www.aclam.org (accessed 30/05/08)

Additional Resources

American Society of Laboratory Animal Practitioners (ASLAP) website http://www. aslap.org (accessed 30/05/08)
http://www.research.cornell.edu/care/index.html (accessed 30/05/08)

Biography

Dr. Bailey is a 1982 graduate of the Ontario Veterinary College and has held the position of Associate Vice Provost for Research Animal Resources at Cornell University since 2001. For the prior 10 years, she directed the Animal Care and Veterinary Services Department at the University of Western Ontario, London, Ontario, Canada. While in Canada, Dr. Bailey was appointed by the Attorney General to the London Police Services Board, which was responsible for the provision of adequate and effective police services in London, Ontario.

Currently, Dr. Bailey is an ad hoc specialist to the Association for Assessment and Accreditation of Laboratory Animal Care International (AAALAC) and a member of the American Society of Laboratory Animal Practitioners (ASLAP) Animal Welfare Committee. In the past, she has served on several committees for AAALAC, ASLAP, the American College of Laboratory Animal Medicine's (ACLAM), and the American Association for Laboratory Animal Science (AALAS).

Dr. Bailey served the Canadian Association for Laboratory Animal Medicine (CALAM) for 13 years as Secretary-Treasurer, Vice President, President, and Past President. She has been a member of various committees and subcommittees for the Canadian Council on Animal Care (CCAC) and a member of CCAC Assessment Panels performing audits of animal research and testing facilities in Canada.

Dr. Bailey served on the Expert Advisory to Health Canada on Xenotransplantation Regulation and represented the Canadian Veterinary Medical Association (CVMA) at Canada's National Forum on Xenotransplantation. She was a member of the Special Emphasis Panel on the Immunobiology of Xenotransplantation for the National Institutes of Health (NIH). She also served on the Ontario Ministry of Agriculture, Food and Rural Affairs' (OMAFRA) Animals for Research Act Review Committee.

In addition to working in academia, Dr. Bailey has experience in the private sector (biologics and pharmaceuticals) and private veterinary practice.

Career Paths in Veterinary Medicine: International Work
(following the light, one step at a time)

David Waltner-Toews, DVM, PhD
Professor, University of Guelph, Department of Population
Medicine, Guelph, Ontario;
Founding President and CEO, Veterinarians without
Borders/Vétérinaires sans Frontièrs—Canada

There is a crack in everything. That's how the light gets in.

— Leonard Cohen

As a professor in the Department of Population Medicine at the University of Guelph, I have taught courses on the epidemiology of food-borne diseases, epidemiology of zoonoses, and ecosystem approaches to health. A lot of my work is international. When I was in veterinary school, most of the subject matter that I now teach either did not exist (e.g., ecosystem health) or was considered too boring for a new graduate (e.g., public health).

If I have had a career path, it has been a winding one, with a lot of it uphill and through wild and dangerous places. I interrupted a degree program in English literature to hitchhike around the world; I ran out of money in India and worked on a development project. I saw what being poor, not having enough to eat, meant. After I came back, I worked in a sawmill and knew I couldn't do that for long. I went back to school and finished my BA, knowing that I had a deep passion for writing but that I also wanted to return to poor southern countries with a useful, transportable skill. At first, I had no idea what that would be. I thought about the poor farmers I had seen and the jungles in Southeast Asia, and I wondered if something having to do with veterinary medicine (like James Herriot and my Mennonite uncles) or wildlife (as on Mutual of Omaha's *Wild Kingdom*) might fit the bill. It was worth a try. I switched gears and studied science.

Fortunately, the late Dr. D. L. T. Smith was on my interview committee at the Western College of Veterinary Medicine (WCVM). When I talked about wanting to do international work, he knew exactly what I meant. There is, in fact, a long tradition of international work among Canadian veterinarians—although it has not always been celebrated or acknowledged, as it should. By the time I graduated from WCVM in 1978, I had a life partner, a new baby, and some debts. I looked at wildlife veterinary jobs. There were none (that I could find). I looked into zoo internships. The only one that appealed to me was in San Diego, and they weren't taking Canadians. I was offered a job working with a dairy cooperative in Barbados, but I would have had to bring all my own equipment and get myself down there. I would live in paradise, but be unable to pay off my student debts. My wife would have trouble getting work. I was terribly insecure about my clinical skills. I went to work for a mixed-animal practice in Grande Prairie, Alberta, and then I worked for a practice in Barrie, Ontario, to get a better sense of what being a veterinarian meant.

With my student debts paid off, I decided to go back to school. I figured I could have lasted a few more years in practice, but I was 32 years old and thought I should get all my formal education done with before I lost all my brain cells. I still wanted something that was exportable and appealing to my generalist instincts. It came down to pathology or epidemiology. I get a headache looking through microscopes at histology slides, and I don't like killing animals, so I picked epidemiology. In 1985, I finished a PhD in epidemiology at University of Guelph, working on diseases of dairy calves. I think, for a few minutes, I was the world expert on the subject.

We again looked at overseas options; this time, we decided that a project funded by the Canadian International Development Agency (CIDA) and executed by the Veterinary Laboratory Services of Ontario was just the right thing. The project was to build an animal disease investigation centre in Java, Indonesia. They needed someone to set up the field investigation programs. It was, as they say, a challenge—both professionally and personally. Disease-wise, the centre covered everything from a rabies epidemic in dogs to an epidemic of *Trypanosoma evansi* in water buffaloes. I learned a lot about how culture, economics, politics, and ecology interact to affect animal disease.

After that two-year experience, our family decided to come back to Canada, largely because my partner had plans to further her education and training. I got a position on faculty at the Ontario Veterinary College (OVC), teaching epidemiology of food-borne diseases and zoonoses. At that time, research teams were looking for epidemiologists. I started off working on projects that looked at diseases of mink and sheep, but I had also made a vow to myself to continue and build on my international involvements. Even in 1987, the world was small, and—at least to some of us—notions of veterinary medicine without regard to ecological, economic, and political globalization were quaint and mostly of historical interest.

In the late 1980s, I got a letter from a Quebecois veterinarian in Nepal. She had been working there for two years and wondered if she could pursue a Masters in Epidemiology at Guelph but do her research in Nepal. "Sure," I said. "If you can get money, we can do anything." With help from me, she got money from the International Development Research Centre (IDRC) in Ottawa, as well as from the CIDA. For 10 years, we worked on a project that started out studying hydatid disease (including infection rates in people, livestock, and dogs). By 2001, this work had transformed into a community-based ecosystem health project.

Over the decade of the 1990s, I became involved in projects in the Caribbean (Caribbean Plant and Animal Health Information Network), Nepal (Hydatid Disease, Ecosystem Health), Kenya (Agroecosystem Health), Peru (human health and natural resource use in the Amazon), Uganda (Sleeping Sickness), and Costa Rica (leishmaniasis, vesicular diseases of cattle)—largely led by student interest. I was based and teaching at Guelph, but, whereas my colleagues were doing research in southern Ontario on production diseases, I chose to focus internationally on public health, epidemiological problems, and information systems.

My epidemiological questioning, both at home and abroad, led me into the newly expanding field of ecosystem health. If we could talk about the health of individual animals and of herd health, could we also talk about the health of farms? Of agroecosystems—the whole agricultural landscape with the people, wildlife, and domestic animals in it? With funding from the Tri-Council (all three national granting councils) in Canada and the IDRC and CIDA (for the overseas work), I was privileged to be a part of various teams of veterinarians and non-veterinarians as we developed both research and teaching curriculum in ecosystem health. Dr. N. Ole Nielsen, the Dean of OVC (who had been dean of WCVM while I was there as well), was a world leader in this area and served as a mentor. Bruce Hunter led the charge on the education side, and I became part of a group that developed an ecosystem health elective that engaged all four of Canada's veterinary colleges.

In 2004, the community liaison for Aeroplan (a major Canadian corporation) was looking for reputable charities to support, and asked me if there was such an organization as Veterinarians without Borders in Canada. If there isn't, there should be, I responded. Within six months, a group of veterinarians from across Canada had volunteered their time, money, and energy to create Veterinarians without Borders/Vétérinaires sans Frontières – Canada, complete with a business plan and charitable status. They made me president. Within a year after that, we had official support from Aeroplan and were sending veterinarians into different parts of the world. Much of this was based on what generous veterinarians were already doing.

The work that I do today did not exist when I started in veterinary medicine. Public health meant inspecting carcasses in a slaughterhouse. Ecosystem Health had been suggested as a possible term in one paper in *Science*, but that was way outside the veterinary literature. Even when I started as a professor at Guelph in 1987, the epidemiology of zoonoses and ecosystem health were marginal fields of inquiry. Today, in the face of global food-borne disease epidemics and emerging infectious diseases (75% of which are of animal origin), ecosystem health and public health are dynamic, rapidly expanding areas of veterinary work. Climate change, population growth, wars over resources such as oil and food, environmental refugees, and global trade are altering how diseases emerge and spread around the world. Veterinarians are—or could be—on the front lines everywhere.

I cannot predict what options will be open to veterinarians 10 years from now, but I can tell you that no education is ever wasted. My English literature degree and the writing and communications skills I have used my whole life are essential to my ability to function as a veterinarian working on issues of public interest. I can also tell you that any issue that mentions health and anything that involves multiple species of animals and comparative medicine should have veterinarians right there in the thick of it. That ranges from food safety and West Nile Virus in Canada to managing elephants and seals in Africa; from smallholder farming in Asia to feral dogs in northern Canada.

My advice is to find things that you love to do and find ways to do them. Talk to people who are doing international work. Go to conferences and talk to the speakers afterward. Find mentors and talk to them. Let them send you off, connect you, and advise you. I find that a lot of my work today is simply helping students to make connections, to plug into one of the many networks of which I have become a member over the past few decades.

Having the right connections is 90% of getting where you want in international veterinary medicine. Get some key technical skills, probably at the graduate level. Pathology and epidemiology are probably the most in-demand skills, but specialties like virology and microbiology are also being called for internationally. Communication skills are essential. If you can't speak publicly and think on your feet, then take one of the many available courses that will help you do so. Find work that almost looks like what you want to do, get hired, and change the job by doing what you think really needs to be done.

To new graduates, I say: Be fearless. Your skills are greater than you realize! Be humble and ask lots of questions. You know less about the world than you think you do. The greatest asset that any new graduate has is the ability to observe carefully and ask questions. Just about everything else you can get from books or the Internet. Think critically. Data are not information, and information is not wisdom. Be adaptable. The world is changing fast. Watch the cultural and ecological waves. Get on that mental surfboard. With a bit of luck, long after the rest of us are beached, you can lead the veterinary profession—you can lead our society—onto the beaches of the unimagined terrain of the late 21st century.

Additional Recommended Reading

What Should a Veterinarian Do? Schwabe C. The Centaur Press, Davis, California, 1972.

VanLeeuwen J, Nielsen ON, Waltner-Toews D. Ecosystem Health: An essential field for veterinary medicine. J Am Vet Med Assoc 1998;212:53-57.

Waltner-Toews D. One animal among many; Veterinarians in the global community. The 1988 DLT Smith Lecture. Can Vet J 1989;30:13-20.

Biography

Dr. David Waltner-Toews is a professor in the Department of Population Medicine, Ontario Veterinary College, University of Guelph. He is known as an essayist, poet, fiction writer, veterinarian, epidemiologist, and specialist in zoonoses and ecosystem health. He is the founding president and CEO of Veterinarians without Borders/ Vétérinaires sans Frontières – Canada (www.vwb-vsf.ca), as well as the founding president of the Network for Ecosystem Sustainability and Health (www.nesh.ca), a not-for-profit organization that employs adaptive ecosystem approaches to help resolve questions in community health, agriculture, and resource management.

He is a scientific advisor to Worldwide Virtual Network of Young Practitioners Working on Science and Society Issues (http://alba.jrc.it/science-society/)

and has been on the editorial boards of several journals dealing with environmental and health issues.

Besides having authored over 100 peer-reviewed scientific papers and conference presentations on animal diseases, public health, and ecosystem approaches to health, he has published four nonfiction books on ecosystems, health, and zoonoses; one book of short stories; and seven collections of poetry. He has at least one murder mystery on the way.

Section 8

YOU AND YOURS:

Preserving Your Good Health and Achieving Balance in Your Life

Introduction

In 1979, I graduated from medical school filled with enthusiasm, optimism, and the vigour of youth. I applied myself to the training process for another two years of dedicated self-sacrifice, and I emerged as a qualified, certified, family physician. I was ready to take on the world! And I believed I was well equipped to do that.

That was only partially true. Along the path to professional competence, I had shed pieces of myself. I had learned that to be a dedicated health professional, I would have to go without sleep, food, fun, and family. I put away my guitar, as there wasn't enough time to practice. My skis were relegated to the basement, since I could never separate myself from the hospital and my patients long enough to spend a day on the slopes. And, despite the image of health professional as a golfer, it would be years before I'd take up the sport, even though there were several beautiful courses in my rural neighbourhood. I believed I was giving my patients the full benefit of my freshly acquired training, even if from an increasingly one-dimensional individual. They seemed to need and enjoy my devotion. I relished their appreciation.

By the mid-1980s, anxious, depressed, exhausted, and abusing substances, I had to stop. Fortunately for me, there were health professionals ready to help. And, when I felt better, my patients and hospital were ready to have me back. So was my family. I was one of the lucky ones.

I learned that good personal health and a balanced approach to life mattered more than anything else. If I could preserve those things, then I could serve others—not the reverse. From treating professionals, friends, and colleagues who had already learned these lessons, I discovered how to attend to the basics. From these chapters that follow, so can you.

Who knew that regular, healthy eating provides energy and chases irritability away, or that we continue to require eight hours of sleep each night despite years of functioning on less? Or that emotional self-awareness and management are as important as intellectual competence? I found out that our most important asset and source of support is our family, not our professional practice. And that it is just as important to take vacations and time away from work as it is to work nights, weekends, and attend conferences. Walking on the uneven ground of a hiking trail became just as important to me as the endless tramping of the corridors at work, and playing the blues can make me feel so good! Ignoring these principles carries considerable risk—for me, certainly, and maybe also for many other accomplished health professionals.

Today, as Director of the Physicians Health Program in Ontario, I and my colleagues respond to the personal needs of doctors, pharmacists, and veterinarians who contact us experiencing difficulties with burnout, substance abuse, depression, and more. While not epidemic in our professions, these kinds of problems are endemic—probably affecting us at much the same rates as the general population. But with a little preparation, advice, and a willingness to care for ourselves and our families as much as our patients, there needn't be unnecessary suffering.

Some of the problems we face are characterized by denial—our own, our families', and our colleagues'. That's why it's important to know about the signs of distress, depression, and substance abuse in particular—in others as well as ourselves—and to be willing to reach out to one another. Please consider this when reading this section, and together we can enjoy good health, balance, and rewarding personal and professional lives.

Michael Kaufmann, BSc, MD, CCFP, FCFP,
CSAM certified Director,
Physicians Health Program,
Ontario Medical Association (OMA),
Toronto, Ontario

Dr. Michael Kaufmann, a former family practitioner, is medical director of the OMA Physician Health Program. Dr. Kaufmann is certified in addiction medicine by the American Society of Addiction Medicine.

Compassion Fatigue

Debbie Stoewen, DVM, MSW, RSW
Pioneer Pet Clinic,
Kitchener, Ontario

> *If you want others to be happy, practice compassion.*
> *If you want to be happy, practice compassion.*
>
> — Dalai Lama

Introduction

Veterinary medicine is distinguished as an ever-evolving profession, although it appears to be changing more to meet the needs of a changing society than the animals under its care. Originally bound within rural roots, the profession has branched outward in innumerable and previously unimaginable directions, offering ever more diversified and progressive expertise. One of the largest growing fields within veterinary medicine has been companion animal practice, and it is within this field that veterinary medicine is best understood as a caregiving profession.

Companion animal practitioners not only know and work with their patients, but with the family that surrounds them. In essence, veterinarians work with "the pet-embedded-within-the-family," or, in other words, a familial social system. Although people are genetically predisposed to becoming attached to other people (especially their own children), people become attached to pets. This is because pets exhibit many of the characteristics that cause attachment of people to people; pets are often thought of as though they were children. Pets can even be regarded as "the perpetual children" within the family, since they remain dependent despite adulthood.[1]

Working within the paradigm of our closest human counterpart, the pediatrician, we not only care for our animal patients, but for the family attached to them. Veterinary healthcare teams impact the lives of these families every day, sometimes facing complicated and often emotional issues with regard to intervention and/or preventative aspects of patient care, and thereby practice "compassionate medicine" that extends beyond the animal patient under their care. Such a broad-based compassion is most typically held by those whose personal passion drives their desire to contribute in this field, and although this passion enhances their ability to practice well, it also makes them vulnerable to be wounded by the very work they love.

Webster's dictionary defines compassion as a "feeling of deep sympathy and sorrow for another who is stricken by suffering or misfortune, accompanied by a strong desire to alleviate the pain or remove its cause." Compassion is based on a passionate connection, promoting a sense of equality within an inherent regard and respect for the other as a fellow human being.[2] Compassion calls for empathy. Empathy is the capacity to accurately understand the emotional perspective of another person and to communicate that understanding. Central to all relationships is the need to understand and be understood. Only when clients feel understood are they able to trust, and trust is the foundation upon which all relationships are built—including the veterinary-client relationship. Although technical competence is absolutely essential in the ever-increasingly complex, technological world of veterinary medicine, the interpersonal skills of empathy, warmth, and respect—all of which foster trust—are as well.

Empathic engagement, however, is a double-edged sword.[2] Just as empathy facilitates caring work, contributing toward optimal outcomes for every member of the family, the act of caring can leave the practitioner vulnerable. When we are exposed to clients' emotional distress, we, too, will feel the effects. Hilfiker sums this up very well: *"All of us who attempt to heal the wounds of others will ourselves be wounded; it is, after all, inherent in the relationship."*[3]

In the last two decades, a link between the empathic sensitivity of healthcare professionals and their vulnerability to be secondarily affected by the suffering of others has been recognized.[2,4] Being around the pain and suffering of others can be "emotionally contagious." As compassionate practitioners, it's impossible to see and care about the suffering of our clients without feeling some pain ourselves. Within such an emotionally charged environment, we may even internalize some patients and clients, taking on unrealistic emotional burdens and sacrificing our own emotional needs for those of others. "Owning" the problems of others, however, is neither necessary nor healthy. Well-intentioned empathy and compassion can give way to unhealthy boundaries, wherein dedication can turn into codependency, empathy can become enmeshment, and commitment can lead to overcommitment and fatigue.[5] Caring, compassion, and empathy as found within compassionate medicine can negatively impact practitioner well-being. It can, in fact, extort a cost – "the cost of caring."

The "cost of caring," as termed by Charles Figley, a psychologist and pioneer in trauma science, is a relatively new condition in the human medical literature, known as "compassion fatigue."[6] However, compassion fatigue is not limited to human medicine and is recognized to afflict a number of healthcare professionals, including those in veterinary medicine. Profoundly significant, compassion fatigue is recognized as *"the greatest threat to personal, professional and financial success among those who truly provide compassionate care."*[7]

What Is Compassion Fatigue?

Despite two decades of research, compassion fatigue still suffers from conceptual limitations.[8] Lack of conceptual clarity hinders and confuses our understanding of it, especially in the field of veterinary medicine wherein it is only newly being recognized and scant literature exists. Within human caregiving fields, researchers have attempted to conceptually differentiate compassion fatigue from other related conditions, such as job burnout, vicarious trauma, and general psychological distress; but the terms even here have remained imprecise.[8] Within the veterinary field, although research has begun, minimal yet exists.

"Compassion fatigue" as a concept and phenomenon was first introduced by Joinson in the nursing literature, describing the condition of nurses worn down by the daily hospital emergencies.[9] It was expanded in the psychology and trauma stress literature by Figley.[10] At that time, the newly acknowledged concept of compassion fatigue finally provided a language for the feelings of those within numerous helping fields who had become challenged by their essential work.

Related terms often used interchangeably with compassion fatigue include empathy fatigue, emotional contagion, countertransference, and vicarious traumatization.[2] Empathy fatigue is considered the emotional secondary stress and grief reactions that occur during helping interactions.[11] Emotional contagion is defined as an affective process in which "an individual observing another person experiences emotional responses parallel to that person's actual or anticipated emotions."[12] Countertransference is the process of seeing oneself in the client, of over-identifying with the client, or of meeting needs through the client.[13] Vicarious traumatization refers to the cumulative effect of the client's traumatic material that affects and is affected by one's world view, differing from compassion fatigue in that one experiences a "transformation" in one's personal and professional belief systems.[2] Although possible, vicarious traumatization would seem least plausible within the veterinary profession. It is doubtful that the emotional material specifically encountered within the usual daily activities of companion animal practice would be profound enough to result in this outcome; however, vicarious traumatization may be possible for the veterinary professional consistently working with victims of extraordinary life events (such as violence, natural disasters, and accidents) or for shelter practitioners and veterinarians of research facilities.

Within the medical literature, compassion fatigue is identical to secondary traumatic stress disorder (STSD) and is equivalent in terms of its symptomatology to post-traumatic stress disorder (PTSD).[11] "Compassion fatigue," given the emphasis on "the cost of caring" for healthcare professionals, is an accepted alternate term and conveys a more user-friendly construct and framework than the more highly "pathologized" STSD identified in the Diagnostic and Statistical Manual of Mental Disorders, Fourth Edition (DSM-IV).

Compassion fatigue can be described as *"the natural consequent behaviours and emotions resulting from knowing about a traumatizing event experienced by a significant other—the stress resulting from helping or wanting to help a traumatized or suffering person."*[14] It emerges as a natural consequence of caring and, accordingly, is not necessarily a problem but more a natural by-product.[10] Defining it by necessary variables, compassion fatigue necessitates a caregiving relationship within which there is an exchange of empathy, emotions, and information between the caregiver and client, along with a strong desire on the part of the caregiver to help alleviate the client's suffering and pain.[8]

Compassion fatigue cannot be clearly differentiated from other environmental stressors. From a systems perspective, compassion fatigue has been conceptualized as the convergence of primary traumatic stress, secondary traumatic stress, and cumulative stress/burnout.[15,16] An interactive or synergistic effect among these three has been discerned, wherein the experience of symptoms from any one appears to diminish resiliency and lower thresholds for the adverse impact of the other two.[15] This may predispose a tridirectionally vulnerable caregiver to a potentially rapid onset of symptoms that may be severe enough to become extremely debilitating within a very short period of time.[15]

Dispelling the Myth

Compassion fatigue is often mistaken as burnout. Despite the recognition of compassion fatigue as a form of professional burnout, the two conditions are, in fact, uniquely different, despite often appearing to feel the same.[6,11] Since the two have uniquely different causes and paths to recovery, it is vital that they be clearly understood and differentiated.[6]

The key differentiating factor is that while compassion fatigue is always related to the process of dispensing care (i.e., it is an occupational hazard of caring), burnout can result from any type of work-related stress.[5] Burnout is brought about by excessive, prolonged, and unrelieved work-related stress, and it is driven by organizational concerns, policies, procedures, and bureaucracy.[6] Essentially, it is the consequence of a disconnection between the individual's expectation around role performance and the organization's structure to support the role.[2] (See Chapter 8-2 on burnout in this section.)

Compassion fatigue and burnout differ with respect to other characteristics as well—specifically, the onset of symptoms, type of symptoms, and treatability. In contrast to burnout, which is a cumulative and sometimes unconscious process, compassion fatigue often emerges suddenly, with little warning, as an acute reaction of physical, emotional, and mental exhaustion.[2,11] Compassion fatigue involves patterns of re-experiencing clients' trauma, avoidance and numbing, and persistent arousal; these patterns induce feelings of helplessness, confusion, and isolation that are disconnected from real causes and triggered by unrelated experiences.[11,16,17] Burnout is characterized by physical, emotional, behavioural, and work-related symptoms that, although comparable, are overall quite different (including exhaustion, sleeping difficulties, somatic problems, irritability, anxiety, depression, guilt, helplessness, aggression, callousness, pessimism, defensiveness, cynicism, avoidance of clients, substance abuse, quitting, poor work performance, absenteeism, tardiness, risk-taking, perfunctory communication, inability to concentrate, social withdrawal, lack of humour, dehumanization, and poor client interactions).[18] And lastly, although burnout is treatable, it may require changing jobs or careers. In contrast, compassion fatigue is highly treatable once recognized and addressed.

Populations at Risk

Compassion fatigue can affect anyone in the role of healer, helper, or rescuer.[14] It occurs across a wide range of care-providing professions, including psychologists, social workers, lawyers, disaster relief workers, nurses, psychiatrists, medical doctors, emergency service professionals, police, crisis phone-line attendants, and shelter workers, among others. Animal care professionals such as humane society workers and veterinary hospital personnel are the most recently recognized. Based on the data obtained from the Humane Society of the United States (HSUS) 2003-2004 mail survey of 200 veterinary practices within the United States (US), one-third of veterinarians are at high or extremely high risk for compassion fatigue. Specific risk factors within veterinary medicine, specifically companion animal practice, make veterinarians especially susceptible. These factors are associated with changing demographics, the nature of the work, and the characteristics inherent to the professional.

Changing Demographics

Once a primarily agriculturally based profession, veterinary medicine has been changed by urbanization. Today, animals are no longer "kept" for primarily utilitarian purposes. Instead they are welcomed into our homes where they often play an integral role in people's personal lives.[6] Animals most often are considered members of families and even referred to as children.[6] Pet "owners" are increasingly identified as guardians or caregivers, with the concept of animals viewed as "property" being long out-dated. In finding meaningful relationships with non-human companions, relationships infused with emotion, new dimensions have been added to the responsibilities of veterinarians. Clients request better preventive and more advanced intervention care. Our patients are therefore living longer and better lives, leading to an absolute increase in the quantity and quality of time shared, and a resultant heightening of the human-animal bond (HAB).[6] Heightened attachment results not just in a stepped-up need for better-quality medical care, but also the associated emotional responsibilities that accompany the provision of that care.[6]

Societal recognition of the beneficial effects of human-animal interaction has increased, with tremendous advances in our understanding of both the physical and mental health benefits of the HAB.[19] There is growing conviction in many spheres of medicine, from cardiology to psychiatry, that the health benefits of pets may reduce human healthcare costs.[19] In some instances, by providing both physical and emotional support, the bond becomes essential for survival.[20] Additionally, interest in and recognition of the benefits of service dogs, medical-assistance dogs, animal-assisted activities, and animal-assisted therapy have all increased, resulting in a higher respect and valuation of human-animal interaction.[19] This contributes toward greater veterinary expectations when clients are seeking care. Animals are no longer just viewed as animals, and services once considered to be in the realm of human healthcare (e.g., hospice care) are becoming part of mainstream companion animal care. Consequently, supervised in-home support of the HAB is likely to expand with increasing client needs and expectations, expanding veterinary involvement in compassionate end-of-life care.

The Nature of the Work

Relative to seven other occupations (including physician, accountant, chiropractor, lawyer, dentist, teacher, and pharmacist), people with pets rank veterinarians first in compassion. The most highly rated factor when choosing a veterinarian is for the doctor to be kind and gentle—elements categorically demonstrative of compassion! Clients value the expression of compassion above and beyond every other factor, including respectfulness and informativeness, reputation for high-quality care, past experience with the clinician, the range of services offered, the location, the convenience of hours, the recommendation from a friend or neighbour, and lastly, the price of services.[19] As veterinary practitioners, although we do care, public perception also compels us to care, and our clientele expects us to care.[6]

An expanding recognition of the importance of the bond between caregivers and their pets has influenced how companion animal practices service their clients and patients.[6] There is mounting awareness that the provision of veterinary care in a manner that acknowledges and appreciates the HAB leads to better outcomes for everyone—patients, clients, and practices themselves.[19] Such an approach is universally accepted as an important determinant of a successful practice, with the HAB considered THE motivating force to seek both routine as well as advanced veterinary care.[6,19] As a response, the veterinary healthcare team and the profession as a whole have placed more emphasis on acknowledging and appreciating the HAB between caregivers and their pets. It necessitates not just attention to the medical needs of the patient, but also the emotional needs of the client.[6]

In human medicine, the responsibility toward the primary, secondary, and tertiary care of the patient is broadly divided between many care providers. In veterinary medicine, responsibilities are not so distributed, and the responsibility for virtually all preventative and intervention care, directly or indirectly, lies solely with the veterinarian as a multi-disciplinarian or generalist. This includes the medical care of the patient and the provision of support for the family. Since clients place their trust and sometimes the lifelong care of their pet in the hands of their veterinarian, they seek the veterinarian as their primary source of support, even when a comprehensively helpful team is in place. Veterinarians are required to not just be medically competent, but to be understanding and supportive as well.

From its origins within veterinarian-centred practice, the philosophy of veterinary medicine has evolved in stages, progressing to client-centred and now finally relationship-centred practice. From the position of patriarchy to one of partnership, instead of telling the client what to think and do, veterinarians now invite clients into communicative relationships by helping them make decisions and planning patient care together. Relationship, by definition, implies and incurs involvement—a more intimate way of being. Within an invited relationship, veterinarians are obliged to support the emotional issues that arise.

Life in companion animal practice can be immeasurably challenging. Despite even the best-made schedules, the unexpected can and often does happen. Practice can change in an instant, depending on the immediacy of presenting needs. The veterinary healthcare team, individually and as a whole, must be prepared and be able to move fluidly between the needs of one situation to the next, even if emotionally charged. It is not easy to move from the shared grief of euthanasia to the delights of a new puppy visit. Similarly, despite best efforts, hoped-for outcomes with sick patients are not always realizable. Emotionally charged situations are termed "critical incidents," and they are experienced by team members on any given day.[6] Companion animal practice is laden with emotional rigors associated with the needs of unique and ever-changing situational challenges.

These rigors have increased in proportion to the explosion in technological advances and skills in the profession. With medical, surgical, and disease prevention and intervention capabilities expanding exponentially, clients are requesting more advanced care as well as better and more complete preventative care.[6] Clients hold greater hopes and expectations and thus suffer greater losses when hoped-for outcomes are not met, exposing the veterinarian, who has invested a great deal of emotional energy in treating the animal and supporting the client, to parallel emotions. Increased contact time with the provision of more complex care increases both veterinary-patient and veterinary-client bonding, and this can increase the risk for compassion fatigue.

As veterinary professionals, we are exposed to death frequently. Veterinarians often care for patients "from the cradle to the casket." Indeed, because of animals' relatively short life spans, veterinarians face patient death five times more than other healthcare professionals.[6,20] Moreover, no other profession deals with the demands surrounding the active ending of life, from the emotional drama of anticipatory grief to the actual act itself. Euthanasia is a complex, often thorny and emotionally charged affair, with the distress of death felt not only by the client, but also by the entire veterinary healthcare team.[20] The profession should recognize the impact that euthanasia has on veterinarians and practice team members. If emotions aren't dealt with, euthanasia-related stress can contribute toward the development of compassion fatigue.[20]

Lastly, not uncharacteristic of the profession, the average veterinarian works more than the standard (40-hour) week.[19] Long hours in what is often an emotionally charged environment can additively increase risk for compassion fatigue.

The Essential Professional

Every helping professional who cares is occupationally vulnerable to compassion fatigue. Certainly some may be considered constitutionally vulnerable, in that they possess certain predisposing factors or personal correlates that may exacerbate or promote the development of compassion fatigue. However, foremost in veterinary medicine, our profession has been identified as "a caring populace."

The 1999 KPMG study clearly conveyed that the veterinary profession is one uniquely characterized by "caring" individuals.[19] One of the key findings that makes veterinarians effective caregivers is that they "love" working with both animals and people. Through their care-giving activities, they experience compassion satisfaction. However, at the same time, they become susceptible to compassion fatigue.[6,21] Those who are especially sensitive, who have an enormous capacity for feeling and expressing empathy, and who are often the best and the brightest, are especially vulnerable. Paradoxically enough, those who feel "the calling" of animal care are more protected from compassion fatigue than those who have sought out the career mostly for money, prestige, or power.[8] This is likely due to the protective effect of compassion satisfaction outweighing compassion fatigue.

Newly graduated veterinarians may be more vulnerable in that they are less experienced with how to develop healthy boundaries and build a balanced lifestyle. Seasoned veterinarians, on the other hand, tend to experience less compassion fatigue, because they have already learned methods to manage the feelings of emotional exhaustion.[11] However, any veterinarian who does not adequately care for him/herself, including making time to replenish and re-energize, enhances the susceptibility to compassion fatigue.[6]

In the 2003-2004 HSUS survey, both male and female veterinarians reported compassion fatigue equally. However, since women are socialized to be the nurturer, caregiver, comforter, peacekeeper, and are conditioned to empathetically engage, we may soon witness an increased prevalence of compassion fatigue within our profession, as women rapidly become the majority in the profession.[19]

Personality type may be a predisposing factor in developing compassion fatigue as well. Type A personalities may deny emotions or not know they have any. They may feel guilty for having or showing emotions, as this takes them away from the source of real value for them, which is to meet standards like a perfectly performing machine. Denying emotions rather than acknowledging and working through them, however, may predispose to compassion stress build-up and resultant fatigue.

Personal predisposing factors that may potentially contribute toward the development of compassion fatigue, as extrapolated from the literature on PTSD, include a history of psychological and behavioural problems, a family and personal history of psychopathology, a family history of psychiatric disorders (e.g., anxiety, depression, or parental PTSD), a history of attachment trauma (such as a prolonged separation from parents in childhood), a history of family instability, previous exposure to trauma (particularly in childhood), and exposure to multiple traumas, even if minor.[16,22] Psychiatric disorders (including depression and other mood disorders), substance abuse, dissociative disorders, other anxiety disorders, and psychotic symptoms or disorders place an individual at greater risk of compassion fatigue. Individuals experiencing an inordinate amount of life disruption related to mental illness or a change in lifestyle, social status, or professional or personal responsibilities, may be especially susceptible to compassion fatigue.[10] In fact, any condition that reduces the ability to modulate emotions puts an individual at risk.

An individual's own world view or cognitive schemas and resultant coping styles influence interpretations of events and, thus, influence how one responds to situations. For example, how a veterinarian processes the act of euthanasia can significantly impact the risk for compassion fatigue, according to experts.[6] If euthanasia is considered to be a service to the animal, done with technical efficiency so as to not harm or scare the animal, then the clinician will be less prone to collecting symptoms and less affected.

In summary, regardless of one's world view and coping styles, mental health, life history, age, gender, personality type, professional experience, or favourable protective and prognostic factors, compassion fatigue may yet be experienced. It is virtually unavoidable.

Symptoms

Consequent to the provision of emotionally demanding services, veterinarians and healthcare team members may experience an array of psychological reactions, including behavioral, emotional, cognitive, and physical symptoms of psychological stress.[6,23] Unfortunately, despite social, psychological, biological, and spiritual consequences, compassion fatigue may go unrecognized or even be denied.[6] Caught in the midst of daily routines and demands, it's not always easy to recognize or admit when one's life is thrown out of kilter. We easily become habituated to circumstances. Moreover, since symptoms of stress and distress occur along a continuum, compassion fatigue may be difficult to definitively identify. The earlier it is identified and addressed, however, the better the outcome for everyone.

Compassion fatigue is characterized by three categories of symptoms: intrusive, constrictive, and hyperarousal symptoms.[15] The hallmark of compassion fatigue is the alternating between intrusive and constrictive symptoms in an all-or-none pattern. Although intrusive thoughts are unwanted, the intentional suppression of them (numbing them out) is counterproductive—they rebound with even greater intensity. Ironically enough, efforts to suppress such thoughts actually increase their occurrence.[24]

Intrusive symptoms can appear spontaneously, day or night, unbidden into consciousness while awake or asleep, interfering with and blurring the boundaries between professional and personal life. Symptoms can range from minimally problematic thoughts concerning a particular family's predicament to more profound, recurrent, intrusive, and distressing recollections and ruminations. One may experience intense psychological distress at exposure to cues that symbolize or resemble an aspect of the trigger situation, and flashback episodes and/or recurrent nightmares may even be experienced.[5] An all-consuming obsessive-compulsive desire to help certain patients and families may develop, and one may find oneself unable to let go of work-related matters while at home.[7]

Constrictive or avoidance symptoms tend to complement intrusive symptoms. There may be active efforts to avoid the thoughts, feelings, activities, and situations that repeatedly remind one of the distressing predicament.[8] A clear sign of compassion fatigue is the urge to avoid, or the act of avoiding, exposure to the patients and clients who have caused distress in the past and have the potential to do so again.[8] There may even be a sense of dread in relation to working with them. In an effort to cope, emotions may be blocked or numbed, but this can spill over from the workplace into personal life, resulting in a reduced interest in self-care and social activities that once brought pleasure or relief from stress. This can exacerbate the situation as well as foster unhealthy isolation. Blocking and numbing of emotions ultimately restricts the range of feelings felt resulting in an overall reduction of affect.[5] Even one's sense of humour can become dulled. Diminished affect results in even greater emotional withdrawal, with greater reluctance to emotionally engage, thereby furthering the isolation. Alienation from colleagues, family, and friends is not uncommon.[11]

As well as the alternating intrusive and constrictive symptoms, compassion fatigue also evokes hyperarousal symptoms, such as sleep disturbances (difficulty falling or staying asleep), general anxiety, difficulty concentrating, exaggerated startle response, feelings of agitation or irritability (including outbursts of anger), and/or hypervigilance.[5,8] Overall, compassion fatigue may disturb the ability to think clearly, modulate emotions, feel effective, or maintain hope.[25] In fact, feelings of helplessness and inadequacy are among the reported symptoms.[7] Over time, one may begin to feel drained and exhausted and experience difficulty separating work life from personal life. Sometimes it may even feel like we are losing our sense of self to the clients we serve.[10] At the extreme, compassion fatigue may bring about modification or even disruptions to important beliefs (called cognitive schemas), which people hold about themselves, other people, and the world.[17] At this point, the sense of self is truly lost.

Although symptoms may be mild and considered the result of a stressful day, they can also be severe, additive, and potentially devastating,[6] involving a cascade of adverse physiological, psychological, and interpersonal consequences.[24] If any of these symptoms are suffered, don't ignore them; the condition is real, as is the threat to your health and welfare.[7] Furthermore, the threat to the health and welfare of your patients, clients, staff, family, and friends—anyone with whom you relate—is real and needs to be taken into consideration.

Impact of Compassion Fatigue

Compassion fatigue affects people personally and professionally, impacting both individuals and organizations. It can affect physical and mental health, professional competence and success, and vocational direction and development. It can even spread "as a contagion" to pan-systemically influence organizational welfare. On the most personal level, compassion fatigue can make a significant contribution to a wide range of physical and psychiatric disorders. Some veterinarians might find themselves dealing with stress-related physical ailments such as headaches, gastrointestinal upsets, and chronic pain and fatigue, while others become predisposed to psychiatric conditions such as dissociative disorders, mood disorders (including anxiety and depression), substance abuse (including gambling, smoking, and alcohol), eating disorders, and personality disorders.[11,24,26,27] Both physical and mental health have direct beneficial or detrimental bearing on personal and professional functioning.

A positive correlation exists between empathy and compassion and the quality of care provided. However, when compassion fatigue is experienced, the veterinarian's ability to empathize, engage with, and care becomes compromised. The obligation to act in a manner that promotes well-being may gradually and nearly imperceptibly wane, risking the potential for less-than-optimal patient and client care and outcomes.[11] Working less conscientiously, some may even find themselves making mistakes.[27]

As wounded caregivers, veterinarians may eventually find professional life disappointing and non-fulfilling. Some may engage in premature job changes, believing the problem to be specific to the place or type of employment. Others, experiencing increasingly poor job performance and plummeting self-esteem, may eventually drop out of private practice as a direct practitioner and take a job that doesn't require much public interaction, in order to avoid any kind of compassion stress.[15,26] Compassion fatigue has driven both promising and seasoned professionals out of their professions entirely, permanently altering the direction of career paths.[6]

Unfortunately, those who persevere, not recognizing or addressing compassion fatigue, act as a reservoir for the "spread" of the "virus" between different members of the veterinary team or caregiving organization. Just as families both breed and destroy stress among its members, depending on coping competencies, so do organizations. As veterinarians who are charged with leadership responsibilities, we may be especially "infectious." Compassion fatigue can also spread through the effort of affected members reaching out to others in the effort to obtain relief.[8,20] As one caregiver reaches out to another, seeking relief from painful emotions, the other, through helping out, absorbs some of that person's pain.[8] Through efforts to seek relief, the "contagion effect" can be transmitted to the entire support system, with everyone in the workplace becoming a potential victim.[28]

Intervention

Professional help may be an answer. Animal health professionals affected by compassion fatigue *"need to talk about their experience and concerns in a safe context that is validating and non-judgmental, offers empathic connection, and supports clear thinking toward effective action."*[25] As well as the provision of psychological first aid, it is important to assist individuals in coping with ongoing stressors and encourage the utilization of natural support systems. These are the key elements of acute intervention.

Intervention has benefits beyond the provision of immediate relief. Equally if not more important, it may be the incentive that leads to the enhancement of professional skills and personal life enrichment, just as crisis tends to precipitate change and growth.[29] Intervention may be the first step to assist one to move toward optimal personal and professional wellbeing, positively reinforcing career aspirations and personal life functioning.[29] We can re-emerge from compassion fatigue renewed and refreshed if we are aware, acknowledging, and open to assistance, whether it be professional assistance or through the care and concern of coworkers, family, and friends.

Prevention

Conceivably, one might wonder whether it is at all possible for us to practice compassionate medicine without becoming wounded caregivers. How can we meet the medical needs of our patients as well as the nonmedical needs of their families while continuing to honour, preserve, and protect the heart of what drew us to this caring profession in the first place? Despite the risk(s) involved in practicing compassionate medicine, certain qualities seem to afford protection.[2]

The first protective quality is acknowledgment. We must acknowledge first that compassion fatigue exists, and second, by the very nature of what we do and who we are, that we are at risk for this condition.[6] Through awareness in tandem with the admission that we are vulnerable, we become enabled and empowered to address it, thus precluding the potentially devastating outcomes that can accompany compassion fatigue. When recognized, compassion fatigue is usually alleviated simply by acknowledging it and taking action to get support.[26]

The second protective quality is self-awareness. It is of utmost importance for each of us to not only be aware of compassion fatigue (awareness is our first defence), but to apply self-reflective skills to continuously self-monitor for fatigue symptom development. With early identification comes the opportunity for early intervention. Self-monitoring can be seen as an obligation that goes hand-in-hand with our commitment to practice, and to practice well. Furthermore, we can and should make use of others around us, whether they be our coworkers, colleagues, friends, or family—they can be external barometers of the changes we may not be able to detect in ourselves. Likewise, we need to be sensitive to the symptoms and warning signs in those we share our working lives with, providing suitable supportive response as warranted. The extent to which we are able to be reflective and responsive, to engage in whatever activities necessary to promote and maintain wellness, will determine our personal and professional happiness and our effectiveness as veterinarians.

The third protective quality: emotional intelligence (see separate chapter on this topic in this section). Emotional intelligence is the degree to which you are attuned to your own emotions as well as those of the people around you.[30] Emotional intelligence has been documented as one of the key factors determining individual and organizational success.[30] Understanding our feelings, where they are coming from, and whether or not they could be detrimental, can help us handle them and prevent the undesirable consequences of compassion fatigue. Sensitivity to the emotions of others can help us to read key signs in them, enabling more effective and appropriate communication.[30] The ability to identify, understand, and appropriately express and respond to emotions can mean the difference between good interpersonal relationships and poor ones, physical/mental health and illness, and success and failure in practice.[30] Emotional intelligence, truly a combination of cognitive and emotional abilities, is the foundation of emotional competence.[30] Emotional competence is a safeguard against compassion fatigue.

The last protective quality is adaptive coping capacity. Coping has been defined as *"the processes that individuals use to modify adverse aspects of their environment as well as to minimize internal threat induced by stress."*[31] Coping may be adaptive or maladaptive; the latter typically involves distractive but ultimately harmful activities that provide only momentary relief. In order to sustain the idealism and joy one has when entering the veterinary field, skills to become resilient and hardy without growing cold-hearted and cynical need to be developed. Learning strategies for building resilience, such as using empathy wisely, avoiding the depletion of emotional reserves, and balancing service with self-care, can go far in preventing compassion fatigue.

The following coping guidelines may be useful in the prevention of compassion fatigue:

- Don't take on others' pain, despite having the capacity to feel and express deep compassion and empathy for animals and each other. We are less able to help when we take ownership of others' problems and pain, because doing so takes so much energy. Let others have their own pain, and use your energy to support and help them.
- Be aware of boundary issues with clients. Remain sensitive and form attachments, but maintain perspective surrounding personal investment, so as to avoid becoming over-involved and overwhelmed. As well, re-

main connected with enough of your own resources so you can contain
it and leave it at the end of the day.

- Let go of things that cannot be controlled, and accept the fact that one's
personal best is good enough. Give yourself a break, and focus on the
things you are doing right.

- Remember that you are not what you do, but rather you are who you
are. Unfortunately, no matter what degree of acknowledgment, self-
awareness, emotional intelligence, or adaptive coping capacity one
may possess, there is no way to avoid compassion fatigue completely.
There are, however, a number of proactive steps and strategies that one
may employ to help manage the consequences.

The Personal Approach: Life Balance and Self-Care

Create balance in your life. Do not allow one area of your life to overpower
or overshadow the entirety of your identity. For veterinarians to keep their professional obligations in check with their personal life responsibilities, priorities need to be established and careful planning implemented.[27] Balance can
be achieved by establishing and maintaining boundaries and limitations on
your availability, involvement, and personal investment in the profession.[6] This
might include "utilizing alternate 24-hour care/emergency facilities, not going
to the office on days off, not sharing home phone numbers with clientele, and
not allowing work to encroach on previously scheduled family time."[6] Sometimes it's necessary to envision a protective island for yourself and the inti-
mates you care about.

It is important to develop and maintain good self-care discipline. If you
don't learn to care for yourself as well as you do your patients and their families, there may be little of quality left to give.[5] The endurance of one's personal
energy and the long-term success and stamina of one's career rests with how
much value is placed upon creating and having a truly personal life. If we do
not devote time and energy to keeping a healthy "number one," all the other
dimensions that depend on us will ultimately suffer the consequences.[32,33]
Thus, it is important to nourish body, mind, and spirit in order to sustain and
maintain both your personal and professional life.

Such "nourishment" or self-care may include whatever works to uplift
and rejuvenate. This may include maintaining a healthy diet, taking daily
walks, getting in touch with nature and the outdoors, interacting with children and animals, exercising, participating in sports, practicing relaxation
techniques, scheduling time to simply relax and read or play, embracing spirituality, volunteering and contributing to your community, and cultivating in-

terests, activities, and hobbies beyond your work.[5,6] Pursue any passions you might have! There are many creative and personally meaningful ways to soothe your senses and make you feel alive, relaxed, and well.[5]

By intentionally affiliating with those who share your values, believe in you, and nurture your growth, you will enhance your own well-being.[5] Anyone who understands and appreciates your empathy and extent of compassion and is willing to engage in meaningful exchange can be an invaluable source of solace.[6] A healthy and strong support system not only offers a buffer to one's working world, but also can be an outlet for good old-fashioned fun!

Self-care is incomplete without the best preventative medicine of all—laughter! Humour, especially laughter, is claimed to have health-enhancing effects.[34] Often regarded as one of the highest forms of coping with life stress, humour is considered a moderator of compassion fatigue.[34] Although we should take what we do seriously, we should not take ourselves too seriously. "Humour may encourage emotional expression, enhance social support, allow reframing of circumstances, facilitate communication, aid physiological functioning, and provide ways of dealing with difficult organizations."[34] Therefore, treat yourself to laughter and laugh at yourself! Good humor is a gift.

The Interpersonal Approach: People Helping People

> *Compassion stress is a function of the general morale and supportiveness of fellow workers. A positive work environment includes workers who care about each other and show it. They genuinely like one another, and they may joke around and/or pitch in when needed and often without being asked to do so. They pick up on even the most subtle mood changes of fellow workers and ask about them in a caring and supportive manner. A negative work environment, on the other hand, is emotionally toxic. Relationships among workers, and especially with supervisory staff, are strained, and staff morale tends to be negative. What is lacking in a toxic work environment is a sense of trust, optimism, and mutual support among and between staff members. As with other social psychological components, the vital resources of supportive colleagues enable the veterinary team members to rebound from emotionally upsetting events.*

> —Charles R. Figley and Robert G. Roop:
> Compassion Fatigue in the Animal-Care Community

The literature and writings about compassion fatigue emphasize the importance of social support. The veterinary healthcare team needs informal and/or formal opportunities to debrief and process heavy emotional material. A positive space for feedback sharing, venting, and support between team members is imperative to healthy individual and team functioning. As professionals in a leadership role, it is not just good practice but our ethical responsibility to ask how our team members are doing.[32] It is equally our ethical responsibility to hear how we ourselves are doing.

Although clinical practice is often demanding, we need to take the time to celebrate the sense of achievement we experience in the many success stories we create.[6] Compassion satisfaction goes a long way to mitigate compassion fatigue.[23] If acknowledged, the rewards found in work can far outweigh the stresses. Through the telling of success stories, we can also celebrate each other, for it is only through interdependency and team effort that such outcomes are achieved. The time for such reflection and acknowledgment can be found in spontaneous conversations in the midst of daily activities or during organized social events. Such events (e.g., birthday and holiday celebrations, organized team-building activities, and staff retreats) can also serve to increase feelings of group cohesion and mutual support.

Especially in large hospital settings, peer support groups (whether peer or professionally led) may be helpful. Group support is considered an adjunct to, not a substitute for, self-care. Group work is powerful in the prevention of compassion fatigue and the promotion of recovery. At the same time, however, there is risk for groups and their members to become "traumatized by concern," with compassion stress "infecting" the entire system after first appearing in only one member.[10] However, within well-led group work, the cultivation of resilience prevails.

The Organizational Approach: Supporting the Membership

Companion animal practices, large or small, need to be mindful of their responsibility and obligation to facilitate their employees' personal and professional growth by addressing issues of secondary stress reactions associated with compassion fatigue. An organizational culture that "normalizes" the effect of working in a helping field of care can provide a supportive environment for health-care team members to address the effects of compassion stress. It can create opportunities for team members to vary their caseload and work activities and participate in multidisciplinary work, which not only brings about relief through variety, but also encourages members to appreciate others' perspectives. It honours the personal lives of staff, supporting members to take care of themselves and their families. It respects time needed for illness and wellness, recognizing how closely personal welfare relates to interpersonal and organizational welfare. It empowers staff through inclusivity in decision-making surrounding policies and procedures. Quite literally, it celebrates the lives of staff.

A comfortable work environment includes physical and emotional space. The provision of a sanctuary or comfort room for healthcare team members, including a coffee maker, soft music, and comfortable furniture, may help staff meet self-care needs.[6,17] Personally meaningful items in the workplace (including pictures of family or travels taken, scenes of nature, or quotes) help people remember who they are and why they are doing this work.[18] Organizations can model the importance of the personal in the professional even further by de-institutionalizing the hospital with inspirational artwork, unique interior decorating, utilizing lighting strategies, "greening the environment," and playing soft background music.

Organizations that promote professional development for their employees recognize it as integral to job endurance. Just as continuing education prepares professionals with the new skills and tools needed to meet the needs of an ever-changing world, trauma-specific education may be the singular ingredient in the prevention of compassion fatigue. Without the ability to name the experience and a framework for understanding and responding to it, compassion fatigue cannot begin to be addressed. Workshops to help team members recognize the phenomenon, as well as support groups to help address it, can be offered.[26]

Organizations that acknowledge compassion fatigue and demonstrate supportive and sensitive attitudes also must sanction debriefing (either informally, in the moment, and/or formally during staff meetings) to allow healthcare team members to discuss the emotional components of various client and patient interactions.[6] Opportunities to talk about the emotional aspects of work—and chances to blow off steam—can help keep compassion fatigue from taking over.[26]

Healthy life balance, nourishing self-care, social sustenance, and organizational support synergistically interweave to prevent and help manage the consequences of compassion fatigue. The nurturance of the individual within the sustenance of the community is key.[10] Although compassion fatigue is a consequence of relationship, it is through relationship (both with ourselves and with others) that we are healed.

Summary

Companion animal veterinary medicine is a social profession. It is not just all about animals or medicine; it is also about people and the bond. The HAB is considered THE motivating force to seek veterinary care. The provision of care in a manner that acknowledges and appreciates the bond leads to better outcomes for patients, clients, and practices themselves. It necessitates not just attention to the medical needs of the patient, but also the emotional needs of the client. It necessitates what is called "compassionate medicine."

Compassionate medicine requires the expression of empathy, the most critical component within the veterinary helping relationship. Caring, compassion, and empathy enhance our ability to practice well, but they also make us vulnerable to becoming wounded by the very work we love. Our work can extort a cost, "the cost of caring," otherwise known as compassion fatigue. When we give more than what we replenish ourselves, it is only a matter of time before we experience a shortage of compassion and a sense of fatigue. This is not a reflection of our character, professionalism, or professional skill level, but it will deleteriously influence these, if not addressed. Compassion fatigue is recognized as "the greatest threat to personal, professional, and financial success among those who truly provide compassionate care."

Compassion fatigue is a term, not a disease! It can be thought of as a label to help us identify where we may benefit from healthy changes in our life. Intervention and preventative approaches can serve not only to alleviate compassion fatigue, but also to move us toward optimal personal and professional well-being and life enrichment. It is our clinical responsibility to make sure we are not harmed by our work. If we don't take care of ourselves, we can't take care of our patients or clients. Clearly, there is no single prescription for compassion fatigue, but through knowledge and awareness, acknowledgment of our inherent vulnerability, and action in response, surely we and the families we serve can thrive through the provision of the best in compassionate medicine.

References

1. Voith VL. Attachment of people to companion animals. Vet Clin North Am: Sm Anim Pract. 1985;15:292.
2. Sabo BM. Compassion fatigue and nursing work: Can we accurately capture the consequences of caring work? Int J Nursing Practice 2006;12:136-142.
3. *Healing the Wounds: A Physician Looks at His Work.* Hilfiker D. Pantheon Books; New York; 1985; :207.

4   Valent P. Diagnosis and treatment of helper stresses, traumas, and illnesses. In: Figley CR, ed. *Treating Compassion Fatigue.* Brunner-Routledge; New York; 2002.

5. Wagner T. What is compassion fatigue? http://www.animalsinourhearts.com/fatigue/balance.htm

6. Mitchener K, Ogilvie G. Understanding compassion fatigue: Keys for the caring veterinary healthcare team. J Am Vet Med Assoc 2002;38:307-310.

7. When Helping Others Hurts You. Special Issue: Veterinary Practice 2005. Vet Econ 2005;46:20-22.

8. Figley CR, Roop RG. Compassion fatigue in the animal-care community. Washington, DC: Humane Society Press, 2006.

9. Joinson C. Coping with compassion fatigue. Nursing 1992;22:116-120.

10. Figley CR. Compassion fatigue as secondary traumatic stress disorder: An overview. In: Figley CR, ed. *Compassion Fatigue: Coping with Secondary Traumatic Stress Disorder.* Brunner/Mazel; New York; 1995.

11. Stebnicki MA. Stress and grief reactions among rehabilitation professionals: Dealing effectively with empathy fatigue. J Rehab 2000;66:23-29.

12. Miller KI, Stiff JB, Ellis BH. Communication and empathy as precursors to burnout among human service workers. Communication monographs, 55(9), 1988.

13. *A Case Approach to Counseling and Psychotherapy.* Corey G. Brooks/Cole Publishing Co.; Pacific Grove, California; 1991.

14. Figley CR. Introduction. In: Figley CR, ed. *Treating Compassion Fatigue.* Brunner-Routledge; New York; 2002.

15. Gentry JE. Compassion fatigue: A crucible of transformation. www.haworthpress.com

16. Voges MA, Romney DM. Risk and resiliency factors in posttraumatic stress disorder. Annals of General Hospital Psychiatry 2003;2:4. http://www.general-hospital-psychiatry.com/content/2/1/4

17. Bell H, Kulkarni S, Dalton L. Organizational prevention of vicarious trauma. Families in Society 2003;84:463-470.

18. *Career Burnout: Causes and Cures.* Pines AM, Aronson E. Free Press; New York; 1988.

19. Brown JP, Silverman JD. The current and future market for veterinarians and veterinary medical services in the United States. J Am Vet Med Assoc 1999;215:161-183.

20. Costello G. Companions, counseling and compassion. Tennessee Alumnus Magazine 2003; Vol.8, No.3.

21. Halpern-Lewis JG. Understanding the emotional experiences of animal research personnel. Contemporary Topics, 1996; Vol.35, No. 6.

22. Yehuda R. Changes in the concepts of PTSD and trauma. Psychiatric Times 2003;20:35-37.

23. Wee D, Myers D. Compassion satisfaction, compassion fatigue and critical incident stress management. Int J Emerg Ment Health 2003;5:33-37.

24. Allen JG. Challenges in treating post-traumatic stress disorder and attachment trauma. Current Women's Health Reports 2003;3:213-220.

25. Geller JA, Madsen LH, Ohrenstein L. Secondary trauma: a team approach. Clinical Social Work Journal 2004;32:415-430.

26. Joslyn H. How compassion fatigue can overwhelm charity workers—and what to do about it. The Chronicle of Philanthropy Website; 2002.

27. Luechtefeld L. The balancing act – A new life skill. Vet Pract News, Feb 2005.

28. Roop R, Vitelli DM. Compassion fatigue in the animal care field. Orendorff B, ed. Selected papers from the 21st NWRA symposium. Wildlife Rehabilitation, 2003;21:146-147.

29. Baranowsky A. Compassion exhilaration: Reclaiming professional mastery through the Accelerated Recovery Program (ARP). Traumatology Institute (Canada). http://www.psychink.com/index.html

30. Stobbs C. Emotional intelligence: how important is a high 'EQ'? In: Practice. September 2003;506-507.

31. Hare D. Editorial – Another ingredient in the recipe for a successful career. Can Vet J 2004:45.

32. Joshua S. Compassion fatigue and vicarious trauma in the veterinary clinic: A silent occupational hazard. Ontario Association of Veterinary Technicians Conference Proceedings, 2006.

33. Wright B. Compassion fatigue: how to avoid it. Editorial. Palliative Medicine 2004;18:3-4.

34. Moran CC. Humor as a moderator of compassion fatigue. In: Figley CR, ed. Treating Compassion Fatigue. New York: Brunner-Routledge, 2002.

Biography

Dr. Debbie Stoewen is an OVC'83 graduate. After four years of becoming familiarized with different practice philosophies and approaches through locum work in small animal general and emergency practices, she opened her own practice, the Pioneer Pet Clinic in Kitchener, Ontario, a relationship-centred companion animal hospital from its outset. Through her work with the Waterloo Region Family and Children's Services from 1995-99, she fostered a number of children-at-risk, becoming exposed to the plight of abused and neglected children and social work as another professional field of care. Motivated to help hurting children as well as hurting animals, she undertook undergraduate studies in Social Development Studies at the University of Waterloo, followed by a Master of Social Work degree at Wilfred Laurier University, completing her studies in 2005.

Although continuing to practice companion animal medicine – her passion as a veterinarian – Dr. Stoewen is ultimately interested in working as an interdisciplinarian within academics, recognizing and promoting the many bridges between veterinary medicine and social work. Her interests include promoting veterinary communication as a professional endeavor and core clinical competency, providing education on the continuum of the human-animal bond and the consequent social responsibilities inherent to the veterinary profession, and developing a multifaceted integration of applied social work within the Ontario Veterinary College (OVC). Dr. Stoewen lectures on the link between animal abuse and family violence, animal-assisted therapy, and compassion fatigue in the schools of social work and veterinary medicine as well as at conferences. She also contributes as a lecturer, coach, and trainer, supporting students and coaches in the clinical communication skills curriculum at the OVC. On a broader level, she hopes to be a force and influential advocate for the promotion of interdisciplinary approaches and appreciations within education.

Burnout

Michael Kaufmann, BSc, MD, CCFP, FCFP, CSAM certified
Director, Professionals Health Program,
Ontario Medical Association,
Toronto, Ontario

Robin Robertson, BA, MBA
President and Principal Consultant, RCR Consulting, Inc.,
Calgary, Alberta
(Co-author for Section III: Personal and Professional Balance)

> *In order that people may be happy in their work, these three
> things are needed: they must be fit for it; they must not
> do too much of it; and they must have a sense of success in it.*
>
> — John Ruskin

Part I: Cause and Condition

Recently, the head of a surgical department in a large community hospital contacted the Physician Health Program (PHP) and asked if I would address medical staff on the topic of physician stress and burnout. It seems several members of the department were feeling so stressed that they were seriously considering resigning their hospital privileges.

A study of the mental health and job satisfaction among rural physicians in British Columbia revealed a self-reported burnout rate of 55%, a rate that rose to a stunning 80% when emotional exhaustion was measured objectively using the Maslach Burnout Inventory.[1] The Canadian Medical Association's (CMA) 1998 physician survey revealed that Canadian doctors feel stressed, overworked, and exhausted.[2] These physicians are at risk for depression, burnout, and substance abuse, and they are among those most likely to leave their communities or even their careers. They are part of a profession that is losing its spirit.

Following are the words of an Ontario family physician whose personal experience with stress and burnout mirrors that of several of his medical colleagues.

It has been an insidious journey. I have to search my memory to really remember when it may have started. About four years ago, I began to ask myself questions like 'where am I?' and 'who am I?' My days were filled with fatigue. I was too afraid to consider where I was going. To get up in the morning, fearful and shaking inside, and try my best to get through the day seemed like all I could handle. Of course, I continued to do a fabulous job at work, without anyone really knowing what was going on inside me. So I began to look outside of myself for the answers. I left a secure hospital-based position and took over a busy community family practice. This may not have been the wisest choice. I had worked with a wonderful team of clinicians at the hospital but wound up in a chaotic, boundary-less, and demanding situation. But you know the saying: 'a change is as good as a rest.'

Well, initially I did feel better. I had more energy and felt more positive. It was only six months until I felt my path lead quickly downhill. Looking back, I feel I had no sense of direction and certainly no dreams; there was no spiritual self. Once again, I became tired. When I was on-call it was all I could do to retain a positive attitude toward my patients. My family felt that it was better for me to stay at work on those days and nights because I became irritable and angry and took it out on them.

I lived in fear that I wouldn't be able to handle the problems I was faced with. My confidence and self-esteem plummeted. I felt overwhelmed, unsatisfied, resentful, angry, and again on a path of spiritual destruction. I tried to set boundaries, but I didn't know what healthy boundaries were. In the attempt I became inflexible. I became increasingly angry with my patients. Why were they doing this to me? I began to have great difficulty waking up in the morning and finding anything to look forward to. I was not excited by work. In fact, I often cried on my way to the office and there were days when I had to fight my way through the door. I wanted to phone in and say I was sick, but my sense of responsibility to my patients took over. I began to withdraw from my partners and only talked to my office staff when I had to. I felt sad, depressed, and afraid. I was so disappointed.

Burnout

Burnout has been described as a career-adversity syndrome.[3] Its components include exhaustion, depersonalization, and a decreased sense of personal effectiveness or accomplishment. It is usually seen in professions that combine prolonged stress with high personal expectations. We might consider doctors—professionals with a highly developed sense of dedication to their patients and their profession—to be particularly susceptible.

Over time, burnout results in the total depletion of the sufferer: physical, emotional, mental, and spiritual. The somatic problems can include headache, gastrointestinal upsets, and many others. The emotional manifestations range from cynicism, resentment, and other negative attitudes to withdrawal and feelings of hopelessness, entrapment, and disillusionment. The mental and spiritual manifestations include depression, anxiety disorders, substance abuse disorders, and a loss of personal direction and purpose. These inevitably lead to some degree of isolation from family, friends, and colleagues, leaving little fulfillment or pleasure from life. Exhausted by prolonged stress, the physician experiencing burnout feels like he or she has nothing left to give. Feeling depleted, service becomes an intolerable demand. At the same time, relaxation and recuperation seem hard to come by.

In the final stages, the isolated doctor feels more and more alone and ineffective. Tapping into the inner sense of inadequacy that some are prone to feel, the "imposter syndrome" is activated. The burned-out doctor lacks confidence in his or her ability to carry out essential responsibilities, s/he feels overwhelmed, and, eventually, no longer capable of living up to the image of a competent health professional.

Sometimes, burnout is confused with depression. Depression is a clinical disorder characterized by persistent low mood and other cognitive, vegetative, and motor signs and symptoms such as poor sleep, declining appetites, decreased motivation, suicidal ideation, agitation or motor retardation, and other symptoms. Clinical depression may result from the continuing stress of burnout in those susceptible and should be diagnosed and treated by a qualified clinician (not the suffering doctor) when it occurs.

There are many reasons why physicians experience burnout. Medicine is practiced today in a constantly changing environment. Conservative by nature, many doctors find difficulty in adapting to the new political, social, and economic realities facing the profession. Hospitals are merging; colleagues and allied health professionals are experiencing low morale and work environments that feel increasingly toxic; primary care is under enormous strain; and there just aren't enough doctors where they are needed. In addition, patient demands are increasing each year as our population ages and becomes more sophisticated, while resources of all kinds fail to keep pace. While not to the same degree, many of these scenarios exist in veterinary medicine as well.

As healthcare professionals, we may feel our autonomy to be in decline and that we are no longer able to control the circumstances of our professional lives. Sensing a loss of status and respect from society, it is easy to feel unrewarded and unappreciated. Pressured by these environmental stresses, some may not have sufficient personal coping skills to prevent burnout. Quality self-care requires an understanding of healthy lifestyle practices and the permission to adopt them afforded by appropriate personal boundaries. In short, individuals who lack the ability to respond to life and career challenges creatively and with resilience are those most likely to experience lack of fulfillment and burnout.

Part II: Personal Factors in Burnout Prevention and Health Maintenance

The honeymoon is over. The practice of medicine isn't fun anymore. The rewards once enjoyed are gone. Compassion fatigue has set in, and patients have joined everyone else on the "other side." The years of toiling under conditions of great and constant stress are taking their toll.

Burnout, an insidious process that can take years to develop fully, is well underway. Exhausted, the doctor drinks cups of coffee or uses other, stronger stimulants to find energy. Irritated, the doctor may turn to alcohol, sedatives, compulsive shopping, gambling, or even indiscriminate sex to feel soothed. Working harder doesn't work anymore, and productivity declines. Relationships with family, friends, and colleagues deteriorate. Now, finally, most everyone knows something is wrong. Unchecked, the burnout syndrome matures into disabling physical, mental, social, and even spiritual illness. Some seek relief by looking for "greener pastures"—new places to work that won't be so stressful. Some, who can't bear the idea of continuing any kind of medical practice, seek new careers in other professions. Some just quit. These are the "lucky" ones. Sometimes advanced burnout results in morbid depression, substance dependence, and even suicide.

It's likely true that even the most developed self-care practices will not protect one from the deleterious effects of a relentlessly toxic work environment. Still, excellent self-care will go a long way to preventing a career-adversity syndrome such as burnout. Even if new work environments are sought, quality personal care and balance remain essential in order to cope, even thrive, in the inevitably stressful medical workplace.

The following is a personal account of one Ontario family physician's successful experience managing stress and burnout, accompanied by a guide to the basics of burnout prevention and health maintenance.

> *I have come far along the path of healing. At this moment, I am sitting, writing in my journal, and glancing outside every so often to watch the birds pecking at their food through the snow. I am thinking how beautiful my garden looks in the winter—the colours of the grass and the red bark of the dogwood are incredible. These are things I would never take the time to notice not so long ago. I am grateful today for so much, but especially the feeling of complete peace, happiness, and freedom. Having the chance to share my journey with others is such a gift. To have hope that things can be different is most important. To feel hopeful at the beginning seemed impossible.*

> *It's difficult to say when the healing began. I think for me it was with the questions I started to ask myself: 'Who am I? What are my dreams and goals? What is really important to me? What is balance? What are boundaries?' As I sought to find the answers to these questions, I believe I stopped looking outside and started looking inside of myself. I soon began to realize that healing would happen from the inside—spiritual growth—not from continuing to focus outside of myself by blaming the system, the workplace, or other people for how I was feeling.*

> *I also know I could not find the answers alone. I started to share my thoughts and feelings with others—my family, my friends, and other physicians. Sharing with other physicians was the scariest of all, because until I did, I thought I was the only*

one, and that to actually talk and share would expose me as the imposter I really was. But as I shared, I received understanding, support, and guidance. I realized I was not alone. And after sharing at the first 'Doctors Anonymous' meeting in Ottawa last year and hearing from other doctors that had actually made some changes that helped them heal, I started to have hope that perhaps things could be different for me.[4]

There was one particular day when the feelings I was experiencing were so intense I was unable to go to work. I spoke with my family, a close friend and colleague, and went to see my family doctor. She listened so patiently and kindly, and instead of diagnosing me with depression, giving me medication, and sending me on my way, she referred me to a psychologist, who also took the time to listen. For the next year and a half, the psychologist helped me find the answers to my questions. She helped me see that it was okay to set boundaries and share them with others; that it was okay to say no and not feel guilty.

Something else that helped me immensely was the '12 Steps for Medical Professionals Who Seek Re-humanizing.'[5] I had been reading the '12 Steps' for some time, but when I made a conscious decision to work through them, I really began to make some headway in my ability to make changes. I needed to begin to make them part of my life. I started to find more time for myself. When my family doctor first suggested this, I thought it sounded ridiculous, impossible. What started out as a reluctant commitment to take five minutes a day for myself is now at least an hour every morning. During this time, I work on my spiritual healing by reading the serenity prayer and applying it to my life today. I also meditate, write in my journal (especially about what I am grateful for today), and watch the birds.

I also started to have more time to re-start some hobbies that I had given up over the years, like listening to music, playing the guitar, and water-colour painting. Having more time with my family, and being more present for them, is one of the greatest gifts of all. We are trying to spend more time outdoors and exercise by hiking, canoeing, bike riding, and swimming. We are also trying to eat healthier. I now make an effort to eat three meals a day. I actually take my lunch to work and take the time to eat it and go for a walk afterward. This past September, my family and I had breakfast together during the week for the first time ever.

I still have many changes to make, and my journey is far from complete. I need to be in touch with my feelings and remain open to help, guidance, and love I receive from others who care about me every day.

Today, I am grateful for my family and friends who walk with me along my journey, never judging, only caring. I am grateful to my higher power who helped me find the courage to heal and find my true path. I am grateful to all individuals who enter my life and share their lives with me and allow me to walk with them.

Burnout Prevention and Health Maintenance: Taking Care of the BASICs

Reverend Edward Reading, of the New Jersey Medical Association Physician Health Program, describes five domains of spiritual health as physical, emotional, social, intellectual, and cosmological.[6] This paradigm has been adapted and applied below to the notion of burnout prevention and health maintenance using the mnemonic acronym, BASIC.

B is for Body

Our body is the vehicle that takes us on the journey. It demands our care and attention or it won't function properly. This is true even for doctors. Though medical training might imply otherwise, doctors must heed the fundamentals of physical health like everyone else.

The first fundamental is nutrition. A healthy diet is a conscious, deliberate thing. Balanced food choices, taken in the right amounts and at the right times, energize and heal. So often doctors skip meals and liquids while attempting to fuel the body with coffee, muffins, and pastries. Malnourished and poorly hydrated, how can one expect to feel truly well, let alone withstand the onslaught of the day's tensions?

The related but opposite consideration is toxin intake. Ingestion of caffeine, nicotine, alcohol to excess, and other drugs of abuse, must be minimized.

The human body requires exercise. The practice of medicine, no matter how needed or noble, doesn't change this fact or fulfill this need. Any fundamentally sedentary job that leaves no time for exercise is unhealthy. Anyone spending so many hours at work that they are unable to exercise even three times a week, 30 minutes each time, is working too much. It can't be stated more clearly.

The human body also needs rest. Some of us need more rest than others, but the need is universal. Medical training leads doctors to believe that a full night's sleep is a luxury, a joyous thing to be had only upon occasion. Physicians learn to go without sleep, or they sleep lightly while waiting to be called into action or for advice. Once again, valiant practice doesn't replace a fundamental need of the organism.

If sleep is rest for the body, the mind and spirit also need refreshment. Here I refer to recreation, hobbies, and holidays—things too often sacrificed upon the altar of insufficient time or importance. Regular breaks from the work to which we are dedicated permit continued attention to it.

Good medical care is another component of physical health. Sometimes the body needs medical attention, either for routine maintenance or in the event of illness. In the experience of the PHP, many physicians don't have family doctors or don't use them properly. Consider the paradox: doctors don't receive good health care, because they don't go to doctors!

B also stands for boundaries and balance. Without the first, the second can't be achieved. Doctors must learn to say "no" once in a while, especially to their work. Eventually, saying no will feel good, and the guilt, worn like a heavy winter coat, will be shed.

A is for Affect

Affect refers to mood, here meaning also attitudinal and emotional health. Medicine exposes its practitioners to the most marvelous and extraordinary circumstances. The vast range of human and animal experience, from exaltation to calamity, confronts the doctor from the very beginning of medical training. The well-trained physician has the knowledge and skill to cope with these things. But often, the emotional intelligence necessary to do so can be lacking. The concept of emotional intelligence as a component of total intelligence and personal coping is well described by Daniel Goleman.[7] Important components of emotional intelligence include self-awareness, ability to manage one's feelings in a positive way, empathy, and delayed gratification, among others.

Anger, resentment, frustration, fear, disappointment, doubt, despair, contentment, sympathy, joy, euphoria, and many more emotions all swirl and intermingle in the psyche like paint on the artist's palate. We all have them. Can we name them and deal with them in a healthy way? Do they balance and blend harmoniously, or do they clash chaotically?

Avoiding burnout demands attention to emotional intelligence. The topic of emotional intelligence is explored further in the chapter of the same title in this book section.

S is for Social

Dr. Michael Myers is a psychiatrist in Vancouver who treats doctors and their families exclusively. When asked for essential components of burnout prevention, he replied in a personal communication:

> *Pay attention to your loved ones—whether family of origin, family of choice, or close friends. They deserve love and connection, and must never be taken for granted. They keep us sane.*

M. Scott Peck, author of *The Road Less Traveled*, makes a stronger statement. The opening words of his book (*The Different Drum – Community Making and Peace*) are "*In and through community lies the salvation of the world.*"[8]

Doctors, like other human beings, are social creatures. We thrive in healthy interdependence, and we suffer in isolation. Honesty, empathy, and respect characterize healthy relationships—the building blocks of healthy communities. In healthy social groups, there is willingness to trust and risk, willingness to give and receive feedback, willingness to support one another even while working through negative feelings, and willingness to experience love and intimacy.

Healthcare professionals are challenged as well to seek support from one another. The task is to transcend the "pseudo-community" of medical staff associations in order to find healthcare professional community groupings where real personal sharing, intimacy, and support are possible. Who, other than a doctor, better understands medical stresses and personalities?

I is for Intellect

Maintaining some components of intellectual health may come more easily for doctors and remains an important component of personal stimulation and burnout prevention. It is as important to make time for hobbies, current events, and reading fiction and non-fiction (according to one's interests) as it is to attend to continuing medical education and medical journals. Striving to learn is essential for humans to thrive, a truth the stressed doctor can forget; however, the doctor's intellect is challenged to a greater degree in other realms. Reading draws our attention to rational and reality-based thought. It invites us to be in touch with the practical realities of the changing world around us, and to define short-term and long-term goals consistent with that reality. This requires regular examination and re-evaluation of one's worldview, belief systems, ethical and moral standards, ideals, values, and expectations.

Entitlement is a component of intellectual reality testing that requires special attention. Sometimes, a physician's worldview results in feelings of entitlement to wealth, social status, or reverence not always earned or appropriate to modern reality. The feelings of frustration that inevitably result when these expectations aren't met contribute significantly to burnout. Most notably, the consequences of poor financial planning resulting from an unrealistic expectation of wealth can drive doctors to work harder and harder, making attention to self-care very difficult.

A thoughtful and maturing individual will, through reflection, integrate his or her experiences into a dynamic philosophy of life and into the proper place of medical practice within that life.

C is for Cosmos

In Rev. Reading's paradigm, this domain refers to cosmological and environmental health. I like to consider one's personal sense of meaning and essential spiritual health in this category. Pressured by the rigours of daily medical practice, the doctor can lose perspective. In an essay entitled, *Recapturing the Soul of Medicine*, Dr. Rachel Remen reminds us that the original meaning of our work is service.[9] She goes on to say: *"Service is not a relationship between an expert and a problem; it is a human relationship, a work of the heart and the soul."* Dr. Remen has challenged doctors to find meaning in their work by seeing it differently, as through the eyes of a poet or writer. Then, physicians can experience the wonder, surprise, inspiration, and even invigoration available to them through their privileged human interactions.

Spirituality also requires pondering larger questions of meaning, such as where we fit in relation to the society of man, the world ecology, and the universe. Also included, of course, is the "Question of God." Is there a Higher Power, a Supreme Being, or a guiding force that defines and powers the universe and mankind on a personal or collective level? It is the practice of prayer (talking to our Higher Power as we understand one) and meditation (listening and contemplating) that are so easily abandoned when we are stressed, and yet these are so necessary to our spiritual health.Rev. Reading also reminds us that cosmological health includes the experience of awe; a form of understanding that encompasses everything in the universe, from micro to macro, and that transcends daily experience.

Summary

Dr. Mamta Gautam is an Ontario psychiatrist whose practice, like that of Dr. Myers', is composed mainly of physicians. In a personal communication, Dr. Gautam summarizes these ideas simply by saying: *"Take care of yourself."* It's tempting to lament that there isn't time to do so, but this notion is an illusion.

It's a matter of priority. If a doctor is to take care of anyone else in an effective and sustained way, he or she must attend to the BASICs of personal care as well. To do otherwise is folly, an act of peril risking burnout and illness.

Part III: Personal and Professional Balance

Both of the previous two parts of this chapter contained an Ontario family physician's first-hand account of professional and personal decline, recovery, and renewal. In Part III, the same physician describes his successful, ongoing efforts to maintain a healthy balance between personal and professional needs and responsibilities.

> Each day on the way to work, I park my car and walk the short distance to the office—all the while looking for familiar faces (patients, friends, shopkeepers) so that I can say 'good morning.'
>
> I thank God for what I have and where I am with my life. I am finally practicing the type of medicine that I love and am doing so in a healthy manner that suits my needs. Although balancing work, home (family and friends), and self-care is still a challenge, most of the time I feel like I'm winning. But this feeling has not come without a great deal of hard work.
>
> The first thing I had to do was overcome the desire to just stop practicing altogether. A journal article on the topic of managing the needs of home life and practice served as a considerable help. The article gave me 'permission' to begin thinking that perhaps I could still practice medicine, but in a different way.
>
> Shortly thereafter, I undertook to document my personal goals. The following is a journal entry from the summer of 2000: 'My goals:
>
> - To be healthy emotionally, spiritually, and physically
> - To be happy and excited about work
> - To not feel overwhelmed, unsatisfied, angry, and resentful
>
> When I am not healthy, I cannot provide the best possible care for my patients. To be healthy, I must:
>
> 1. Know my boundaries and share them with others
> 2. Work on balance between work, home, and self
> 3. Do more of the type of practice that I enjoy

4.   *Talk about my stress and feelings and do something about it, knowing that I can't change the system myself, but that, individually, I can have a better day'*

I had already worked hard at taking care of myself, by making time to do the things that I enjoy. I had been working on my spiritual healing as well. This provided the foundation that gave me the strength and courage to embark on the journey of making changes at work. I began by setting boundaries. I worked with my psychologist to accept the need to establish boundaries and then proceeded to put them in place. I had to work hard on overcoming feelings of guilt and the fear of the possible consequences that I would face when I communicated these boundaries to my patients. I realized, however, that once I became comfortable with setting boundaries, and communicating them clearly to patients, that they, for the most part, would understand and respect my position.

Although I wasn't able to change my workplace immediately, this was an example of how I was able to make an important initial step forward. I felt more freedom, which in turn led to the realization that I did have choices. This empowered me to relinquish on-call and hospital work (which was causing me the most stress) and eventually leave my practice to start a new practice doing the type of medicine that I love.

This could not have happened without support from family, friends, colleagues, and other professionals. Working through the PHP's "12-Steps for Medical Professionals Who Seek Rehumanizing" was also extremely helpful.[5]

Through all of this, I continued to work on my spiritual healing. Many days I asked God for answers and direction. The answers came slowly through other people who were also walking this path. Eventually, my path was revealed to me and I had the strength and courage to move forward and practice medicine in the way that was meant for me.

I am sharing my story with the hope that others will read it and see that change is possible, and balance is possible.

Burnout occurs when the perception of personal stress places an individual in a position of "energy overdraft." People suffering from the early phases of burnout are often able to extricate themselves from the situations at hand. However, as the condition progresses through its various stages, those affected often require professional help in order to recover. Research on burnout and the "phase model" shows that individuals in the earliest phase have surplus emotional resources available to cope with stressors, while those in the final phase are in a deficit condition.[10] The following will consider issues pertinent in the medical workplace and across the health-care profession as a whole.

Individual Considerations and Strategies in the Workplace

Each of us brings our "personhood" to work each day, which includes our physical, emotional, and spiritual selves. The following steps suggest a path to help influence work so that it becomes more meaningful, even joyful, given who we are as individuals.

Control Thoughts and Attitudes

Three parents of young children are sitting in a busy, noisy playground. When asked what they are doing, the first parent responds, *"I am sleep-deprived and exhausted, but I have to be here to watch these kids play."* The second responds: *"I am doing my job as a parent by providing a safe and caring environment for my kids to play."* The third responds: *"I am raising future physicians and healers, and this is the most important place I could be right now."* All three parents are doing the same work, yet each views the world and their work very differently. The connection between their respective views and levels of satisfaction is obvious.

Do you view your work in a way that contributes to positive feelings, enhances the level of service you provide, and ultimately changes the environment in which you work?

Know and Live Your Values and Goals

When did you last analyze your values and goals to ensure that they are reflected in your professional practice? Is the amount of energy you expend in the workplace creating a lifestyle that you want to sustain?

Consider a physician with a young family who is working a schedule of extended hours in order to sustain a material lifestyle that, upon closer examination, is neither meeting the needs of his family, nor fulfilling his personal views on child rearing. Clearly, something must change. The physician may, for example, choose to restrict lifestyle expenses (e.g., travel or entertainment) or perhaps adopt a more modest residence in order to have the opportunity to work fewer hours and spend more time with the young children. This way of living may be more in line with the physician's personal values.

Understand Your Personality and Preferences

Consider a physician who received many accolades and rewards for his laboratory research. Out of a desire to examine his life and better balance the time spent between work and family, the physician kept a log over a two-week period, along with a note describing how each area of work made him feel. The analysis showed clearly that work with patients in a clinical setting, surrounded by a team of healthcare workers, made the physician feel energized and fulfilled. His laboratory research, on the other hand, made him feel worn out, actually resulting in stomach aches. The journal exercise helped the physician to decide not to reapply for research funding and to focus instead on clinical work.

Be Present for the Moments of Wonder

Healthcare professionals have the opportunity to daily experience wonder in life. Challenge yourself each day to find something in your work that inspires you. We cannot always control the feedback received from others, but we can take notice of that which moves us and is a natural part of our work.

Set Boundaries

Each day you are bombarded by demands from clients, patients, and others. Each of these clients, individually, is unaware of the cumulative effect these demands may have. However, you are well aware of the stress and strain you experience. Only you can establish boundaries to protect yourself.

There are two essential boundaries to set: those pertaining to personal time and those that protect family time. Along with boundary setting comes the skill and discipline needed to enforce them. Learn how to say "no." Gather people around you and seek their help to encourage you to stick to your plan. The receptionist or office manager can be one of your greatest allies if he or she is aware of, and trained in, how to protect your boundaries.

Workplace Considerations: What Makes a Healthy Workplace?

A healthcare professional who works in a community hospital was asked, *"What would make your workplace a healthier place to be?"* Her response: *"Reduce the hierarchy, red tape, and politics,* adding, *we say we are patient-focused, and that's what draws me to the work, but it seems to be forgotten sometimes."*

This response mirrors what we know about healthy workplaces. Workplaces that allow us to thrive embody a combination of factors:

- The structure of the organization facilitates our work. Hierarchies can become too steep, thus impeding good decision-making and diminishing an organization's flexibility and ability to respond.
- Systems, policies, and procedures enhance workflow in a meaningful way. They do not create barriers or prevent staff from living out a core value, such as patient-centered care. They do not hold people back from doing what is right!
- The culture facilitates trust, open communication, and accountability. Culture is like the air quality in a building—it is impossible to see, and yet we know whether it is healthy or not.
- Positive "people practices" create satisfying work.
- People are provided with opportunities to contribute to the greater whole.

To feel good about our work, the work itself must provide a balanced exchange of energy and remuneration that is in line with our values and goals; a sense of accomplishment and awareness that our gifts are being utilized; a sense that we are appreciated by others; and, finally, a balance between the job demands and our ability to meet or control those demands.

Communication, support for one another, and agreement on workplace norms (including how disagreements will be handled) are areas within a work group's influence. High-performing workplaces are known for their willingness to invest time and energy into creating healthy, working teams.

Schedule time as a group to discuss aspects of the workplace. Hire a facilitator, if necessary, to gather data on the current situation, to assist the group in identifying current gaps and future goals, and then create a plan for change.

Systemic Considerations

Creating satisfaction and preventing burnout in medical practice are challenges that require attention at every level, from the beginning of medical training to retirement and beyond. Indeed, a change in the culture of medicine is indicated. Medical schools need to continue to improve training for students in the principles and values of emotional intelligence, self-awareness, and self-care, along with the core curriculum. Clinical teachers must model these skills and behaviours and abandon once and for all the attitude that sacrificing personal health for that of patients is a virtue. Viewed in the context of burnout and dwindling physician human resources, this is an absurd and dangerous belief.

Continuing education opportunities increasingly include physician health as a theme or component. Medical communities must be encouraged to seek and create events that support doctors' health. Hospital policies can be enhanced to acknowledge the importance of staff health, including physician health, as a core value. Hospitals can form physician health committees. Medical associations, both provincial and national, can and do support these policies and practices, but there is room for improvement.

The profession must acknowledge and reward doctors who live balanced, self-respecting lives.

Conclusion

When there is balance in our lives, we are more resilient. Resilience is important when it comes to stress and burnout. It's tempting to estimate the impact of stress in one's life simply by counting the number and severity of stressors. But we each experience stress differently, and what may be devastating to one person can be energizing to another.

Underlying both reactions is an individual's life balance—emotional, social, intellectual, spiritual, occupational, financial, and physical—or lack thereof. Living in balance provides the energy supply we require to deal with stress, avoid burnout, and extract the greatest meaning and joy from everything life has to offer.

References

1. Thommasen HV, Lavanchy M, Connelly I, Berkowitz J, Grzybowski S. Mental health, job satisfaction, and intention to relocate—Opinions of physicians in rural British Columbia. Can Fam Physician 2001;47:737-744.

2. Sullivan P, Buske L. Results from the CMA's huge 1998 physician survey point to a dispirited profession. Can Med Assoc J 1998;159(5):525-528.

3. *The Handbook of Physician Health.* Goldman LS, Myers M, Dickstein L, eds. Pearson T. Physician Life and Career Health and Development. Published by the American Medical Association.

4. Chicken Soup for the Doctor's Soul: Unique Day in Physician Health a Resounding Success. Ontario Medical Review, February 2001:29.

5. 12 Steps. Ontario Medical Review, October 1999–April 2000. www.oma. org/php/12steps.htm

6. Reading EG. Clinical Spirituality: A New Paradigm; Proceedings of the Ruth Fox Course for Physicians, April 19, 2001; American Society of Addiction Medicine, 4601 No. Park Ave., Ste. 101 Upper Arcade, Chevy Chase, MD 20815, USA.

7.   *Emotional Intelligence—Why it Can Matter More than IQ.* Goleman D. Bantam Books; 1995.

8.   *The Different Drum – Community Making and Peace.* Peck MS. Simon and Schuster; 1987.

9.   Remen RN. Recapturing the soul of medicine. West J Med 2001;174:4-5.

10. Golembiewski RT, *et al.* Estimates of burnout in public agencies: Worldwide, how many employees have which degrees of burnout, and with what consequences? Public Administration Review; Jan/Feb 1998:Vol. 58(1).

Biographies

For Dr. Kaufman's biography, please see the Section 8 Introduction on page 507.

Robin Robertson brings more than 20 years of experience to organizational consulting, including involvement in organizations with both small and large-scale systems change projects. Her extensive experience includes over 300 projects including cultural change projects and work-life balance initiatives. Robin's experience extends to the healthcare, oil and gas, defense, government, not-for-profit, and service industries. She is the former director of a provincial physician and family health program.

Robin has taught at the University of Calgary, S.A.I.T., N.A.I.T., Mount Royal College, Grant MacEwen Community College, Lethbridge College and Medicine Hat College. Robin is an accredited Insights Discovery facilitator and an EQ-i (Emotional Intelligence) practitioner.

Prior to launching RCR Consulting Inc. in 1990, Robin worked as a Senior Organization Development Consultant, Corporate Training Consultant, Leadership Development Consultant, and Recreation Manager.

CHAPTER 8-3

Depressive Conditions

Joy Albuquerque, MD, FRCP(C)
Associate Medical Director, Physician Health Program,
Ontario Medical Association,
Toronto, Ontario

> *There are no classes in life for beginners; right away you are asked to always deal with what is most difficult.*
>
> — Rainer Maria Rilke

Introduction

Many of us have been touched at some point with feelings of sadness or anxiety about things in our lives. For about one-fifth of us, the experience will go beyond just feeling "stressed out" to a more debilitating state. The word *depression* covers a lot of ground, due at least in part to its widespread use in everyday conversation, in pop psychology, and in clinical settings. Keeping this in mind, the term *depression* can be divided into levels of psychological distress with the associated symptoms and behavior along a continuum, as depicted below.

Mild distress indicators	→ → →	Severe clinical depression/suicide

While the specific relationship between mild distress and clinical depression is poorly understood, most mild symptoms do not progress to a clinical threshold. Loosely stated, all distress is not depression. It is conceivable that identifying and modifying things in your environment can relieve milder forms of psychological distress.

Is veterinary training stressful? Yes, it is. With such a steep learning curve comes the need for a lot of time for study and preparation. But not all stress causes distress—we can learn to manage lots of situations, and many stressors ameliorate with time and experience.

Stress

There is a complex relationship between stress, health, and illness. While it is clear that some stress is essential to living, prolonged, heightened, or abnormal stress in a vulnerable person can be damaging. Researchers consider the negative aspects of stress as "allostatic load."[1] A terrific book, written by stress researcher Robert Sapolsky and titled, *Why Zebras Don't Get Ulcers*, gives a good and entertaining discussion on stress management.[2]

Often referred to as "burnout" in the literature, excess workplace stress has become part of our everyday language. Burnout tends to occur under conditions of prolonged work stress that leads to an imbalance between our sense of control and the demands of work. Burnout can lead to decreased sense of satisfaction in one's work, to emotional exhaustion, and to problems with coworkers.

The cornerstone in the treatment of distress or burnout is self-evaluation—being attentive to various elements of one's physical, emotional, social, and spiritual health. This reevaluation often illuminates disparities, which can then be resolved.

Depression

Clinical depression refers to a broad range of mental health problems characterized by key symptoms, such as low mood or a loss of interest and enjoyment in things that are normally associated with pleasure. The syndrome has a range of associated emotional, cognitive, physical, and behavioural symptoms. As illustrated in Table 1, distinguishing the mood changes of major depression and those occurring because of adverse experiences or stressful circumstances remains a challenge because of symptom overlap. Clinically, the persistence, severity, and the degree of functional and social impairment are used to sort these closely related phenomena.

Table 1
Clinical Depression Versus Psychological Distress

Clinical Depression	Psychological Distress[3]
• Depressed mood, sadness	• Depressed mood
• Disinterest or anhedonia	• Feeling overwhelmed
• Worthlessness	• Anxiety / worrying
• Excessive guilt	
• Problem with concentration/ attention	• Difficulty concentrating
• Difficulty making decisions	
• Poor memory	
• Sleep disturbances	• Sleep disturbance
• Appetite change/weight change	• Appetite change/possible weight change
• Fatigue/low energy	• Fatigue/chronic tiredness
• Agitation or restlessness	
• Poor motivation	• Procrastination
• Suicidal thoughts or ideas	
• Physical symptoms: headaches	• Physical symptoms: headaches

Major Depressive Disorder

Major depressive disorder, as defined by the acronym DSM-IV, is associated with significant disability, chronicity, and relapses/recurrences.[4] The incidence of depression in the general population from the Baltimore ECA (epidemiological catchment area) study was estimated at 3/1000 per year, with the lifetime prevalence of approximately 16%; the gap between incidence and prevalence reflects chronicity and recurrence.[5-7] The World Health Organization (WHO) ranks the illness burden of this disorder as the fourth leading cause of disability (measured as the years lived with disability) worldwide, and this is expected to rise to the second leading cause by 2020 for all ages and both sexes.[8]

Many people who have suffered a clinical depression realize, in retrospect, that symptoms had been ongoing for some time before they sought help. The average age of the onset of depression tends to be in the mid-20s. It follows that if there can be early recognition of symptoms, effective treatment may reduce the course of the episode.

Apart from the personal suffering, depression significantly impacts a person's physical health and their social and occupational functioning. Furthermore, the stigma associated with mental illnesses and the worry of being considered "unbalanced" or "weak" is a major deterrent, especially for professionals. This forms a serious barrier to obtaining the necessary help and effective treatment. But we must remember that there is room for optimism. The majority of those who seek help for depression have successful outcomes.

Predisposing Factors
As defined in Table 2, predisposing factors may be divided into "non-modifiable" (uncontrollable) and "modifiable" (controllable) factors.

Treatment
Treatment of depressive disorders can be loosely divided into pharmacological and psychotherapeutic interventions. For mild to moderate depression, the individual's treatment preference is one of the best guides in treatment choice; a previous successful treatment is also a reasonable choice in recurrent depressive episodes. Pharmacologic treatments for depression usually involve antidepressant medications, and there are a number of antidepressants available with relatively tolerable side effects.

Though there are a number of psychotherapies used to treat depression, cognitive-behavioural therapy (CBT) and interpersonal therapy (IPT) are time-limited and manual approaches. CBT focuses on negative thoughts and behaviours and develops countering techniques to reduce psychological distress.

Table 2
Non-Modifiable and Modifiable Factors in Depression

Non-Modifiable Factors	Modifiable Factors
Biological	
• Positive family history of psychiatric disorder, substance use disorder, or suicide	• Physical illnesses associated with depression, such as thyroid disease
• Gender: women are more likely to suffer from a mood disorder	• Treatment of underlying psychiatric conditions
• Other psychiatric diagnoses, such as anxiety disorders	• Good sleep routine
	• Good nutrition and weight control
	• Regular exercise
Psychological and Social	
• Adverse childhood chaotic upbringing	• Modifying maladaptive traits, such as a need for perfection, a marked sense of responsibility, controlling behaviour, chronic low self-esteem or negative view of self
• History of trauma	
• Low socioeconomic status	
• Stressful living circumstances	• Having at least one good friend or person you can depend on
• Unemployment	
• Being single	• Varied coping mechanisms to deal with life stressors
	• Minimizing unhealthy behaviours such as excessive substance use
	• Improving healthy habits

IPT concentrates on social factors and interpersonal problems to alleviate symptoms. Often a combination of medication and psychotherapy is appropriate. Other treatments might include light therapy for a seasonal component.

Barriers to seeking help are particularly important in the case of professionals (Table 3). A colleague may improve the odds of a depressed person receiving help by voicing their concerns. Institutions can reduce barriers to obtaining help by creating an environment that recognizes the importance of mental health and supports those in distress getting treatment.

Table 3
Barriers to Seeking Help for Depression

- Denial or lack of insight

- Worry about confidentiality

- Belief that livelihood wil be lost

- Fear

- Shame

- Stigma

- Minimizing or rationalizing situation

- Absence of hope

- Insurance worries

Specific Relevance to Veterinary Practice

The literature on mental health issues among professionals is in its nascency. At least two studies have examined suicide risk in veterinarians, with the rates for suicide both in men and women exceeding those of the general population. One study showed that suicide rates among veterinarians are higher than rates in medicine and dentistry. Similar to medical physicians, there appears to be a gender distinction, with suicide in men to be at least twice that of the general population. The rate for female veterinarians compared to the females in general is even higher.[9,10]

A recent study, performed in 2000 by the American Veterinary Medical Association (AVMA), looked at wellness issues affecting veterinarians and identified several areas of interest, with the "impaired veterinarian" being a chief concern. Emerging areas of interest were mental health issues as underscored by the following article excerpt:

> *The Committee has broadened its scope to include emerging wellness issues such as depression, stress and burnout, and suicide, and is considering the development of a workshop in the near future that would address the changing face of wellness within the veterinary profession.*[11]

The AVMA wellness committee in 2003 found that an overwhelming 94% of veterinarians felt that wellness issues were important or very important.

Being in a respected profession with a fair degree of control over one's life does not automatically confer immunity from depression. The study of veterinary medicine is exceedingly challenging and may have a negative effect on emotional development and maturity. Table 4 illustrates what can be stressful from students' perspectives.

There has been interest in identifying modifiable stressors in veterinary training. Developing programs to address stress-related problems as well as other mental health issues at the university level is one approach to addressing this complex matter. A program or identified person, within the university or institution, can work collaboratively with existing resources to reduce the impact of illness, impairment, and stigma. Easy access to information about any program or resources can be provided for students and staff. Finally, staff can play an active role in modeling effective coping strategies and being available to mentor trainees.[3,13,14] Having an approach that takes into consideration the individual, the group, and the institution can reduce much of the morbidity from mental illness.

What Can You Do?

Learn about stress and take care of the "BASICS." Stress refers to the situation, and the stress response is your body's attempt to handle it. Nurturing the com-

Table 4
Identified Stressors for Veterinary Students[9,11,12]

Veterinary Student Stressors	Veterinary Practice Stressors
• Debt and financial difficulties	• Perceived lack of control of workload
• Excessive workload	• Long hours
• Unsatisfied personal or family relationships	• Emergencies
• Lack of time for social and recreational activities	• Unexpected deaths/euthanasia
• Competition with peers	• Treatment failures
• Poor personal health	• Diagnostic mistakes
• Physical disabilities	• Client grief
	• Difficult clients
	• Conflict with staff

plex reward pathways of the brain, and having healthy hedonic tone, appears to be involved in increased resiliency. Healthy resiliency requires the **BASICS**.

B stands for body. Take care of your body by eating well, sleeping well, and exercising regularly. If you are having problems with sleep, your gastrointestinal tract, weight, or pain, then make the time to get to a family doctor.

A stands for affect. Be aware of your feelings/emotions and how you react. Recognize when you are anxious, frustrated, or increasingly irritable; take a moment to remember your reasons for wanting to study veterinary medicine, your values, your ideals, and your goals.

S stands for social. How are you treating your friends, family, and coworkers? Are you taking time to socialize, or are you avoiding it and perhaps feeling excluded? What is your support network?

I stands for intellect. How is your thinking? Veterinary medicine is a challenge in reading, digesting, and remembering countless details. Are you coping well intellectually? Are you rigid? Do you harbour resentments? What is your attitude?

C stands for community. We form and inform our community. Young veterinarians are often the force that determines change.

S stands for spirituality. All of us struggle from time to time with "big questions." Changes in our lives and too much stress can challenge our cherished views of the world and of ourselves, and our purpose in being. We need to take time to deliberate, to discuss, and discover our spiritual beliefs and essential humanity.

Veterinary training is time-consuming, and if there are times when you realize you cannot do the BASICS as you would like, remember that this sense of being out of control does not last. It is just as important to recall the BASICS when life becomes more manageable.

References

1.   Charney DS. Psychobiological mechanisms of resilience and vulnerability: Implications for successful adaptation to extreme stress. Am J Psych 2004;161:195-216.

2.   *Why Zebras Don't Get Ulcers. 3rd ed.* Sapolsky RM. Henry Holt and Company, LLC; New York; 2004.

3.   Collins H, Foote D. Managing stress in veterinary students. J Vet Med Ed 2005;32:170-172.

4.   Diagnostic and Statistical Manual of Mental Disorders. 4th edition, American Psychiatric Association, Washington, DC; 1994.

5.   Eaton WW, Anthony JC, Gallo J, *et al.* Natural history of Diagnostic Interview Schedule/DSM-IV depression. The Baltimore Epidemiological Catchment Area follow-up. Arch Gen Psych 1997;54:993-999.

6.   Kessler RC, Berglund P, Chiu WT, *et al.* National Comorbidity Survey Replication. The epidemiology of major depression: results from the National Comorbidity Survey Replication (NCS-R). J Am Med Assoc 2003;289:30953105.

7.   Hollon S, Shelton R, Wisniewski SR, *et al.* Presenting characteristics of depressed outpatients as a function of recurrence: Preliminary findings from the STAR*D clinical trial. J Psych Res 2006;40:59-69.

8.   National Collaborating Center for Mental Health. Depression: Management of depression in primary and secondary care. National Institute for Clinical Excellence; 2004.

9. Halliwell REW, Hoskin BD. Reducing the suicide rate among veterinary surgeons: how the profession can help. Vet Rec 2005;157:397-398.

10. Mellanby RJ. Incidence of suicide in the veterinary profession in England and Wales. Vet Rec 2005;157:415-417.

11. The Results of the Spring 2000 Questionnaire. The Wellness Report: A newsletter of the AVMA Committee on Wellness [fall] 2000:1-4.

12. Gardner GH, Hini D. Work related stress in the veterinary profession in New Zealand. New Zealand Vet J 2006;54:119-124.

13. Gelberg S, Gelberg H. Stress management interventions for veterinary students. J Vet Med Ed 2005;32:173-181.

14. Williams S, Arnold P, Mills J, Todd S, Wilson P, Wright C. Coping with stress: A survey of Murdoch University veterinary students. J Vet Med Ed 2005;32:201-212.

Biography

Dr. Joy Albuquerque joined the PHP in 2004 as the Associate Medical Director. She worked as a family physician prior to completing her psychiatric training. Dr. Albuquerque has extensive experience in general clinical psychiatry and has a special interest on the impact of stress on psychiatric conditions and quality of life. She has published articles in peer-reviewed journals on mood disorders and in the area of disease construction. Her current interests include understanding modifiable risk factors and identifying specific signs of distress among professionals, with the long-term aim of implementing effective interventions. As part of her work with the PHP, Dr. Albuquerque enjoys presenting on topics involving stress, distress, and resiliency as it relates to professionals. Outside of clinical medicine, Dr. Albuquerque pursues long-standing interests in the history and philosophy of medicine.

Substance Abuse and Addiction: Recognition, Intervention, and Recovery

Michael Kaufmann, BSc, MD, CCFP, FCFP, CSAM certified
Director, Physician Health Program,
Ontario Medical Association
Toronto, Ontario

> *Remember that we deal with alcohol—cunning, baffling, powerful! Without help, it is too much for us.*
>
> — "Big Book" of Alcoholics Anonymous

Introduction

The Ontario Medical Association (OMA) Physician Health Program (PHP) was founded in 1995 with an initial mandate to provide assistance to physicians who experience problems with drug and alcohol abuse and addiction. Since its inception, the program has assisted hundreds of health care professionals (including veterinarians) troubled by substance use disorders, and much has been learned about the problem.

Definitions

The salient features of a diagnosis of substance dependence or addiction usually include the inability to control one's use of these substances, preoccupation about using drugs or drinking, continuing to do so despite adverse life consequences, and physiological tolerance and withdrawal symptoms. It is important to view drug or alcohol dependence as a primary disorder that is often progressive and possibly fatal, if left untreated.

Substance abuse is characterized by the repeated, inappropriate use of a mood-altering substance that, in some way, interferes with health and/or quality of life. This diagnosis can be made if substance dependence diagnostic criteria are not met. Substance abuse may progress to dependence if unaddressed. Callers to the PHP who suffer from drug or alcohol problems fall into both categories. Expert assessment is sometimes required to differentiate between substance abuse and dependence.

Prevalence

The prevalence of drug and alcohol problems within the medical profession has been the subject of speculation and misconception. Research indicates that such problems are not likely to be more common among physicians than the general population. In a 1986 review of the issue, author J.M. Brewster stated, *"Extreme statements regarding the prevalence of problems with alcohol and other drugs have often been made without empirical support."*[1] In 1992, Hughes, *et al.* reported that in a survey of more than 9,000 physicians in all specialties, almost 8% reported substance abuse or dependence problems at some time in their lives.[2]

Regardless, if a health care professional is impaired due to a substance use disorder, patient care can be affected, and the health care professional risks serious personal morbidity or even death.

Commonly Abused Substances

It is prudent to regard substance dependence as a single entity, rather than a collection of addictions. The majority of health care professionals treated for addiction acknowledge abusing many drugs and alcohol. Still, alcohol is most often identified as the drug of choice.

Data collected by PHP reveals that 47% of doctors monitored by the program list alcohol as their drug of choice. Of these, half have a history of abusing a range of other drugs as well. Thirty-five percent of the PHP participants were dependent upon opioids as their drug of choice, 7% used cocaine, 5% used sedative and hypnotic drugs, and the remaining 6% used a variety of other drugs, such as cannabis, solvents, and anesthetic agents.

Risk Factors

Although data tend to suggest that substance dependence affects doctors in ways similar to the general population, there are some considerations pertinent to medical professionals that merit discussion.

In 1972, Vaillant, *et al.* reported on the psychological vulnerability of physicians. According to this prospective study, doctors were more likely to experience problems with drugs and alcohol, require psychotherapy, and have marital problems than were other matched non-health-professional controls.[3] The authors believed that physician vulnerability was related to unmet personal needs; some doctors choose a medical career to help themselves by helping others.

While many dispute the existence of a "medical personality," PHP staff has observed personality traits common among health care professionals seeking assistance. These doctors are usually compassionate people, dedicated in the extreme to the well-being of their patients—to their own detriment and often that of their families. They tend to be perfectionists, obsessive, and rigidly self-controlled. Stressed and lacking healthy coping strategies, some find ease and comfort in drugs or alcohol. Thus, the seeds of abuse and dependence are sown, especially when there is a family history of substance use disorders.

Access to mood-altering drugs is another consideration, although not the most important. Self-treatment with prescription drugs is always ill-advised. But self-administration of mood-altering drugs is a dangerous and risky proposition. Anesthetists who self-administer potent opioids (e.g., fentanyl) are a special case illustrating this point, as these drugs are particularly dependency prone. Many doctors experiencing problems with drugs and alcohol are reluctant to request help. They may deny the magnitude of the problem in their lives, just as others around them might deny what they are observing, due to their own discomfort, lack of knowledge about how to help, or other factors. The suffering doctor may also be fearful that to reach out might result in a report to regulatory authorities and represent the end of his or her career. This is seldom the case.

But, together, these factors and others mean that doctors experiencing drug and alcohol problems seldom receive assistance early in the course of the disorder.

Recognition

There is rarely a single observation that will clearly identify an addicted colleague. As with other illnesses, an accurate diagnosis is made by a physician familiar with the signs and symptoms of chemical dependence. Still, there are clues readily apparent in doctors affected by drug or alcohol abuse that can be appreciated by any caring observer, especially if they are familiar with the doctor's baseline behaviour prior to the substance abuse becoming problematic. Many of these observations have been previously described in the Ontario Medical Review.[4]

Generally, the affected health care professional will appear moody, withdrawn, and more irritable than expected. Previously decisive, reliable, and predictable, he or she may have difficulty making decisions, fail to meet professional commitments, and change routines—perhaps arriving at the hospital to do rounds at odd hours. Excessive use of alcohol at social and continuing education events (e.g., conferences), and alcohol on the breath at work, are worrisome signs. Any doctor who insists on administering parenteral narcotics to patients personally, and who has heavy "wastage" of drugs, must be viewed with concern. Addicted doctors often become depressed and, in advanced cases, may make suicidal gestures. Some will be successful. These clues and others are listed in Table 1, originally prepared by Dr. Graeme Cunningham, director of alcohol and drug services at the Homewood Health Centre in Guelph.[5]

It is important to recognize that the suffering doctor is very sensitive to the shame and stigma that accompanies a drug or alcohol problem. Such health care professionals will go to great lengths to conceal their disorder from colleagues, even when they are no longer able to disguise their problems at home. For this reason, observations made in the workplace might well represent illness that is fairly advanced and demanding of immediate attention.

Help

It is not unusual for health care professionals in a community to be aware that one of their colleagues is struggling personally in some way. In the earlier stages, the nature of a problem might not be clear. Caring individuals will offer help. One or two friendly colleagues can approach the doctor and share their observations and concerns. If especially concerned, a clinical resource, such as a psychiatrist or therapist, might be made available in advance of approaching the troubled doctor. An offer to facilitate an appointment with that

Table 1
Signs of Addiction in Health Care Professionals

Personality change

Loss of efficiency and reliability

Increased sick time and other time away from work

Patient and staff complaints about physician's changing attitude/behaviour

Indecision

Increasing personal and professional isolation

Physical changes

Unpredictable work habits and patterns

Moodiness, anxiety, depression, suicidal thoughts or gestures

Memory loss

Uncharacteristic deterioration of handwriting and charting

Unexpected presence in hospital when off-duty

Heavy "wastage" of drugs

Inappropriate prescription of large narcotic doses

Insistence on personal administration of parenteral narcotics to patients

Long sleeves when inappropriate

Frequent bathroom use

Alcohol on the breath

Wide mood swings

resource is an affirmative, helpful action. It is also necessary to follow-up with the doctor to verify that positive action has been taken and to affirm support.

Unfortunately, in the case of the addicted doctor, denial is often present. This often results in deliberate, conscious deception of others, as well as less conscious self-deceit and minimization of the severity of the problem. Dependent health care professionals also likely feel guilt and shame about what they have done and how they see themselves as a result of their illness. When these psychological forces are at play, the doctor who is confronted in an informal manner, no matter how well-intentioned and thorough, may not respond favourably.

Two myths must be confronted when considering addicted doctors. The first is that they must "want help" before intervention is successful. The second is that they must "hit bottom" before they will be receptive to assistance. These myths represent serious misconceptions. Confronting an impaired colleague, while difficult, must be done swiftly and competently. It can be a life-saving action.

The process of helpful confrontation is called intervention. It has been well described by Vernon Johnson and others, and an outline of the intervention process has been published in the Ontario Medical Review.[6,7] Intervention should be carried out as early as possible when impairment due to substance abuse is suspected. The intervention, which must be properly planned and re-hearsed, is conducted by at least two individuals in a position of importance in the affected physician's life (such as a partner, department head, or chief of staff). Sometimes family members are also involved. The dependent physician is presented with objective, documented evidence of his or her behaviour of concern in a caring but firm manner. The minimum goal of the intervention is to motivate the physician to follow through with an expert clinical assessment, arranged in advance.

Sometimes, in more advanced cases, the preferred outcome is to discontinue clinical practice immediately following the intervention and enter treatment directly. An expertly conducted and highly motivational intervention will likely yield the preferred result. Still, many impaired health care professionals thus confronted will resist assessment and treatment, preferring to handle the problem themselves in their own way. Such measures usually fail.

The PHP believes that it is essential for interveners to be prepared to notify regulatory authorities in some way if the dependent health care professional refuses to comply with the intervention. Outlining a clear consequence for lack of compliance usually results in the desired outcome. Some suggest that such an intervention, especially if there is a "threat" to notify authorities, places the suffering doctor at risk of suicide. This risk is minimized by arranging helping resources in advance and making sure that the time from intervention to assessment or treatment is short. Sometimes this is achieved by escorting the doctor to treatment directly from the intervention. At the least, interveners and other caring individuals should remain in close contact with the doctor until his or her safety is ensured. To do less is not acceptable. For a more complete description on effective intervention, see

Chapter 8-5 in this section titled *After the Call: Accessing Substance Abuse Assistance Programs.*

Health care professionals have a moral and ethical obligation to do their best to help dependent colleagues, even if the actions taken on a colleague's behalf are personally difficult. The PHP is available to offer advice about intervention or to participate directly when required.

Treatment: Substance Abuse and Addiction

Health care professionals who have been diagnosed with substance abuse (but not dependence) benefit from education about the benefits of abstinence or low-risk use of mood-altering substances. An addiction medicine physician, knowledgeable family physician, or other substance abuse professional can provide this information.

Once a substance dependence/addiction diagnosis is confirmed, treatment programs designed specifically for the physician/patient are available. Inpatient treatment is not always required, but it is the norm when a period of detoxification or a respite from medical practice, personal circumstances, and stress is required. It is often difficult for health care professionals to assume the role of patient, and inpatient programs designed specifically for health care professionals and other health professionals can facilitate this transition. Most inpatient facilities do not segregate health care professionals in treatment, but rather they offer therapy groups for health professionals in parallel to those offered for the entire patient population. These groups give recovering doctors an opportunity to address special issues arising from their professional lives.

Inpatient treatment is followed by formal aftercare that lasts several months to several years. Recovering doctors are usually encouraged to make use of community-based mutual help programs (e.g., Alcoholics Anonymous) or other 12-step or similar programs. Most also attend peer support groups (often called Caduceus groups), where they join other health professionals in recovery. These and other elements of a comprehensive recovery program are listed in Table 2.

Special mention should be made of the addicted health care professional's family. Addiction affects the entire family, and programs exist that provide education, counseling, and support for spouses and other family

Table 2
Components of a Recovery Program

Outpatient aftercare: group and individual therapy

Caduceus peer support group

Mutual help group: Alcoholics Anonymous (AA), Narcotics Anonymous, International Doctors in AA (IDAA), Women for Sobriety

Pharmacotherapy (e.g., disulfiram, naltrexone)

Proper nutrition

Regular exercise

Healthy spiritual life

Healthy balance between work, rest, and leisure activities

Assessment and treatment of concurrent problems (e.g., psychiatric, marital)

Family treatment and support

Rigorous monitoring, including random body fluid analyses

members. An untreated and unsupported family suffers needlessly and can predispose a relapse into addictive behaviour by the health care professional.

Monitoring

In Ontario and many other North American jurisdictions, there are formal monitoring programs that recovering doctors may use to enhance their recovery program. Monitoring includes regular interviews to ascertain the health status of the recovering individual, as well as to encourage full compliance with all prescribed recovery activities. Progress reports are received from treating clinicians, and random urine toxicology screens are performed.

The PHP conducts such a comprehensive monitoring program, which also provides case management services and advocacy for the doctor in recovery. These programs usually continue for five years or longer.

Outcomes

The prevalence and expression of substance use disorders in health care professionals is much like that in the general population. But outcomes, especially among those doctors enrolled in monitoring programs, are better. The PHP experience to date reveals that of the first 100 doctors monitored in recovery, more than 70% have enjoyed sustained remission of their substance dependence, never experiencing a relapse. There are similar reports from many other jurisdictions.

Substance dependence is, nevertheless, a disease of relapse. Relapse, when it occurs, should be treated seriously and promptly. Breaks in abstinence can be minor or life-threatening. Once again, careful monitoring goes a long way toward prevention and early detection of relapse events. The experience of relapse can be helpful to the recovery process, pointing out untreated problems or revealing components of the recovery program that need strengthening. The majority of doctors who experience relapse make the appropriate adjustments and continue to enjoy good health. In fact, it has been the experience of the PHP that more than 90% of the health care professionals monitored return to excellent health and productivity.

Conclusion

Substance use disorders affect health care professionals just as they affect members of the general population. Medical training does not confer immunity, nor does it result in excessive risk. Denial (by health care professional, family, and colleagues) is a major symptom and a significant obstacle to timely diagnosis and treatment. Thoughtful intervention does work, and effective treatment is available. Once the addictive disorder is in remission, sustained abstinence, productivity, and healthy lifestyles are the expected norm. There are also treatment and support programs for families of recovering doctors.

Recovery from chemical dependence means improved physical, psychological, and emotional health. Social lives are improved and families are rebuilt. Even matters of the spirit flourish. This is the beauty of recovery.

So it falls to each of us as health care professionals to care about the well-being of our colleagues, to be watchful for signs of drug or alcohol problems, and to be prepared to respond. With respect to this problem, we really are our brothers' and sisters' keepers.

References

1. Brewster JM. Prevalence of alcohol and other drug problems among health care professionals. J Am Med Assoc 1986;255:1913-1920.
2. Hughes PH, Brandenburg N, Baldwin DC, *et al.* Prevalence of substance use among U.S. physicians. J Am Med Assoc 1992;267:2333-2339.
3. Vaillant G, Sobowale MC, McArthur C. Some psychologic vulnerabilities of physicians. New Eng J Med 1972;287:372-375.
4. Kaufmann M. Recognizing the signs and symptoms of distress. Ont Med Rev 1999;66:46-47. www. phpoma.org/pdf/May99.pdf.
5. Cunningham GM. Paying attention to substance abuse in physicians. Can J Diagn 1993;10:76-88.
6. *I'll Quit Tomorrow.* Johnson VE. Harper and Row; New York, NY; 1980.
7. Kaufmann M. After the call: the Physician Health Program referral and intervention process. Ont Med Rev 1999;66:54-56. www.phpoma. org/pdf/Mar99.pdf.

Additional Recommended Reading

Talbott GD, Gallegos KV, Angres DH. Impairment and Recovery in Physicians and Other Health Professionals. In: *Principles of Addiction Medicine.* American Society of Addiction Medicine, Chevy Chase, Maryland; 1998.

All Physician Health and related columns published in the Ontario Medical Review are posted on the Physician Health Program Web site: www.phpoma.org/articles.html.

Biography

For Dr. Kaufman's biography, please see the Section 8 Introduction on page 507.

After the Call: Accessing Substance Abuse Assistance Programs

Michael Kaufmann, BSc, MD, CCFP, FCFP, CSAM certified
Director, Physician Health Program,
Ontario Medical Association,
Toronto, Ontario

> *Sometimes it's not so much seeing the light as feeling the heat.*
>
> — Anonymous

Introduction

Health-care professionals, regardless of the species or discipline upon which they focus, are at risk for substance abuse. This risk is due to the often long-hours worked, neglect of overall life balance, and easy access to restricted substances. Self-recognition of a potential substance-abuse problem is the first step in the process of recovery. However, taking the initiative of seeking assistance often is delayed or halted due to uncertainty over the process involved, particularly over fear of public humiliation (whether from friends, colleagues, or the community in which s/he lives). This fear applies equally to friends and colleagues, who are willing to intervene on behalf of the troubled individual, but concerned over "making things worse." However, the various programs in place have defined protocols designed to encourage participation for those in need, based on mutual trust and confidentiality.

Various programs are available with information easily accessible through provincial veterinary medical associations. In this chapter, I will use the Physician Health Program (PHP) to highlight the processes in place that are common to all substance-abuse assistance programs. From a veterinary perspective, the PHP is also available to veterinarians in Ontario; in Nova Scotia, the Physician Support Program also services veterinarians; for other provinces and territories, information on assistance programs is available through the respective provincial veterinary medical association.

Denial

Your colleague always has been the "life of the party." At social events and continuing education meetings, he drinks more than everyone else. And twice, lately, you have had to drive him home. You aren't aware of any problems specifically relating to his drinking, but rumours suggest his marriage is in trouble. You aren't sure what you should do, if anything. An opportunity arises to talk to him. Despite your discomfort, you take him aside and ask if he has a problem with alcohol. He becomes upset and denies any problem. He says he likes to drink, but never when he is working. He leaves, and you feel nothing has been accomplished.

Physicians suffering from drug- or alcohol-abuse frequently experience such significant denial that they are not capable of seeking out help on their own. Intelligent, carefully selected for medical training, knowledgeable about drugs and therapeutics, some physicians may feel immune from the perils of substance dependency. Once in trouble, embarrassment, shame, and fear of losing one's medical license or privileges, fuel the fires of personal denial. Families also may deny the problem for a time, fearing loss of status and economic stability. As the illness progresses—finally appearing in the workplace— more denial is encountered.

Health-related institutions deny such problems exist, and seldom are policies in place to deal with impaired staff. Very few offer education about impairment prevention, detection, and management. Colleagues may deny a problem in their midst. They don't want to upset the troubled doctor, risk his or her professional status, lose a partner who shares practice costs and workloads, or risk retribution if they do act. Some colleagues may have personal or family issues that generate uncomfortable feelings when they suspect drug or alcohol problems in a co-worker.

Obligation

You call the PHP with your concerns. Advised to speak to a colleague in a position of authority, you learn from the chief of staff that other reports of possible impairment have been filed.

The Canadian Medical Association (CMA) Code of Ethics contains several references to physicians' obligation to themselves, their patients, and colleagues to practice medicine free of impairment. In addition, they have an obligation to report any unprofessional conduct by colleagues (such as practicing while impaired) to appropriate authorities. In Ontario, the Regulated Health Professions Act states that any physician who has employment or hospital privileges interrupted due to impairment, or who resigns to avoid these consequences, must be reported to the College of Physicians and Surgeons of Ontario (CPSO).

Confidentiality

All calls to the PHP regarding impairment, or even suspected problems regarding a physician colleague, are kept confidential unless otherwise dictated by law (e.g., records subpoenaed by the court or in cases involving suspected child abuse). A caller's name is never revealed without first obtaining the caller's permission. The PHP never reports concerns expressed by a caller at the point of intake to any authority, including hospitals and the CPSO; this applies for veterinarians and their licensing body as well. Program staff simply will advise the caller about his or her responsibilities as previously described. No "down side" exists to calling the PHP with concerns, or for advice.

Intervention

The chief of staff calls the PHP and an intervention is planned. Documentation is reviewed, and participants who share your concerns are selected. Then, joined by a representative of the PHP, you all meet with the doctor one morning in the hospital boardroom. The process is essentially the same for veterinarians however, rather than the chief of staff, the process usually involves partners or senior administrators from the veterinary facility.

A physician's illness is advanced by the time s/he appears impaired in the workplace. The affected physician is using all available energy to maintain an appearance of normal health and job functioning. Family and friends are bound up already with their own losses, pain, and denial. Intervention is the necessary process that must be undertaken by colleagues to avoid further enabling this destructive condition. Presuming the suffering physician is not willing to call for help on his or her own, the PHP works with referral sources toward a safe and effective intervention. Following is a listing of conditions that help promote a successful outcome:

- The intervention is conducted by more than one individual (i.e., a team). This team is led by someone knowledgeable about the process and, whenever possible, also is trained and experienced.
- Other members of the team share concern for the doctor and are respected by him or her.
- Interveners are taught that intervention is a caring, compassionate procedure. It is not punitive.
- Interveners are screened and prepared, so that they understand the documented concerns. They are firmly like-minded regarding the intervention outcome goals.
- The intervention is rehearsed. Defensive responses should be anticipated and prepared for in advance.
- Time and place selection is critical. Whenever possible, a time should be chosen that minimizes the likelihood that the physician will be intoxicated. The site should be calm, quiet, and available for as long as is required.
- Specific assessment and/or treatment resources have been identified previously and are made available to the physician immediately following the intervention.
- A support system of family, friends, and colleagues should be identified prior to the intervention, and made available to the physician upon completion of the intervention.
- Sufficient time must be taken to gather appropriate documentation of concerns, then to plan and execute the intervention.
- Appropriate contingencies, if any, for non-compliance with the intervention recommendations must be specified clearly. If non-compliance results, the contingencies must be implemented and enforced.

It is the role of the PHP to facilitate, and participate in, this process. We help identify appropriate interveners, gather documentation, and guide the process. We protect the physician's confidentiality by speaking only to those who contact us. We arrange assessment and treatment resources. We work with callers on their terms.

Participants, in turn, share observations. The chief of staff explains that he expects the doctor to proceed promptly to undergo expert assessment of his health and alcohol use. The assessment already has been arranged by the PHP. The chief of staff is prepared to recommend interim suspension of hospital privileges if the doctor refuses, mandating a report to the CPSO. The doctor agrees to the assessment process.

With the doctor's permission, the PHP meets with his wife to explain the assessment process and offer support. A detailed history of the impact of the doctor's drinking now can be obtained.

PHP staff members understand that this is a very difficult and emotional process for the interveners, as well as the suffering doctor. We will "debrief" intervention participants afterward, and remain available as a support for those who need it. We will offer support to spouses and family members. We know that successful intervention leads to successful treatment and quality recovery for the majority of physicians who suffer from chemical dependency. We know it's worth it.

Barriers

Usually, callers to the PHP are reluctant to do anything more than receive advice. They may feel their concerns are minor. They don't understand, or accept, that even "minimal" signs suggesting drug or alcohol abuse in the workplace may indicate advanced disease. This general lack of understanding about how the problem can be managed effectively is a serious barrier to action.

Reporting physicians may fear retribution. They don't understand that outcomes are favourable and recovering physicians express gratitude, not resentment. Litigation following intervention is rare, and not likely to be successful, should it occur after action taken in good faith. Some physicians believe that a suffering colleague must "want help" before intervention is likely to be successful. This is a myth. Waiting allows the disease to progress and possibly to be fatal.

Colleagues may resist using "clout." They may not want to report an impaired physician to institutional or regulatory authorities, for fear that the doctor will lose his or her licence and livelihood. They don't understand that hospitals and the CPSO (and veterinary licensing bodies, as well) embrace rehabilitation, and not a punitive approach, for dealing with impaired medical professionals. Sometimes, colleagues may not be able to overcome their personal experiences with alcoholism or drug addiction in their own families—the PHP can help in these cases as well.

Outcome

The assessment process results in a diagnosis of alcohol dependency and the doctor enters treatment. Upon discharge, he enrolls in the PHP monitoring and advocacy program. Three months after the intervention, he returns to work clean and sober.

Summary

Intervention works. When properly planned, executed, and with contingencies in place, the majority of physicians experiencing intervention go on to assessment and, often, treatment. It has been the experience of the PHP that interventions fail mostly when no consequences threaten a physician's right to practice medicine. The PHP tries to avoid an intervention without clout.

Once treated, physicians in recovery do very well. Over 90 per cent of the physicians monitored by the PHP remain abstinent from drugs and alcohol, and are enjoying improving physical, emotional, and professional health and productivity. Some of them have caring and compassionate colleagues, who overcame the barriers and personal discomfort inherent in intervention, in order to help them on their way to recovery.

Where impairment is concerned, intervention can be a life-saving procedure. In this regard, we are indeed our brothers' (and sisters') keepers. Make the call.

Additional Recommended Reading

Talbott GD, Gallegos KV. Intervention with health professionals. Addiction and Recovery, 1990;10:13-16.

Biography

For Dr. Kaufman's biography, please see the Section 8 Introduction on page 507.

8-6

Emotional Intelligence for Veterinary Professionals

Patsy Marshall, MSc, BASc
President, Train On Track,
Guelph, Ontario

> *It's often our attitude, not our aptitude,
> which determines our altitude in life!*
>
> — Anonymous

Introduction

The introductory quote above relates to emotional intelligence, and it is as relevant today as it was over 150 years ago. As a professional, it is imperative to be in touch with your mind, body, and spirit and to heed warning signs if one, two, or all three of the above are not in sync. Individuals employed in veterinary medicine need to be up-to-date in their skills; possess physical, mental, emotional, and spiritual health (this may not involve organized religion); experience a balance between family, work, and social life; and have a passion for the vocation.

Veterinary medicine professionals need to appreciate the importance and relevance of balancing medical, surgical, and technical abilities with important life skills such as collaboration, personal leadership, and emotional intelligence (EI)—often measured as an Emotional Intelligence Quotient (EQ). According to Daniel Goleman, EI is not about IQ (Intellectual Quotient) but about an ability, capacity, or skill to perceive, assess, and manage the emotions of one's self, of others and how well they work in a team, and our ability to lead other people.[1] With equal intellectual and technical competencies, the way of engagement with others makes a huge difference to fulfillment. People who rise to the top of their field—whether it be psychology, law, veterinary medicine, teaching, or engineering—aren't just good at their jobs; they are affable, flexible, resilient, confident, and optimistic. Leaders and business owners, in particular, require high EI, because they represent the organization to the public, they interact with the highest number of people within and outside the organization, and they set the tone for employee morale. This chapter will look at the five dimensions of EI (selfawareness, self-regulation, self-motivation, empathy, and social skill/nurturing relationships) as they relate to overall well-being and business success.

Self-Awareness

Self-awareness implies being aware "in the moment" of what you are feeling and thinking. Since the 1950s, psychologists have been aware that professionals need to be in touch with their emotions and how to express them constructively. If not, misunderstandings, frustrations, and inner wounds relating to self-esteem tend to surface and may lead to implosion (e.g., developing headaches, gastrointestinal problems, anxieties, depression, addictions, etc.) and/or explosion (e.g., becoming irritable, having outbursts, becoming aggressive, etc.). Regardless of degree, implosions and explosions are painful and risky and may even lead to serious health problems or a lawsuit. They diminish (at times even annihilate) the efficiency and effectiveness of the individual professional and the practice team, who may not be fully functioning because of strained relationships. Your emotions are present all the time, just like your body, soul, brain, and heartbeat. Listen to your heart, not just your head!

Self-Regulation

Self-regulation involves having the skills to be able to choose the emotions you want to experience, while not letting others "push your buttons." Self-regulation relies on the ability to suspend judgment and to think through the consequences of a behaviour. It is the choice or decision made between the stimulus and the response! Self-regulation includes the capability to bounce back quickly and to soothe or comfort yourself.

Self-Motivation

Self-motivation is the ability to stifle impulses, direct emotions toward achievement of goals, and delay gratification. Professionals with high self-motivation use their emotions to take positive action, to think critically, to be confident, and to persistently pursue goals even in the face of significant adversity or difficulty. They are accountable and disciplined and appreciate autonomy as well as working within a team approach.

Empathy

Empathy is not to be confused with sympathy; it involves possessing the ability to listen effectively and accurately enough to put yourself in the other person's shoes. Having empathy does not necessarily mean you agree with the other person, but you truly understand the situation from the other's point of view in order to improve communication, problem solving, and trust. Individuals who possess strong empathic skills are aware of and are able to respond favourably to the needs of others by showing compassion, understanding, and forgiveness. They are also astute to nonverbal communication and recognize its tremendous significance to understanding feelings as well as thoughts.

Social Skill

Social skill involves managing the emotions of others and the ability to nurture relationships. It is crucial, through word and deed, to demonstrate appreciation for people's efforts and contributions. Those individuals high in social skill are able to set a positive tone of cooperation no matter how difficult the situation or conversation, because they are able to manage their own emotions and the emotions of others. They truly have the best interests and emotions/feelings of others in mind while focusing on achieving goals to create win-win outcomes.

Test Yourself

To determine your EI score based on these five dimensions, you may go on-line to http://ei.haygroup.com/resources/content-ieitest.html or http://www.helpself.com/iq-teat.htm

The Importance of EI

Why is EI so important? According to an online article entitled, "Self-Help Tips for Professionals – Why Emotional Intelligence is Important?" here are the 10 reasons:[2]

1. Your career success depends on it—75% of careers are derailed for reasons related to emotional incompetence.
2. Emotional intelligence can impact your client retention—70% of the reasons why customers and clients are lost are EI related.
3. Potential effect on your business success—50% of time wasted in business is due to lack of trust.
4. Educational success is related to EI. Low levels of empathy predict poor scholastic performance.
5. Intelligent people also need EI. Veterinary medicine practitioners require both technical and affective skills.
6. Medical professionals need to diagnose their EI. Professionals with poor EI get sued more often.
7. People need EI from each other. Empathy is comforting to both recipient and provider.
8. Lack of EI can be fatal. It can lead to debilitating health and even death.
9. Health care feels the effects—75% to 90% of visits to primary care physicians in the United States and Canada are due to stress-related problems.
10. Emotional intelligence can balance your life. Enjoy your family, your career, your relationships, and your life!

Variations in EI

Goleman states that different jobs call for different types of EI.[1] Professionals in veterinary medicine require the empathic ability to gauge a customer's mood, whether it be the animal itself or the owner, and the interpersonal skills to discern when to recommend a course of treatment and when to keep quiet. By comparison, success in painting or professional tennis requires a more individual form of self-discipline and motivation.

Stein found that after administering EQ assessments to 4500 men and 3200 women, that women score higher than men on empathy and social responsibility, but men outperform women on stress tolerance and self-confidence measures.[3] Women and men are equally as intelligent emotionally, yet they are strong in different areas. Patterns of EI are not fixed. Those who wish can boost their EQ by building their emotional abilities where they are lacking. This enhancement can occur through education, training, practice, and reinforcement. For example, women can hone their assertiveness skills and can learn stress management techniques such as meditation, yoga, time-use management, and swimming. Men can learn the importance of listening to coworkers and customers, reading their moods, and winning their trust—all of which are increasingly important aspects of leadership, teamwork, customer service, and lifestyle change.

Remember, EI is NOT about being soft! It is a different way of being smart and having the skill to use your emotions to make choices in-themoment and have more effective control over yourself, your impact on animals, and relationships with others.

Conclusion

Professionals need to take care of both tasks and relationships. It is important to develop a capacity for working with, even honouring, differences in people. Each person has a unique journey of life that may be surprising, intriguing, or frustrating. Creating a synergy between intellectual, technical, and emotional competencies will increase overall well-being of each professional on the team. Improved EI gives those in veterinary medicine the chance of becoming more at ease, competent, and efficient in providing the very best care to animals and to humans (including themselves).

References

1. *Emotional Intelligence: Why it Can Matter More Than IQ.* Goleman D. Bantam Books; New York; 1995.
2. Dunn S. Why Emotional Intelligence is Important. http://www.pldynamics.com/archived-self-help-tips-3.php
3. *The EQ Edge: Emotional Intelligence and Your Success.* Stein SJ, Book HE. Stoddard Publishing Co.; Toronto; 2000.

Additional Recommended Reading

Apter N. Emotional Intelligence. <u>UNSPECIAL</u> No 610, September 2002.

Murray B. Does Emotional intelligence matter in the workplace? Amer Psychol Assoc 1998;29.

Timmins RP. How does emotional intelligence fit into the paradigm of veterinary medical education? J Vet Med Ed 2006;33:71-75.

"Who Needs Emotional Intelligence Skills?" http://www.byronstock.com/home.html

Biography

Patsy Marshall has held positions in all employment areas: entrepreneur, private sector, public sector, and not-for-profit. She has been the President of her own training and development company for 13 years. Patsy has extensive adult education experience - 29 years with Conestoga College and she also presently teaches with the University of Guelph, the University of Waterloo, and Brock University in their Bachelor of Education program. She has held full-time positions as Manager of Training and Development with Sun Life, Director of Education with Homewood Health Centre, and Executive Director of the Lung Association, Wellington Chapter.

Patsy has a MSc degree and a BASc degree from the University of Guelph. She is not only a business owner and teacher/trainer, but also a keynote speaker and author. In addition, she has always supported her community and presently volunteers with several organizations. In July 2006 she was given a Paul Harris Award from Rotary International for her exemplary volunteer commitment to her community and to Rotary.

Break Away From Work: The Restorative Value of Effective Vacationing

Michael Kaufmann, BSc, MD, CCFP, FCFP, CSAM certified
Director, Physician Health Program,
Ontario Medical Association,
Toronto, Ontario

> *Take a rest; a field that has rested gives a bountiful crop.*
>
> — Ovid

Well, doctor, what did you do on your summer vacation? Chances are you took one. In fact, an Ontario Medical Association (OMA) survey conducted in 2003[1] discovered that Ontario doctors, on average, take a little more than four weeks of vacation time per year. But we also work very hard. The same survey reported that, collectively, we work an average of nearly 65 hours per week, excluding on-call time! The Canadian Medical Association (CMA) Physician Resource Questionnaire (PRQ) for 2001 reported that a majority (64%) of Canadian doctors believe their workload is heavier than they would like it to be, and that their personal and family lives have suffered because they were physicians (58%).[2] And last year's PRQ suggested that nearly half the doctors surveyed were experiencing advanced stages of burnout.[3]

Medical practice can insinuate itself into our time away from the office or hospital as well. Of course, when we're on-call, we're tense, waiting for the phone to ring, prepared to spring into action—even if we're sleeping—when the call comes in. In a sense, we're very much at work while on-call. In Ontario, doctors are on-call an average of 46 hours per week, actually working 11 of those hours.[1] Add these to the 65 hours mentioned above, and it's hard not to conclude that doctors are an overworked lot. Similar work figures have been published for veterinary medicine as well, indicating that regardless of whether one is an MD or DVM, the term "overworked" applies equally to both medical callings.

Even when not at work or on-call, it can be difficult to stop thinking or worrying about our patients and other work-related problems. I wonder if four weeks of vacation per year is enough! Just what is a vacation? My Funk and Wagnall's dictionary defines *vacation* as "an interlude, usually of several days or weeks, from one's customary duties, as for recreation or rest." Sounds good. Of course, it doesn't explain how important that interlude is, how to arrange it, or how to make the most of it. So, as my summer ends— and with it go the memories of my vacation in early July—I thought it appropriate to consider the *vacation* a little more carefully.

All work and no play is not a good thing. In Japan, a country with a culture that values long hours of dedicated work, the people have a word for the phenomenon of death caused by overwork: karoshi. The Japanese describe such death to be caused by cardiovascular diseases, peptic ulcer disease, asthma, and suicide, among others.[4] Dr. Mel Borins, family physician, psychotherapist, author, world traveler, and friend, cited the Framingham study in his book entitled, *Go Away Just For the Health of It*. The study reported that women who take fewer vacations than others had an increased risk of suffering heart attacks and cardiac mortality.[5] Let's face it. Work is stressful for most, and prolonged work without relief renders that stress toxic. Therefore, vacations—real opportunities for departure, both physical and mental—are a good idea.

I'd like to focus briefly on this latter notion and look at how we spend our vacation opportunities. Are they always genuine departures from work? I don't have research to cite in this instance, but I certainly have personal observations and experience. I believe doctors' personalities make it difficult to really break away from work. So, during our time off, we allow work to "contaminate" our breaks. Catching up on medical reading, taking files with us, checking e-mail (hard to resist those Internet cafes and airport kiosks) and voice messages, even attending continuing education events in combination with vacation (a personal favourite) detract from the restorative value of a true departure from work.

Wayne and Mary Sotile, who are consultants, counselors, and therapists, recognize the value of effective vacation as one strategy physicians can use to enhance their resilience.[6] They recommend that physicians use their resources to take vacations and use them wisely as times of play. They also remind us of the value of spending vacation time with family, reporting that the families of physicians they counsel value the memories of their physician-parents during vacations—the only times they saw their parents truly relaxed and playful.

So, we probably don't take as much genuinely restorative time off as we should. Why not? There are many barriers to effective vacationing. Travel vacations cost money. And in a fee-for-service environment, time off is time without pay. For many doctors, "carving out" time away from medical practice and patient demands is difficult. Locums to cover medical practices for any length of time are hard to find, and we are loathe to "saddle" our colleagues with our practice demands. Then, of course, there is the onslaught awaiting our return that prompts us to wonder why we ever took a break in the first place.

Finally, the culture of medicine in which we trained and continue to work, teaches us to value our long hours of hard work and devotion to our patients, even if it means sacrificing our personal needs. This is a hard one to overcome. But overcome it we must, if we truly seek the work/life balance and the personal and family health that are required to extract the most from our human journey—including, ironically, optimal professional performance.

So below are some ideas about effective vacationing.

- Going away is a good idea. A change of environment and exposure to new people, cultures, and interests are marvellous distractions from work and from the pervasive and intrusive thoughts work bestows upon us.
- Vacations to locales away from home can be romantic interludes with our partners or be times enjoyed with our children (but seldom both, the Sotiles suggest, so plan accordingly[6]).
- Vacations offer opportunities for healthy physical activity, such as golf, hiking, water sports, skiing, etc.
- Hobbies such as photography, collecting (anything), or painting (art, not houses) can be indulged, stimulated, and developed while on vacation.
- Social connections are made or restored when on vacation.

These are all good things. Dr. Borins reminds us that where there is a will, there is a way to plan and enjoy getting away from home and office. He offers many suggestions to address practical and financial concerns that may block vacation planning, such as traveling by bus, lodging with friends and family, and more.

Can we vacation effectively at home? I believe so, but this can be more difficult. For many of us, home is close to work and our patients, increasing the temptation to incompletely sever that connection. And, if there is a home office set-up, deliberate strategies barring access are likely required. (On one such attempt to vacation at home, my wife had to seal the door to the home office with duct tape and post a sign there stating that access was forbidden until the vacation ended.) But home is where our friends and social networks are, our recreation, and likely, interesting attractions and venues that others come to see. Why not try being tourists in your own backyard? Remember, effective vacation time is not meant to be spent on household chores, arranging to take the kids to camp or university, or going to dental appointments. You might use it that way, but it's unlikely you'll arrive back in the office feeling rested as a result.

Then there's doing nothing, or nothing in particular. That's hard to contemplate, especially for focused, task-oriented professionals. Just imagine meandering randomly through the day, pressure free, like a dust particle in the air. Sit and listen, re-read a favourite novel, paint a chair, play with the dog, go for a bike ride with your spouse, swing in the park with your kids, sleep in the hammock. Delicious.

What about returning to work after a vacation break? Again, the Sotiles have some good advice.[6] They remind us that the relaxation and rejuvenation benefits of a good vacation can be quickly erased by a work binge immediately upon return. Many physicians find it helpful to use the last day or two of vacation time to "re-enter" gradually. This allows time to check messages, review events that occurred while away, and catch up on mail and paperwork before resuming a full schedule.

How much vacation is enough vacation, and how often? I don't know. I suspect that this depends on the individual, tolerance to stress, enjoyment of work, occupational realities, personal interests, family circumstances, and so on. But we probably need more than four weeks of genuine vacation, and it needs to be properly spaced. One vacation per year is not likely going to offer restorative value that lasts. Many would prefer to vacation about every three to four months. Even the anticipation of a vacation, the knowledge that our next break isn't far off, is valuable. Dr. Mamta Gautam, psychiatrist and specialist in physician health, and others, have offered the "Tarzan Principle" of vacation planning: Never complete one vacation without knowing when the next one will be.[7]

So, to quote Dr. Borins: *"Go away just for the health of it."* Close the office door, change the message on the voice mail greeting, turn the computer off, stow the pager and the Blackberry, and take a vacation. We deserve them. We need them.

References

1.   Ontario Medical Association Human Resource Committee (OHRC), Survey of Ontario Physicians; 2003.
2.   Canadian Medical Association. 2001 Physician Resource Questionnaire. Ottawa, ON: Canadian Medical Association; 2001. Available from: http://www.cmaj.ca/cgi/data/ 165/5/626/DC1/33. Accessed: August 30, 2004.
3.   Canadian Medical Association. 2003 Physician Resource Questionnaire. Ottawa, ON: Canadian Medical Association; 2003. Available from: http://www.cmaj.ca/cgi/data/ 169/7/701/DC1/34. Accessed: August 30, 2004.
4.   Nishiyama K, Johnson JV. Karoshi—death from overwork: Occupational health consequences of Japanese production management. Int J Health Serv 1997;27:625-641.
5.   *Go Away Just for the Health of It.* Borins M. Wholistic Press; Toronto, Ontario; 2000.
6.   Sotile WM, Sotile MO. The resilient physician: Effective emotional management for doctors & their medical organizations. American Medical Association; Chicago, Illinois; 2001.
7.   *Iron Doc: Practical Stress Management Tools for Physicians.* Gautam M. Book Coach Press; Ottawa, Ontario; 2004.

Biography

For Dr. Kaufmann's biography, please see the Section 8 Introduction on page 507.

CHAPTER 8-8

Giving Something Back

John Tait, BSc, DVM, MBA, CFP, ADR
Managing Partner, Ontario Veterinary Group,
Toronto, Ontario
Assistant Professor, Ontario Veterinary College,
Guelph, Ontario

> *Real unselfishness consists in sharing the interests of others.*
>
> — Ovid

One of the questions that the profession of veterinary medicine will face over the years to come is, "Who will lead the profession?" Whether it be self-interest veterinary medical associations (VMAs), regulatory bodies, or veterinary colleges, the profession will need volunteers to contribute their expertise and forward thinking in a variety of areas and to represent the profession on issues of the day.

Without representation from all parties of the profession, including various areas of practice (e.g., species interest, geographic location) and career stages/ages, moving the profession forward with a depth of informed opinion will be a difficult task.

While volunteering to be part of "organized" veterinary medicine does take up time and represents an "opportunity cost," it can be a very rewarding experience to participate in shaping the future direction of the profession. I would encourage everyone to become involved—if even for a short period of time—at some level, over some topic, project, or initiative. Your efforts and time can often facilitate positive short- and long-term change for the betterment of the profession. Organized veterinary medicine needs everybody from students to retired veterinarians to be involved, or the profession's voice will be weakened by fragmentation, equating to missed opportunities and a stagnating profession.

Participation has its benefits. It allows you to become exposed to the most current knowledge, issues, and controversies—and, best of all, it allows you to take a leadership role in addressing those issues and controversies. The networking opportunities are abundant, and volunteering provides an opportunity to meet and work with other like-minded individuals and groups, learn about other organizations and their roles, and learn many skills that will augment your development and maturation as a veterinarian—no matter what career path you choose. For many career advancement paths, volunteering also brings added credibility and an enhanced skill and knowledge set.

I recommend spending some time doing a bit of due diligence on any voluntary role that you may be considering. Ask current or former members in the same role about their experience and time commitment; research the organization or group to review their mission and values, to see if they are compatible with your own; and check your own availability and time that you are able to commit. In the early stages of assuming a volunteer position, avoid over-committing to a lot of extra committee work and participation in multiple projects until you feel comfortable with your role and the time commitment involved.

New graduates and students often feel they are not experienced or well versed enough on issues to be valuable volunteers to the profession. In fact, the opposite is often true. New graduates and students bring an up-andcoming perspective to issues. They will be the leaders of tomorrow, having to live the longest with the decisions made today. Therefore, it is important and constructive to provide your input as early on as possible.

Without volunteers among our profession, we would not have progressed as far as we have today in a number of areas. The momentum of progress can only be sustained if new generations of veterinarians make the same commitment to the advancement of the profession. So...what are you waiting for!?

Additional Recommended Reading

Associate's Survival Guide. Fassig SM, Ed. AAHA Press, Denver, CO; 2005.

Biography

For Dr. Tait's biography, plesase see the Section 1 Introduction on page 3.